Theory and design of active RC circuits

The progress in active *RC* circuits over the past decade is illustrated dramatically by the two photographs shown on the inside cover pages. On the bottom right is a photograph of a bandpass network using negative-immittance converters. Each of the cards contains an NIC (negative-immittance converter) as well as other active and passive elements.* On the top right page is shown a photomicrograph of an integrated realization for a gyrator. The die size is approximately 0.087 by 0.065 in.†

* Reprinted by permission of the copyright owner, the American Telephone and Telegraph Co., and the author. This picture originally appeared in the article by B. K. Kinariwala, Synthesis of Active RC Networks, *Bell System Tech. J.*, vol. 38, pp. 1269–1316, 1959.

† The gyrator photomicrograph was provided by R. W. Newcomb of Stanford University. The gyrator is described in the article by H. T. Chua and R. W. Newcomb, Integrated Direct-Coupled Gyrator, *Electron. Letters*, vol. 3, no. 5, pp. 182–184, May, 1967.

McGraw-Hill Series in Electronic Systems

John G. Truxal and Ronald A. Rohrer, *Consulting Editors*

Huelsman: *Theory and Design of Active RC Circuits*

Schultz and Melsa: *State Functions and Linear Control Systems*

Stagg and El-Abiad: *Computer Methods in Power System Analysis*

Timothy and Bona: *State Space Analysis: An Introduction*

Theory and Design of Active RC Circuits

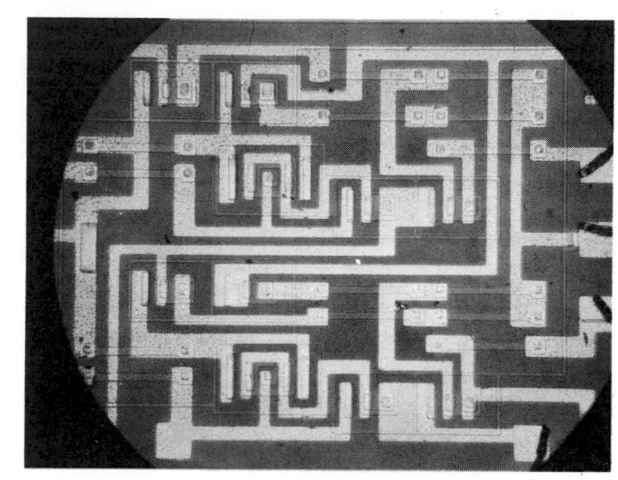

Lawrence P. Huelsman
Professor of Electrical Engineering, University of Arizona

McGraw-Hill Book Company
New York, St. Louis, San Francisco, Toronto, London, Sydney

Theory and Design of Active RC Circuits

Library of Congress Catalog Card Number 68-14756
30848
1234567890 MAMM 7543210698

To Jo

Preface

As the name implies, an active RC circuit is one composed solely of resistors, capacitors, and some form of active element. Such circuits, being inductanceless, are attractive for applications where weight and size must be minimized. They reduce the problem of incidental dissipation which complicates synthesis procedures, and they permit more precise adjustment of the final realization than is possible in many purely passive networks. In addition, they are applicable to integrated circuits where, in general, the realization of inductors is not feasible. Thus, the subject of active RC circuits is of practical as well as theoretical interest.

The purpose of this book is to provide an introduction to the theory and design of active RC circuits. More specifically, the goals of this text may be enumerated as follows:

First, to lay the foundation for a general approach to the theory of active RC circuits. Such a theory should be applicable both to the analysis and the synthesis of such circuits. From an analysis point of view, it should illustrate any similarity of fundamental realization mechanism inherent in techniques which, superficially at least, appear to be widely divergent. This theory should also provide a means of comparing results of the application of such techniques. From a synthesis point of view, it should permit the network designer to manipulate intelligently the parameters of the network in such a way as to be able to adjust the network characteristics.

Second, to provide the network theorist with an integrated treatment of the state of the art of active RC circuits. This treatment applies to the general problem and emphasizes a broad approach. It includes considerable coverage of the theoretical variations from the well-trodden paths that have been followed in the past.

Third, to give the practicing graduate engineer an overall viewpoint of the general area of active RC circuits, to indicate the advantages and disadvantages of the various types of realizations, and to illustrate actual practical realizations while at the same time indicating the theoretical basis behind these realizations.

Fourth, to provide a single source of background material both in text and in bibliography for the reader who wishes an up-to-date starting point for his own researches in this area.

A few comments about the arrangement of the material may be helpful to the reader. Chapter 1 provides a brief review of the most significant properties of passive *RC* networks. It then defines the classes of active *RC* networks that will be of primary concern in this book and introduces the properties of these classes to enable the reader to quickly achieve some depth of perspective from which later developments may be viewed. In Chapter 2, the basic mathematical processes which are common to the analysis and synthesis of all active *RC* realizations are discussed. The concepts of sensitivity and polynomial decomposition are introduced, developed, and illustrated. No prior knowledge of these subjects is assumed. This material forms the foundation for the detailed study of the various classes of active *RC* circuits which follows. In Chapter 3, the basic types of controlled sources are defined. General techniques whereby these sources may be applied to the realization of transfer functions are introduced. The application of the underlying concepts of Chapter 2 is stressed. The techniques are then applied to some specific common filtering problems. Detailed design procedures and example realizations are given. The realization of the controlled sources is also discussed. The pattern of Chapter 4 is similar to that of Chapter 3, except that a different active device, the negative-immittance converter, is treated as the active element. Similarly, Chapter 5 treats realizations using gyrators, and Chapter 6 treats realizations with infinite-gain elements. A common pattern that runs through Chapters 3, 4, 5, 6 is the manner in which the basic concepts developed in Chapter 2 are applied. Appendix A provides a comprehensive theoretical treatment of the properties of driving-point functions for the various classes of active and passive *RC* networks. This material is based on the energy-function approach and is included for the reader who wishes to establish more rigorously the basic properties of these classes of networks. Appendix B provides a similar comprehensive theoretical treatment of the z and y parameters for various classes of active and passive *RC* networks, including a discussion of the restrictions placed on these parameters because of the choice of network configurations. The results of this treatment are applied to develop the properties of various transfer functions. Appendix C contains a proof of the Horowitz decomposition. Together with Appendixes A and B, this appendix comprises the most theoretical portion of the book. Appendix D contains an extensive bibliography broken down into subject categories corresponding to the major topics of the various chapters.

There are several ways in which the book may be used. The instructor who wishes to use this material for a one-semester senior or graduate-level course in the theory of active *RC* networks would most logically start with the material in Appendixes A and B. The material in Chapter 2 would then be treated next, supplemented by additional material on sensitivity and polynomial decomposition taken from the references given in the chapter and from the bibliography. The presentation of the material from these parts of the book can be spread over a half to two-thirds of a semester, depending on the depth of coverage. The rest of the semester can be used to cover the remaining chapters. In note form, the material has been used in this manner by the author at the University of Arizona and has been found to provide a logical development. The engineer who wishes to give himself a thorough working background in active *RC* circuits might follow directly through the book from Chapters 1 to 7. The less theoretically inclined engineer will find it possible to skip most of Chapter 2 without appreciable loss of continuity in the material; however, he will not fully appreciate the extent to which all of the specialized techniques are extensions of a single theoretical approach. Finally, the engineer-in-a-hurry has the option of turning directly to the closing sections of Chapters 3, 4, and 6 and looking to see if there is a circuit there which will satisfy his needs.

I would like to express my most sincere appreciation to the Burr-Brown Research Corporation for their support of some of the research that materially contributed to this book and for their permission to use portions of their "Handbook of Operational Amplifier Active RC Circuits." I am especially grateful to Tom Brown, Henry Koerner, Tom Fern, and Dale Dukes of that company for their encouragement of this project. I would also like to acknowledge the most capable assistance of Jim Whalen of Burr-Brown for his work in testing the example circuits. Finally, my thanks to Dr. Gabor Temes of the Ampex Corporation and Professors Donald Pederson and Ronald Rohrer for their most helpful comments on the original manuscript.

Lawrence P. Huelsman

Contents

Theory and design of active RC circuits

Chapter 1 *Introduction*

The past decade has seen a rapid growth of interest in active *RC* circuits. The attention of both the network theorist and the practicing engineer has been drawn to the study of these circuits. The result has been a rapid increase in the amount of knowledge in this field. This increase has been described in a variety of places, including journals of varying purpose from various countries. Thus, the person who desires to acquaint himself with this area of network theory faces a sizable literature search at the very outset. Nor is this his only problem. The various realization techniques that have been propounded by the different authors who have considered this subject bear little resemblance to each other. The active elements that are required range from such commonplace ones as the transistor to quite esoteric-sounding ones such as the negative-immittance converter. The engineer who has a use for active *RC* circuits is thus faced with the problem of evaluating the various realization techniques and trying to decide which one is best for his particular application. Thus, the question is raised as to whether there is a common method of approach to the general problem of active *RC* circuit realizations, in the light of which all the detailed techniques that have been proposed may be evaluated and compared. The development of such a basic theoretical approach from which not only present realization techniques, but also future ones, may be viewed is one of the goals of this text.

Some of the significant properties of active *RC* circuits may be of interest to the reader. An active *RC* circuit is one which consists of time-invariant resistors and capacitors and some form of active element. Thus, by definition, it is a circuit which does not contain inductors. There are many advantages to be realized from the elimination of inductors from network realizations. In practical circuit applications inductors may create problems because of their associated magnetic fields and also because of their nonlinear behavior. In synthesis procedures, inductors complicate network design because of their winding resistance and core loss. In many applications the size and weight of inductors make them undesirable. Finally, it is virtually impossible to realize practical inductors in integrated circuits. For all these reasons, and others, the concept of eliminating inductors from network realizations without relinquishing any of the properties that such inductors provide is a most attractive one. In the pages of this book we shall show how active *RC* circuits fulfill this role.

Let us begin our study of active *RC* circuits by first considering a passive *RLC* network. Such a network is shown in Fig. 1.1. For the element

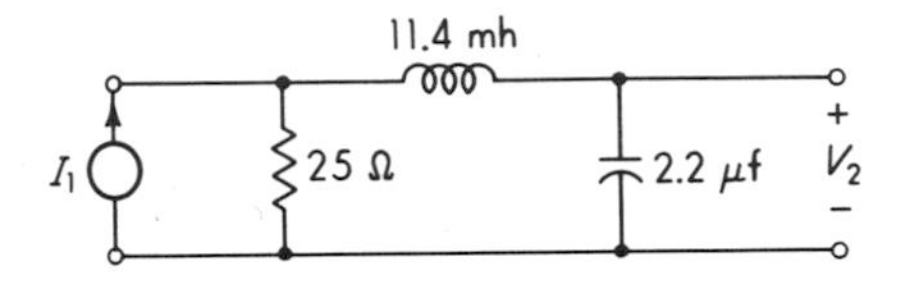

***Figure 1.1** A passive RLC circuit.*

values given in the figure the transfer impedance is

$$\frac{V_2}{I_1} = \frac{10^9}{p^2 + 2.2 \times 10^3 p + 40 \times 10^6} \tag{1}$$

where p is the complex-frequency variable. A Bode plot, i.e., a plot of the logarithm of the magnitude of V_2/I_1 as a function of frequency (on a logarithmic scale), for the function given in (1) is shown in Fig. 1.2. The

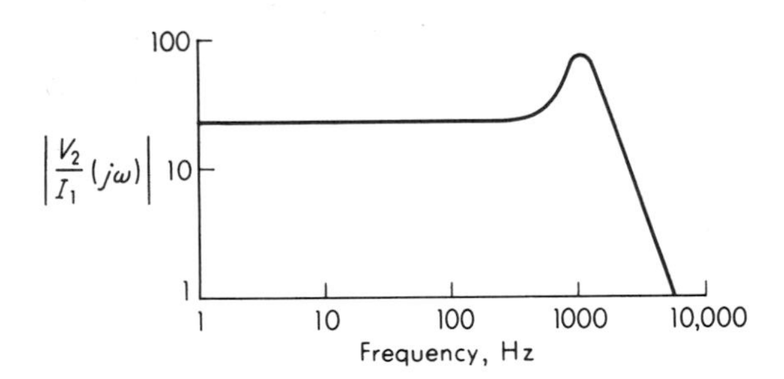

***Figure 1.2** A Bode plot for the circuit shown in Fig. 1.1.*

hump in this frequency-response curve at 1000 Hz is usually referred to as the "resonant" effect produced by the combination of the inductor and the capacitor. Such a resonant effect cannot be produced by passive *RC* networks. For example, consider the network shown in Fig. 1.3. For the

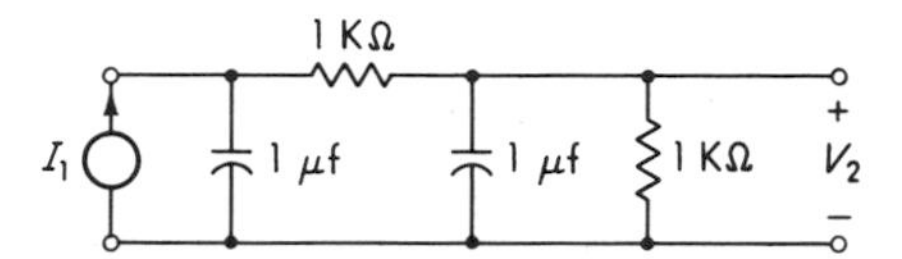

Figure 1.3 A passive RC circuit.

element values given in the figure it has the transfer impedance

$$\frac{V_2}{I_1} = \frac{10^9}{p^2 + 3 \times 10^3 p + 10^6} \tag{2}$$

A plot of the magnitude of V_2/I_1 for (2) as a function of frequency is shown in Fig. 1.4. Clearly, no resonant hump is evident.

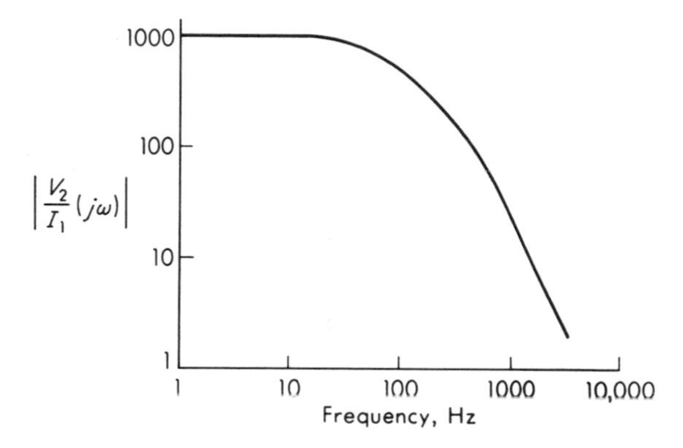

Figure 1.4 A Bode plot for the circuit shown in Fig. 1.3.

Now let us convert the passive *RC* circuit shown in Fig. 1.3 to an active *RC* circuit by adding a single transistor. To keep our representation simple, we shall use the small-signal-equivalent T circuit for a transistor in a common emitter configuration shown in Fig. 1.5. We shall assume that any transistor base resistance will be absorbed by the network connected to the transistor. If we combine the passive *RC* network shown in Fig. 1.3

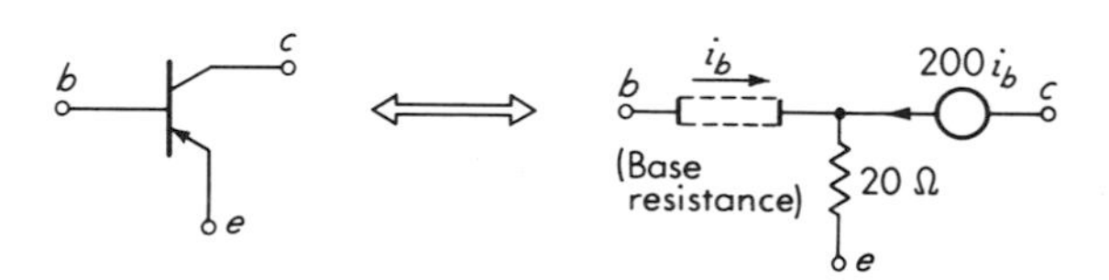

Figure 1.5 A transistor and a small-signal-equivalent model.

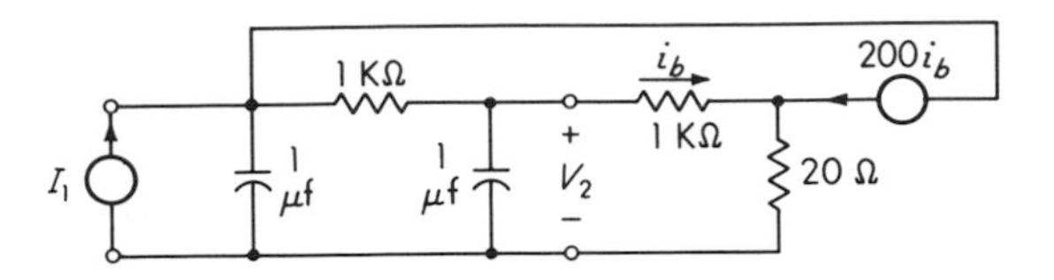

Figure 1.6 A transistor RC circuit.

with the transistor model shown in Fig. 1.5 to produce the circuit shown in Fig. 1.6, we obtain the transfer function

$$\frac{V_2}{I_1} = \frac{10^9}{p^2 + 2.2 \times 10^3 p + 40 \times 10^6} \tag{3}$$

This is exactly the same transfer function as was given in (1) for the *RLC* circuit shown in Fig. 1.1. Its frequency-response curve is therefore also given by Fig. 1.2, and it thus exhibits the resonant effects normally associated with *RLC* circuits. Thus, at least in this simple example, we see that an active *RC* circuit can be used to replace a passive *RLC* circuit. To show that this is true in general will be one of the goals of this book. Indeed, we shall show not only that active *RC* circuits can be used to provide all of the characteristics obtainable with passive *RLC* networks, but also that they will provide many additional network capabilities which are not possible in the passive case.

In studying network synthesis techniques, whether for passive or for active networks, one comes early to the conclusion that it is possible to find many different network configurations which can be used to synthesize a given network function. The same is true of active *RC* circuits. As an example of this nonuniqueness of synthesis procedures, consider the use of an ideal noninverting voltage amplifier as the "active" part of an active *RC* circuit. By "ideal" we mean that the amplifier has high input impedance and negligible output impedance. If such an amplifier with a gain $K = 2.65$ is connected to a passive *RC* circuit as shown in Fig. 1.7, we find the transfer impedance is

$$\frac{V_2}{I_1} = \frac{106 \times 10^9}{p^2 + 2.2 \times 10^3 p + 40 \times 10^6} \tag{4}$$

If we compare (4) with (3), we see that this second active *RC* circuit,

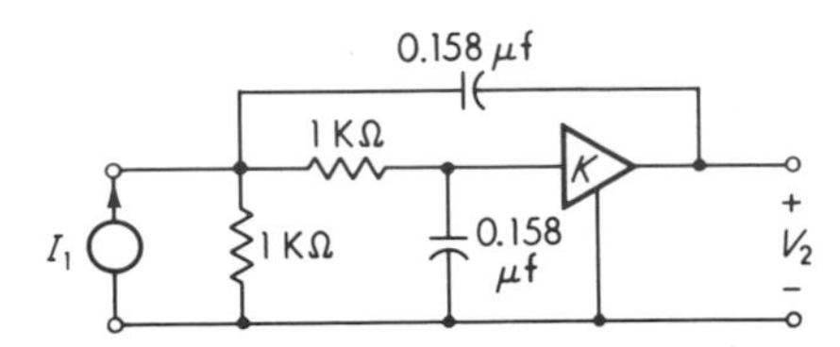

Figure 1.7 An active RC circuit.

using a noninverting voltage amplifier, produces a transfer impedance with the same resonant effect as the active *RC* circuit (shown in Fig. 1.6) which uses a transistor as the active element. Only the overall gain constant is different. Given such similar realizations, the question naturally arises as to the relative merits of the two circuits or, in other words, whether one is better than the other. Before such a question can be answered we must, of course, define what we mean by the word "better"; i.e., we must set up criteria by means of which the performance of the two active *RC* circuits can be judged. One of the major goals of this text will be the development of such criteria and their application to a variety of active *RC* circuit design techniques.

As a further introduction to the subject of active *RC* circuits, in this chapter we shall define several classes of such circuits and discuss their properties. In general, no proofs of these properties will be presented; however, a detailed and more rigorous discussion of the properties of the different classes is given in Appendixes A and B, to which the interested reader is referred.

1.1 *The passive RC class of networks*

As a review, let us first consider the class of networks that consists of positive-valued (i.e., passive) resistors and capacitors. This will be referred to as the passive *RC* or the $+R$, $+C$ class of networks. The natural frequencies of this class are restricted to the negative-real axis of the complex-frequency plane (including the origin and infinity), and they must be simple, i.e., of the first order. The zeros of driving-point functions are restricted to the same region; however, the zeros of transfer functions may be located anywhere on the complex-frequency plane. It should be noted, however, that to produce complex zeros (which must occur in conjugate pairs) in general requires the use of parallel networks. If a restriction is made to the more practical three-terminal (i.e., common-ground) passive *RC* network, then the zeros of transfer functions are excluded from the positive-real axis. These properties are summarized in Fig. 1.8.

1.2 *The $\pm R$, $+C$ class of networks*

The first class of active *RC* circuits that will be defined is the class consisting of positive- and negative-valued resistors and positive-valued capacitors. This will be referred to as the $\pm R$, $+C$ class of networks.

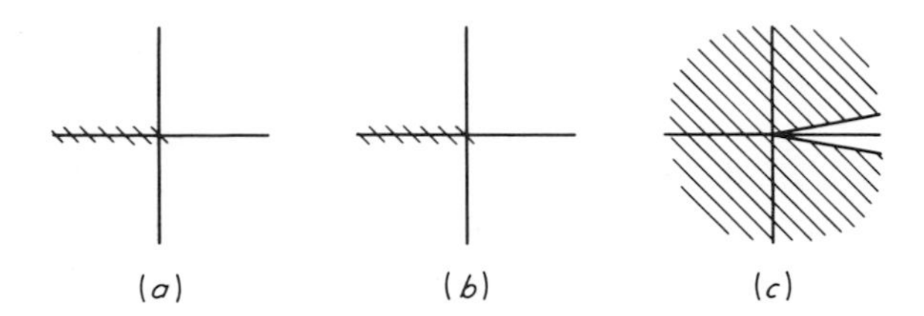

Figure 1.8 The passive RC network. (a) Possible location of natural frequencies. (b) Possible location of zeros of driving-point functions. (c) Possible location of zeros of transfer functions (of a three-terminal network).

There is considerable practical motivation for considering such a class since many negative-resistance devices, such as tunnel diodes and double-base diodes, are available as actual circuit elements. The natural frequencies of this class of networks may, of course, be located on the negative-real axis, as was possible for the passive RC class. In addition, they may be located on the positive-real axis, although application of this possibility is, in general, precluded by stability considerations. Only simple natural frequencies are permitted. The zeros of driving-point functions are also restricted to the real axis. The zeros of transfer functions may be located anywhere on the complex-frequency plane; however, paralleled networks are required for complex zeros. For this class of networks, restriction to the three-terminal configuration does not exclude zeros on the positive-real axis as it did in the passive RC case. The properties of this class of networks are summarized in Fig. 1.9. It should be noted that relatively little is gained in terms of useful frequency characteristics by adding negative-valued resistors to the passive RC class of networks. It should be noted, however, that the $\pm R$, $+C$ class is capable of voltage

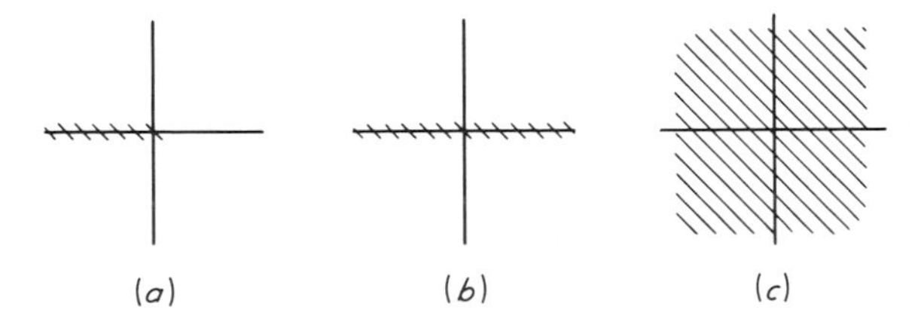

Figure 1.9 The $\pm R$, $+C$ network. (a) Possible location of stable natural frequencies. (b) Possible location of zeros of driving-point functions. (c) Possible location of zeros of transfer functions.

gain over the entire frequency range. A detailed discussion of the properties of this class of networks may be found in Appendixes A and B.

1.3 *The RC-gyrator class of networks*

A more interesting class of active *RC* networks than the one described above is the class consisting of positive-valued resistors and capacitors and an active element called a *gyrator*.* This will be called the *RC*-gyrator class of networks. The gyrator will be discussed in detail in Chap. 5. Here it will suffice to describe it as a two-port nonreciprocal device with the property that the input impedance seen at either port is the reciprocal of any impedance connected to the other port. Thus a capacitive termination at one port produces two-terminal behavior identical to that of an inductor at the other port. Obviously, the *RC*-gyrator class of networks must have properties at least as general as the passive *RLC* class of networks, i.e., the class composed of positive-valued resistors, capacitors, and inductors. Thus, the natural frequencies for this class of networks may be located anywhere on the left half of the complex-frequency plane, including the $j\omega$ axis. Any $j\omega$-axis natural frequencies must be simple. The zeros of driving-point functions are also restricted to this region. The zeros of transfer functions, however, may occur anywhere on the complex-frequency plane. The above properties are summarized in Fig. 1.10. In addition, it should be noted that because of the nonreciprocal nature of the gyrator, this class of networks is also capable of nonreciprocal behav-

* Actually, the gyrator, as it is usually defined, has the property that the sum of the input powers to its two ports is zero. As such it is a lossless element and may therefore be considered as passive. Practically, however, its realization requires the use of active devices; therefore, for our purposes, it will be considered as an active element.

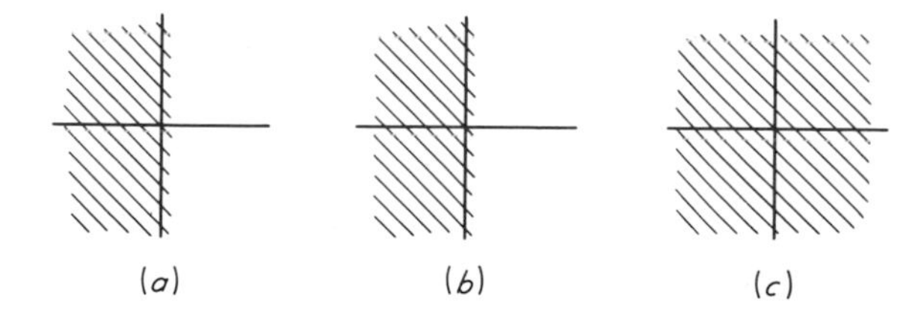

***Figure 1.10** The RC-gyrator network. (a) Possible location of natural frequencies. (b) Possible location of zeros of driving-point functions. (c) Possible location of zeros of transfer functions.*

ior. This behavior is not possible in the passive RC or the $\pm R$, $+C$ classes of networks.

1.4 *The $\pm R$, $\pm C$ class of networks*

Next let us consider the class of active RC circuits whose elements are positive- and negative-valued resistors and positive- and negative-valued capacitors. This class will be called the $\pm R$, $\pm C$ class of networks. It is shown in Appendixes A and B that this class of networks is completely general in the sense that any rational function, i.e., any ratio of polynomials in the complex-frequency variable with real coefficients, may be realized either as a driving-point function or as a transfer function. Thus, the natural frequencies may be located anywhere on the complex-frequency plane and may be of any order. Stability, of course, dictates that they be limited to the left half-plane and the $j\omega$ axis. It also requires that the natural frequencies located on the $j\omega$ axis be simple. Similarly, zeros of either driving-point or transfer functions may be located anywhere on the complex-frequency plane. These properties are indicated in Fig. 1.11. From the above, we see the addition of negative-valued capac-

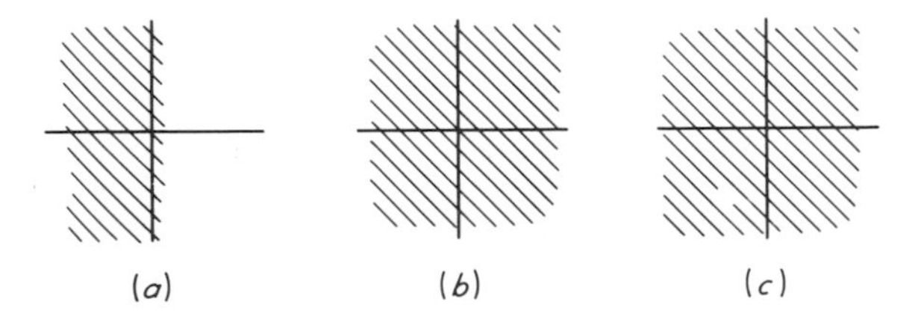

***Figure 1.11** The $\pm R$, $\pm C$ network. (a) Possible location of stable natural frequencies. (b) Possible location of zeros of driving-point functions. (c) Possible location of zeros of transfer functions.*

itors to the $\pm R$, $+C$ class of networks, i.e., the one with only positive-valued capacitors, results in a drastic improvement in the capabilities of this class of networks. It is easily shown that the use of negative-valued capacitors in connection with the passive RC class of networks does not achieve this same improvement; i.e., generality requires both types of negative-valued elements. It should be noted that since the $\pm R$, $\pm C$ class of networks is comprised entirely of two-terminal elements, this class of networks is always reciprocal in behavior.

1.5 *The RC-NIC class of networks*

Unlike negative-valued resistors, negative-valued capacitors are more difficult to realize as physical devices. Thus, we are led to seek a means of producing them from positive-valued capacitors. Such a means is found in an active element called a *negative-immittance converter* (NIC). The properties of such an element will be discussed in detail in Chap. 4. Here it will suffice to describe it as a nonreciprocal two-port device with the property that the input impedance seen at either port is the negative of any impedance connected to the other port. Such a device may obviously be used to produce two-terminal behavior identical with that of either a negative-valued resistor or a negative-valued capacitor, from a positive-valued resistor or a positive-valued capacitor, respectively. Thus the class of networks consisting of positive-valued resistors and capacitors and NICs is at least as general as the $\pm R$, $\pm C$ class described above. We shall call this class of networks the RC-NIC class. It should be noted that since the NIC is a nonreciprocal device, this class of networks may also exhibit nonreciprocal behavior, a property that is not possible with the $\pm R$, $\pm C$ class.

1.6 *The RC-controlled-source and the RC-infinite-gain classes of networks*

We may define a *controlled source* as an ideal voltage or current source whose output is controlled by some other voltage or current. Such sources will be treated in more detail in Chap. 3. This type of active element is of considerable interest since many physical devices have properties which approximate those of controlled sources. It will be shown in Chap. 4 that a controlled source may be used to realize an NIC; thus, this class of networks is as general as the RC-NIC class of networks. A class of controlled sources which is of very practical interest is the infinite-gain class. The properties of such devices will be explored in Chap. 6. Here, however, we may point out that an operational amplifier is an example of such an element. Since these devices provide excellent stability in circuit applications through the use of feedback, they are of considerable interest as active elements. We will call the class of networks comprised of positive-valued resistors and capacitors and infinite-gain active elements the RC-infinite-gain class. It is shown in Chap. 4 that since an infinite-gain active element may be used to realize an NIC, this class of networks is as general as the RC-NIC class.

1.7 Conclusion

In the preceding sections we have introduced several classes of active networks, and we have used simple examples to define some of the goals of this text. In the pages that follow, we shall seek to realize these goals. Specifically, in Chap. 2 we shall develop criteria by means of which various types of active *RC* circuits may be evaluated and compared. In Chaps. 3, 4, 5, and 6 we shall apply these criteria to the four different classes of active *RC* circuits, namely, those realized, respectively, by controlled sources, negative-immittance converters, gyrators, and operational amplifiers. Finally, in Chap. 7 we shall summarize our findings and administer the final deathblow to the archenemy of circuit theory, the inductor.

Chapter 2 *Sensitivity in active RC circuits*

Our goal in this chapter will be to develop some of the criteria by means of which the performance of various types of active RC circuits can be evaluated and compared. As an example of the differences that we can expect to find in circuits which have similar terminal properties, let us consider the two examples of active RC circuits which were introduced in Chap. 1. The first of these is shown in Fig. 1.6. It uses a transistor as an active element. If we make appropriate frequency and impedance normalizations on the elements of this circuit so that the passive resistors and the capacitors are both set to unity values, the circuit appears as shown in Fig. 2.1.* For this figure the transfer impedance function originally given in (3) of Chap. 1 becomes

$$\frac{V_2}{I_1} = \frac{1}{p^2 + 2.2p + 40}$$

* An impedance normalization is achieved by making the transformation $Z = z_n Z'$, where Z is the original impedance, Z' is the normalized impedance, and z_n is the normalizing factor. In this case $z_n = 10^3$; thus, resistors of value 1 kilohm become unity-valued resistors, and capacitors of value 1 μF become capacitors of value 1000 μF. A frequency normalization is achieved by making a transformation of the complex-frequency variable $p = k_n p'$, where p is the original frequency variable, k_n is the normalizing factor, and p' is the normalized complex-frequency variable. In this case, $k_n = 10^3$; therefore, the capacitors of value 1000 μF resulting from the impedance transformation become unity-valued capacitors. The gain of the transistor, being dimensionless, is not affected by either of these transformations.

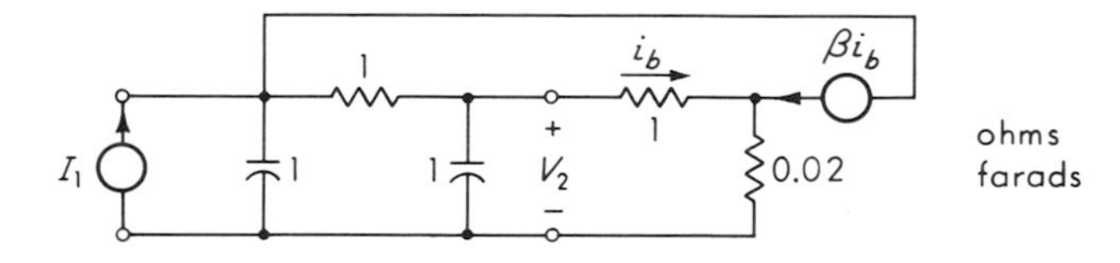

Figure 2.1 A normalized transistor-RC circuit.

This equation assumes that β, the gain of the transistor, has a nominal value of 200. If we retain β as an explicit variable, the transfer impedance function for the circuit of Fig. 2.1 may be written in the form

$$\frac{V_2}{I_1} = \frac{1}{p^2 + [2 + 1/(1 + 0.02 + 0.02\beta)]p + (1 + \beta)/(1 + 0.02 + 0.02\beta)}$$

Now let us consider the effect of changes in the value of β on the transfer impedance of the circuit. In Fig. 2.2 a Bode plot is presented showing the

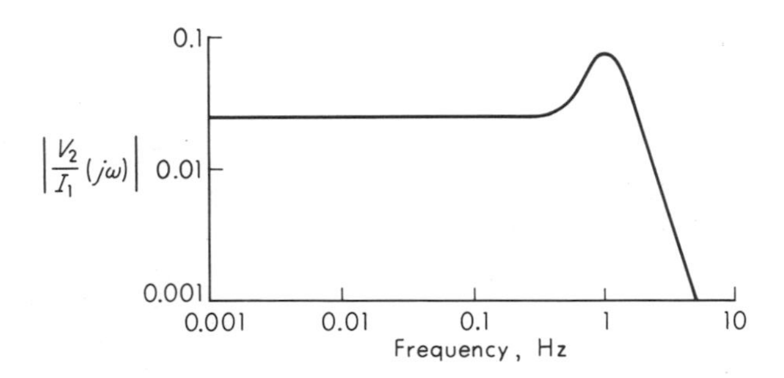

***Figure 2.2** A Bode plot for the circuit shown in Fig. 2.1.*

magnitude of the transfer impedance given above for $\beta = 200$. If we make ± 10 percent changes in the value of β, the plot is virtually unchanged. Actual computation shows that at the normalized resonant frequency of 1 Hz, the total percentage variation in the magnitude for ± 10 percent changes in β is approximately 1.6 percent.

Now let us consider the second active circuit which was introduced in Chap. 1 (shown in Fig. 1.7). If we make frequency and impedance normalizations identical to those that were made for the transistor circuit, the normalized circuit is as shown in Fig. 2.3. The transfer impedance function

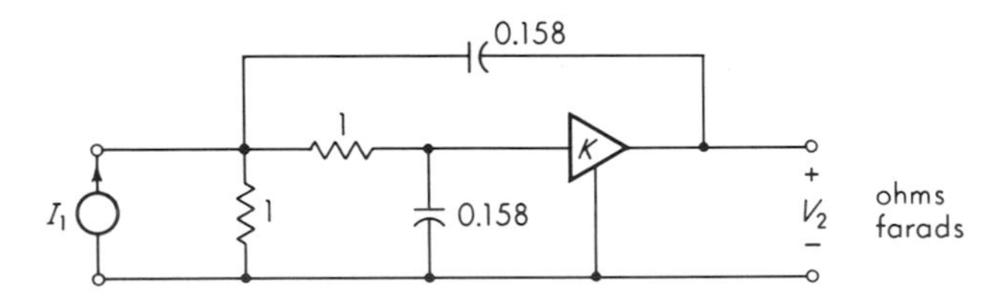

***Figure 2.3** A normalized active RC circuit.*

originally given in (4) of Chap. 1 becomes (for the gain K equal to 2.65)

$$\frac{V_2}{I_1} = \frac{106}{p^2 + 2.2p + 40}$$

If we retain the gain K of the noninverting voltage amplifier as an explicit variable, the transfer impedance may be written as

$$\frac{V_2}{I_1} = \frac{40K}{p^2 + 6.32(3 - K)p + 40}$$

Now let us evaluate the effect of changes in the amplifier gain K from its nominal value of 2.65. In Fig. 2.4 we show the variation that occurs in the

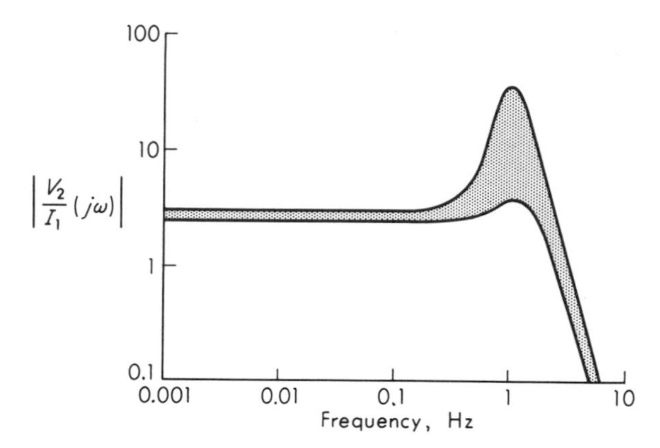

***Figure 2.4** Variations in the Bode plot for the circuit shown in Fig. 2.3.*

Bode plot for the magnitude of the transfer impedance as a result of making ± 10 percent changes in the value of K. The effect is drastically greater than was produced by corresponding percentage changes in β for the transistor circuit. In the case shown in Fig. 2.4, an actual computation shows that at the normalized frequency of 1 Hz, the total percentage variation in the magnitude is about 400 percent! If stability in the magnitude characteristic is our goal, the transistor circuit must certainly be considered as the one to be chosen since its magnitude characteristic at resonance is considerably less "sensitive" to variations in the characteristics of the active element.

The word "sensitive" introduces the material of Chap. 2, which is devoted to a study of *sensitivity*, i.e., the way in which changes in a network characteristic are caused by changes in the network itself.

2.1 *Classical sensitivity*

Sensitivity may be considered as a measure of the change in some performance characteristic of a network resulting from a change in the nominal value of one or more of the elements of the network. The symbol S is used to denote sensitivity. In addition, a superscript character is used to indicate the performance characteristic that is changing, and a subscript character is used to indicate the specific network element that is causing the change. One of the earliest definitions of sensitivity was made by Bode.* The performance characteristic that is used is the network function itself. If we let $N(p,x)$ be any network function and x be any parameter, the *classical sensitivity* is usually referred to as $S_x^N(p,x)$ and defined as

$$S_x^N(p,x) = \frac{dN/N}{dx/x} = \frac{d(\ln N)}{d(\ln x)} \tag{1}$$

Now let us define the numerator and denominator polynomials of $N(p,x)$ as $Q(p,x)$ and $P(p,x)$, respectively. Thus

$$N(p,x) = \frac{Q(p,x)}{P(p,x)}$$

It may be easily shown that

$$S_x^N(p,x) = x\left(\frac{Q'}{Q} - \frac{P'}{P}\right) \tag{2}$$

where

$$Q' = \frac{\partial Q(p,x)}{\partial x} \qquad P' = \frac{\partial P(p,x)}{\partial x}$$

Classical sensitivity is useful when it is desired to determine the variation of the magnitude or phase of a network function caused by parameter variations. To see this, we may write

$$\ln N(j\omega,x) = \ln |N(j\omega,x)| + j \arg N(j\omega,x)$$

If we evaluate (1) along the $j\omega$ axis and substitute from the above equation, we obtain

$$S_x^N(j\omega,x) = \frac{d|N(j\omega,x)|/|N(j\omega,x)|}{dx/x} + j\,\frac{d \arg N(j\omega,x)}{dx/x} \tag{3}$$

Thus we see that *the real part of the sensitivity specifies the normalized change in the magnitude of the network function and the imaginary part specifies the change in the phase function.* The concept of classical sensitivity will not be used extensively in this text. An example, however, is included below to demonstrate the application of the concept.

* H. W. Bode, "Network Analysis and Feedback Amplifier Design," p. 52, D. Van Nostrand Company, Inc., Princeton, N.J., 1945. The definition used here is the reciprocal of Bode's definition and is usually attributed to S. J. Mason. See J. G. Truxal, "Automatic Feedback Control System Synthesis," p. 120, McGraw-Hill Book Company, New York, 1955.

As an example of the concept of classical sensitivity, consider the network function

$$N(p,x) = \frac{p}{p^2 + xp + 3}$$

where x has a nominal value of unity. A physical example of such a function is the driving-point admittance of the network shown in Fig. 2.5,

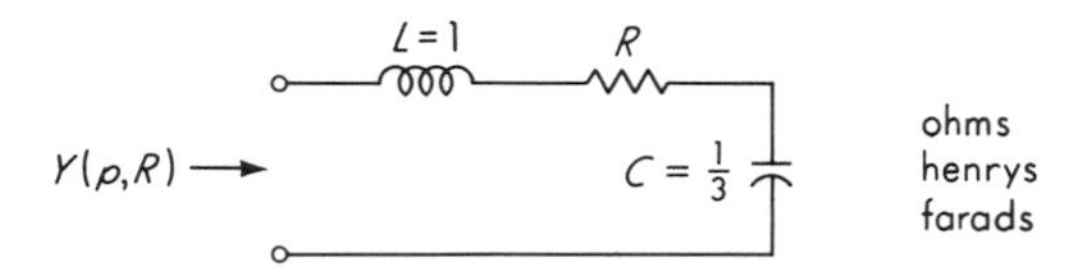

***Figure 2.5** A driving-point admittance.*

since for the indicated normalized values of L and C for this network we obtain

$$Y(p,R) = \frac{p}{p^2 + Rp + 3}$$

The sensitivity function may be found from (2). Thus we see that

$$S_x^N(p,x) = \frac{-xp}{p^2 + xp + 3}$$

Thus, for the nominal value of x, evaluating the sensitivity function along the $j\omega$ axis, we obtain

$$S_x^N(j\omega,1) = \frac{-\omega^2}{(3 - \omega^2)^2 + \omega^2} + j\frac{-\omega(3 - \omega^2)}{(3 - \omega^2)^2 + \omega^2}$$

For example, let us consider the network behavior at $\omega = 2$ rad/sec. For this case

$$S_x^N(j2,1) = -0.8 + j0.4$$

Comparing this with (3), we see that the normalized change in the magnitude of $N(j\omega,1)$ with respect to a normalized change in x, at the frequency of 2 rad/sec, is -0.8, and that the change in the argument of $N(j\omega,1)$ with respect to a normalized change in x at the same frequency is 0.4 rad. It is interesting to compare these values of the classical sensitivity with the actual changes in the magnitude and phase of the network function. First let us consider a relatively small change by letting x go from its nominal value of unity to a value of 1.01. For the network function we may calculate

$$\frac{[|N(j2,1.01)| - |N(j2,1)|]/|N(j2,1)|}{0.01/1} = -0.797$$

Similarly, for the phase function, we obtain

$$\frac{\arg N(j2,1.01) - \arg N(j2,1)}{0.01/1} = 0.398 \text{ rad}$$

We note that quite good agreement is obtained with the computed sensitivity figures, as is to be expected when small incremental changes are considered.

Now let us investigate the effect of a larger change on the parameter x. If we let x go from its nominal unity value to a value of 1.1, we find that

$$\frac{[|N(j2,1.1)| - |N(j2,1)|]/|N(j2,1)|}{0.1/1} = -0.747$$

$$\frac{\arg N(j2,1.1) - \arg N(j2,1)}{0.1/1} = 0.369 \text{ rad}$$

As is to be expected, since the sensitivity function of (1) is not an exact relation when incremental quantities are considered, the use of larger increments leads to greater inaccuracies. Plots of the magnitude and phase of the network function for $x = 1$ and $x = 1.1$ are given in Fig. 2.6. The real and imaginary parts of the sensitivity function are also plotted in the figure for a value of x equal to unity. It should be noted that although the change in the magnitude function as given by the real part of the sensitivity function reaches its maximum value at $\omega = \sqrt{3}$ rad/sec, the change in the phase reaches a maximum at considerably different frequencies.

The concept of classical sensitivity finds an important general application to network functions in which the denominator is of the second degree. Such a function may be written in the form

$$N(p) = \frac{Q(p)}{p^2 + b_1 p + b_2}$$

Let us consider the situation where only b_1 is a function of some parameter x. Thus we may write

$$N(p,x) = \frac{Q(p)}{p^2 + pb_1(x) + b_2}$$

If this function is evaluated at $p = j\sqrt{b_2}$, i.e., the frequency at which the denominator is purely imaginary [if $N(p)$ is a bandpass function, $Q(p) = Hp$, and $\omega = \sqrt{b_2}$ is the "resonant" frequency], we obtain

$$N(j\sqrt{b_2},x) = \frac{Q(j\sqrt{b_2})}{j\sqrt{b_2}\, b_1(x)}$$

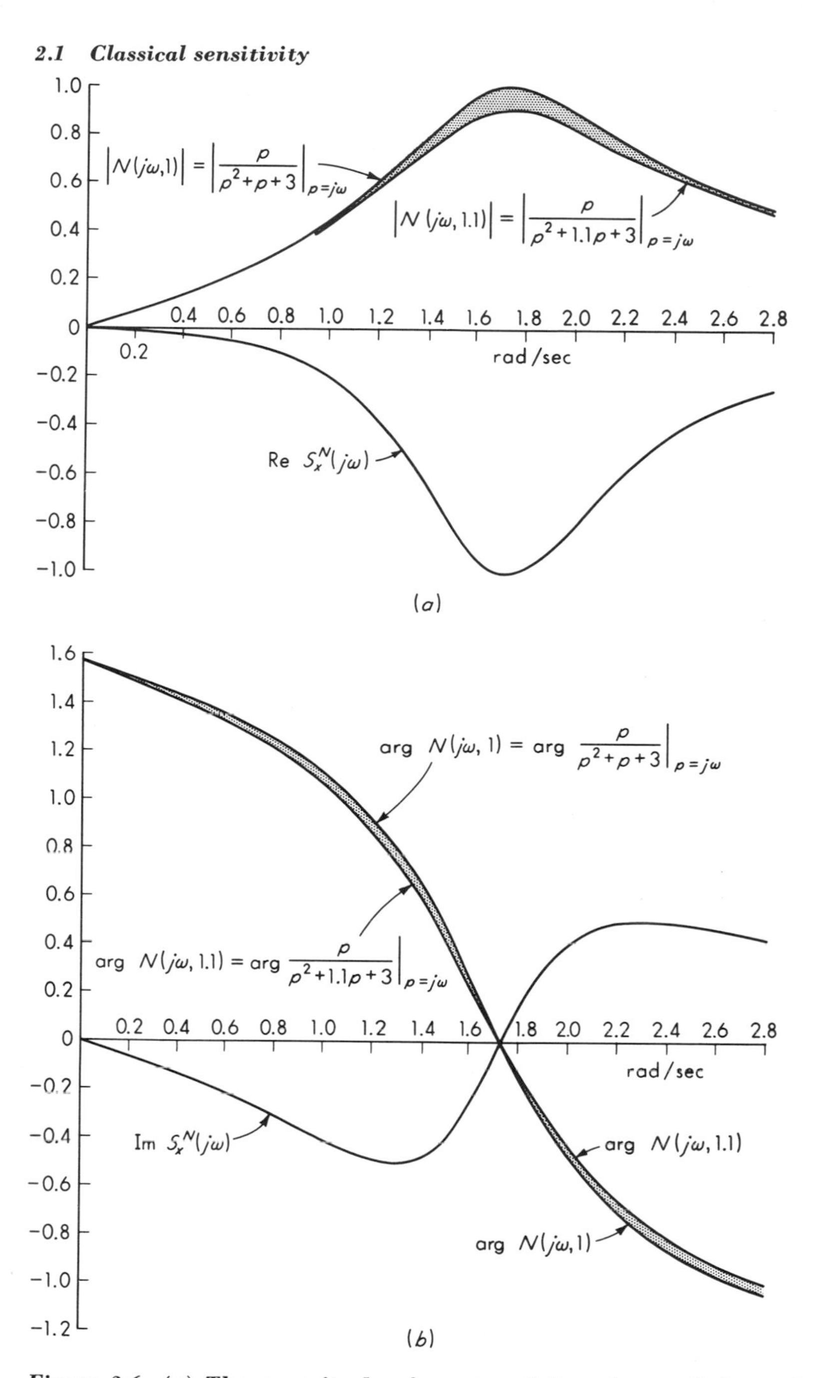

***Figure 2.6** (a) The magnitude of a network function and the real part of the sensitivity for that function. (b) The argument of a network function and the imaginary part of the sensitivity for that function (arguments are specified in radians).*

From (2) we may derive the sensitivity

$$S_x^N(j\sqrt{b_2},x) = \frac{-\partial b_1}{\partial x}\frac{x}{b_1} \tag{4}$$

Now let us consider three different ways in which the coefficient b_1 may depend on the parameter x and the resultant effect on the sensitivity of (4). These lead to the following properties:

Property 1 *If the dependence of the coefficient b_1 on some parameter x may be written in the form $b_1 = a_0x$, then*

$$S_x^N(j\sqrt{b_2},x) = -1$$

This is easily verified by direct substitution in (4). Note that for this case, a bandpass network, the sensitivity is independent of the Q of the network.*

Property 2 *Assume that the dependence of the coefficient b_1 on some parameter x may be written in the form $b_1 = a_0 + a_1x$, where a_0, a_1, and x are all positive. For this case, the sensitivity approaches the value*

$$S_x^N(j\sqrt{b_2},x) = \frac{-a_1x}{a_0 + a_1x}$$

and the magnitude of the sensitivity is always less than unity.

Property 3 *Assume that the dependence of the coefficient b_1 on some parameter x may be written in the same form as property 2, but that only a_0 and a_1 are positive while x is negative. This may be written $b_1 = a_0 - a_1|x|$. For the sensitivity we obtain*

$$S_x^N(j\sqrt{b_2},x) = \frac{a_1|x|}{a_0 - a_1|x|}$$

It should be noted that for the bandpass case and the dependence defined in property 3, as the Q of the network approaches infinity, the sensitivity also approaches infinity. We shall find applications for these properties in developments in later sections.

The concept of classical sensitivity is readily extended to the multiparameter case. Let N be a function of n parameters x_i. Thus $N = N(p, x_1, \ldots, x_n)$. Considering variations in the x_i, we may write

$$dN = \frac{\partial N}{\partial x_1}dx_1 + \cdots + \frac{\partial N}{\partial x_n}dx_n$$

* The Q of a network with a single pair of complex conjugate poles is usually defined as the magnitude of the distance from either pole to the origin divided by two times the magnitude of the real part of the pole locations. Thus, for the case discussed here, $Q = \sqrt{b_2}/b_1$.

This is readily put in the form

$$\frac{dN}{N} = d(\ln N) = \sum_{i=1}^{n} S_{x_i}{}^{N} \frac{dx_i}{x_i} \tag{5}$$

Thus we may define a *multiparameter sensitivity* $\mathbf{S}^N$ which is a gradient vector with elements $\partial(\ln N)/\partial(\ln x_i)$. Similarly, let the set of normalized parameter variations be represented by the vector $\mathbf{d}(\ln \mathbf{x})$ with elements $d(\ln x_i)$. Thus (5) may be written*

$$\frac{dN}{N} = d(\ln N) = (\mathbf{S}^N)^t \, \mathbf{d}(\ln \mathbf{x}) \tag{6}$$

The real part of $\mathbf{S}^N$ defines the change in the magnitude of N resulting from the change in the x_i, and the imaginary part of $\mathbf{S}^N$ defines the change in the argument of N. Like the other relations defined in this section, (6) is an exact relation when differential quantities are considered and may, of course, be used as a linear approximation by considering incremental quantities.

2.2 *The bilinear dependence of network functions on parameters*

In the preceding section one type of sensitivity, i.e., classical sensitivity, was defined and illustrated. Before going on to discuss other types of sensitivity, it will be helpful to study the manner in which an arbitrary network function depends on a given parameter, i.e., the manner in which the network function varies as the parameter is varied. By parameter, here we mean any passive or active component on which the network function depends, i.e., of which it is itself a function. If we let x be the parameter and consider $N(p,x)$ as the general network function, we may define the following relation:

$$N(p,x) = \frac{C(p) + xD(p)}{A(p) + xB(p)} \tag{7}$$

where $A(p)$, $B(p)$, $C(p)$, and $D(p)$ are polynomials with real coefficients which are not functions of x. The function $N(p,x)$ defined in (7) is said to be a *bilinear function of x*.†

* A. J. Goldstein and F. F. Kuo, Multiparameter Sensitivity, *IRE Trans. Circuit Theory*, vol. CT-8, no. 2, pp. 177–178, June, 1961.

† This was originally pointed out for driving-point and transfer impedances by H. W. Bode, "Network Analysis and Feedback Amplifier Design," p. 223, D. Van Nostrand Company, Inc., Princeton, N.J., 1945.

As an example of such bilinear dependence, consider the active RC circuit shown in Fig. 2.7. The triangle shown in the figure indicates an

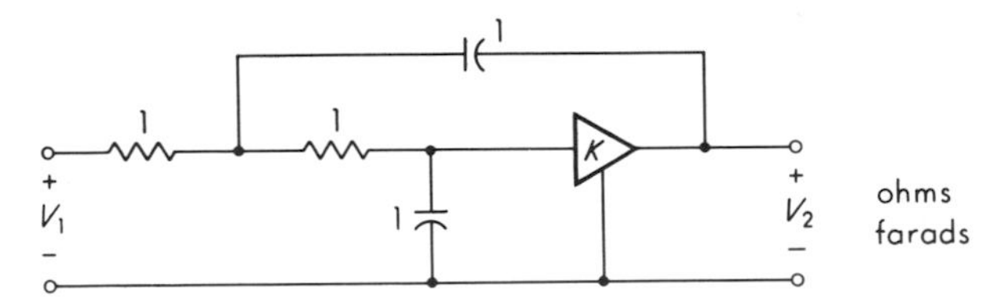

***Figure 2.7** An active RC circuit.*

ideal noninverting voltage amplifier of high input impedance, low output impedance, and gain K. For the normalized element values given in the figure, we may write the voltage transfer function in the form

$$\frac{V_2}{V_1}(p,K) = \frac{K}{p^2 + 3p + 1 - Kp}$$

Thus we see that, for this example, $A(p)$ of (7) is $p^2 + 3p + 1$. Similarly $B(p) = -p$, $C(p) = 0$, $D(p) = 1$, and $x = K$.

Although other types of dependence are encountered, the bilinear dependence of a network function on a parameter encompasses by far the majority of active and passive network situations. Other situations can usually be treated as bilinear by suitable changes of parameters.*

The bilinear dependence of network functions is readily established with respect to two-terminal elements. As an example of this, consider the RC network shown in Fig. 2.8. The transfer impedance for this network is

$$\frac{V_2}{I_1} = \frac{1}{(3p + 1) + C_0(2p^2 + 2p)}$$

which is certainly bilinear in C_0. This result may be shown to be true in general. To see this, consider an arbitrary network with a nodal admittance matrix $\mathbf{Y}$. This network may also be considered as an arbitrary

* See I. M. Horowitz, "Synthesis of Feedback Systems," p. 71, Academic Press Inc., New York, 1963.

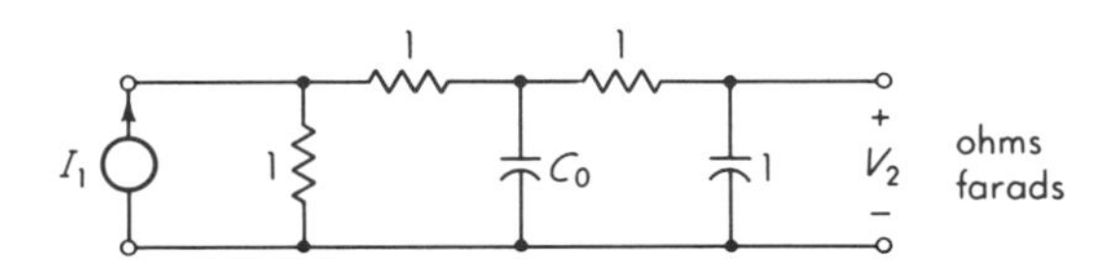

***Figure 2.8** A passive RC circuit.*

two-port network by using the jth and ith nodes as the terminals of port 1 and the mth and nth nodes as the terminals of port 2 as shown in Fig. 2.9.

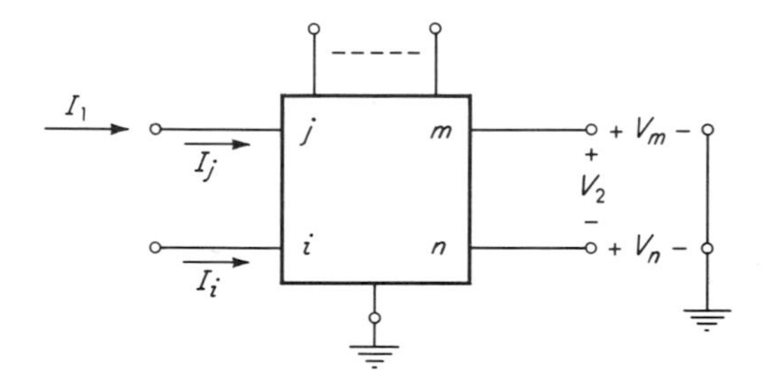

***Figure 2.9** A network which uses four arbitrary nodes to define two ports.*

Now consider the effect of adding an admittance Y_0 between any two nodes of the network. Without loss of generality these may be taken as node 1 and ground, since the nodes defining the input and output ports are unspecified. Let $\mathbf{Y}'$ be the nodal admittance matrix for the network with the admittance Y_0 added. If we write the matrix $\mathbf{Y}$ for the original network in the partitioned form

$$\mathbf{Y} = \left[\begin{array}{c|c} y_{11} & \mathbf{Y}_{12} \\ \hline \mathbf{Y}_{21} & \mathbf{Y}_{22} \end{array}\right]$$

then we may write $\mathbf{Y}'$ as

$$\mathbf{Y}' = \left[\begin{array}{c|c} y_{11} + Y_0 & \mathbf{Y}_{12} \\ \hline \mathbf{Y}_{21} & \mathbf{Y}_{22} \end{array}\right] \tag{8}$$

Now let us derive the open-circuit transfer impedance for the two-port network shown in Fig. 2.9. In terms of the nodal currents defined in the figure we may write

$$\frac{V_m}{I_j} = z_{mj} = \frac{Y'_{jm}}{\det \mathbf{Y}'}$$
$$\frac{V_n}{I_j} = z_{nj} = \frac{Y'_{jn}}{\det \mathbf{Y}'}$$
$$\frac{V_m}{I_i} = z_{mi} = \frac{Y'_{im}}{\det \mathbf{Y}'}$$
$$\frac{V_n}{I_i} = z_{ni} = \frac{Y'_{in}}{\det \mathbf{Y}'}$$

where the z_{qr} are the elements of the inverse of the $\mathbf{Y}'$ matrix and the Y'_{qr} are cofactors of $\mathbf{Y}'$. Taking into account the relations

$$V_2 = V_m - V_n$$
$$I_1 = I_j = -I_i$$

we obtain

$$z_{21} = \frac{V_2}{I_1} = \frac{Y'_{jm} - Y'_{jn} - Y'_{im} + Y'_{in}}{\det \mathbf{Y}'} \tag{9}$$

The determinant of $\mathbf{Y}'$ may be written in the form

$$\det \mathbf{Y}' = \det \mathbf{Y} + Y_0(\det \mathbf{Y}_{22}) \tag{10}$$

Thus we see that the denominator of z_{21} in (9) is a linear function of Y_0. Similarly, expansions for any of the cofactors Y'_{qr} yield expressions that are linear in Y_0. Since the sum and difference of such expressions will also be a linear function of Y_0, we see that the numerator of z_{21} in (9) is also a linear function of Y_0. We may conclude that z_{21} is a bilinear function of the two-terminal element Y_0; thus, it may be written in the form given in (7), where the quantity x is replaced by Y_0.* Since the element Y_0 was chosen arbitrarily, we may conclude that the transfer impedance of an arbitrary network is a bilinear function of any two-terminal admittance in that network.

Now let us consider the driving-point impedance z_{11} of the two-port network shown in Fig. 2.9. It may be shown that this is

$$z_{11} = \frac{V_1}{I_1} = \frac{Y'_{jj} - Y'_{ji} - Y'_{ij} + Y'_{ii}}{\det \mathbf{Y}'} \tag{11}$$

Proceeding as before, we see that z_{11} is also a bilinear function of any two-terminal admittance Y_0 in the network. Since the open-circuit voltage transfer function for a two-port network $V_2/V_1 = z_{21}/z_{11}$, from (9) and (11) we see that such a function will also be a bilinear function of any two-terminal admittance Y_0. An argument similar to that used above may be employed to show the bilinear nature of short-circuit transfer admittances and current transfer ratios with respect to any two-terminal impedances. The proof is left to the reader as an exercise.

Network functions are also bilinear with respect to controlled sources. For example, consider a network with a nodal admittance matrix $\mathbf{Y}$. For convenience in future developments, let us partition the matrix as follows:

$$\mathbf{Y} = \left[\begin{array}{cc|c} y_{11} & y_{12} & \mathbf{Y}_{12} \\ \hline y_{21} & y_{22} & \mathbf{Y}_{22} \\ \hline y_{31} & y_{32} & \\ \cdot & \cdot & \\ \cdot & \cdot & \mathbf{Y}_{32} \\ \cdot & \cdot & \\ y_{n1} & y_{n2} & \end{array}\right] \tag{12}$$

* If Y_0 is a function of the complex-frequency variable p, such dependence is usually included in the polynomials $B(p)$ and $D(p)$. Thus, x is usually treated as a real number.

Now let us connect a voltage-controlled current source* of transconductance G from node 1 to ground, controlled by the voltage from node 2 to ground. Let the resulting matrix be defined as $\mathbf{Y}'$. We see that

$$\mathbf{Y}' = \left[\begin{array}{cc:c} y_{11} & y_{12} + G & \mathbf{Y}_{12} \\ \hdashline y_{21} & y_{22} & \mathbf{Y}_{22} \\ \hdashline y_{31} & y_{32} & \\ \cdot & \cdot & \\ \cdot & \cdot & \mathbf{Y}_{32} \\ \cdot & \cdot & \\ y_{n1} & y_{n2} & \end{array}\right] \tag{13}$$

The proof of the bilinearity of the network functions with respect to G follows from the same arguments as were used in the case of a two-terminal admittance. Duality can be used to prove the bilinear dependence on a current-controlled voltage source.

It may also be shown that network functions are bilinear with respect to voltage-controlled voltage sources. To see this, let us again consider a network with a nodal admittance matrix $\mathbf{Y}$, partitioned as shown in (12). Now let us place a voltage-controlled voltage source from node 2 to ground, controlled by the voltage from node 1 to ground and of gain K. Thus, we establish the constraint on the network $V_2 = KV_1$. It may be shown that the effect of such a constraint is to multiply the second column of $\mathbf{Y}$ by K, add it to the first column, and also to delete the second row and second column of $\mathbf{Y}$.† Let the resulting matrix be defined as $\mathbf{Y}'$. We see that

$$\mathbf{Y}' = \left[\begin{array}{c:c} y_{11} + Ky_{12} & \mathbf{Y}_{12} \\ \hdashline y_{31} + Ky_{32} & \\ \cdot & \\ \cdot & \mathbf{Y}_{32} \\ \cdot & \\ y_{n1} + Ky_{n2} & \end{array}\right] \tag{14}$$

It is easily shown that all the determinants and cofactors of $\mathbf{Y}'$ are linear in K. For example, consider det $\mathbf{Y}'$. This is easily shown to be

$$\det \mathbf{Y}' = y_{11}Y'_{11} + Ky_{12}Y'_{11} + \sum_{i=3}^{n} y_{i1}Y'_{i-1,1} + K\sum_{i=3}^{n} y_{i2}Y'_{i-1,1} \tag{15}$$

* Such a source will be defined more formally in Chap. 3. Here it may be considered as a two-port device satisfying the relation $I_2 = GV_1$.

† A. Nathan, Matrix Analysis of Constrained Networks, *Inst. Elec. Eng. (England)*, Monograph No. 399E, pp. 98–105, Sept., 1960.

where the Y'_{j1} are the cofactors of $\mathbf{Y}'$. The cofactors in (15) do not involve any of the elements in the first column of $\mathbf{Y}'$, and therefore, they are not functions of K. Thus, det $\mathbf{Y}'$ is linear in K. Similar expressions may be derived to show that all other cofactors of $\mathbf{Y}'$ are linear in K. Thus, all transfer impedances and driving-point impedances and all other related network functions will be bilinear in K. It will be shown in Chap. 4 that a voltage-controlled voltage source may be used to realize a negative-immittance converter. Therefore, we see that the network functions are also bilinear with respect to the gain of such a device.

In this section we have shown that network functions, in general, have a bilinear dependence on both active and passive network elements. There are some exceptions to this relationship. For example, it may be shown that the dependence on the coefficient of coupling of a pair of coupled coils is not bilinear. Such exceptions, however, are of relatively little significance to this study. Thus, it will be convenient in the material that follows to consider that the network functions are bilinear with respect to all the parameters of the network unless otherwise stated.

2.3 *Root sensitivity*

In the first section of this chapter, the concept of sensitivity was introduced. It was pointed out that various types of sensitivity could be defined, depending on the criterion of network performance which was chosen. In this section we shall introduce a very important and useful sensitivity, one which has as its criterion the change in position of the poles and zeros of the network function. This sensitivity will be referred to as *root sensitivity*.

There is, of course, a close correlation between classical sensitivity and root sensitivity. This correlation will be developed explicitly in the following section. Here, by way of example, let us again consider the network shown in Fig. 2.5. Its driving-point admittance is

$$Y(p) = \frac{p}{p^2 + Rp + 3}$$

If the resistance R is varied from 1 to 3, the poles of the admittance function move as shown in Fig. 2.10. The corresponding change in the magnitude characteristic is shown in Fig. 2.11.

We may define *root sensitivity* as the change in the position of a pole or a zero, i.e., a "root" of the denominator or numerator polynomial of a network function, with respect to a normalized change in one of the network parameters. If we let p_j be the location of the jth root of the numerator or

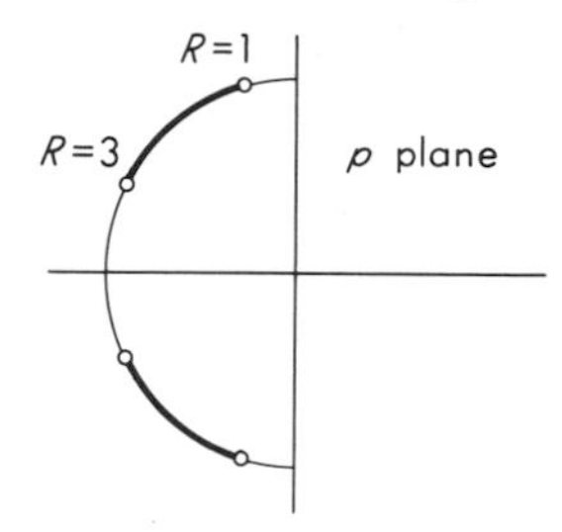

***Figure 2.10** Variation of the poles of a network function.*

denominator polynomials and x be any parameter, we may define the root sensitivity as*

$$S_x^{p_j} = \frac{dp_j}{dx/x} \tag{16}$$

The concepts of root sensitivity, being based on the roots of a polynomial, obviously apply equally well to either a numerator or a denominator polynomial. For the sake of conciseness, we shall restrict ourselves to a discussion of root sensitivity as applied to the roots of a denominator polynomial, i.e., to the poles of a network function. The treatment for the zeros is identical.

If we let $P(p)$ be the denominator polynomial of an arbitrary network function, then by reason of the bilinear dependence of network functions on parameters demonstrated in the last section, we may write†

$$P(p) = A(p) + xB(p) \tag{17}$$

* Several other forms of the root sensitivity have been presented by various authors, mostly differing in a normalization term of the form $1/p_j$ or $1/|p_j|$. This definition appears to be of most utility and is due to I. M. Horowitz, Active Network Synthesis, *IRE Conv. Record*, part 2, pp. 38–45, March, 1956.

† Actually, instead of writing $P(p)$, we might have written $P(p,x)$ as was done in the preceding section. To simplify our notation, however, the functional dependence on x will not be shown explicitly in the remainder of this section.

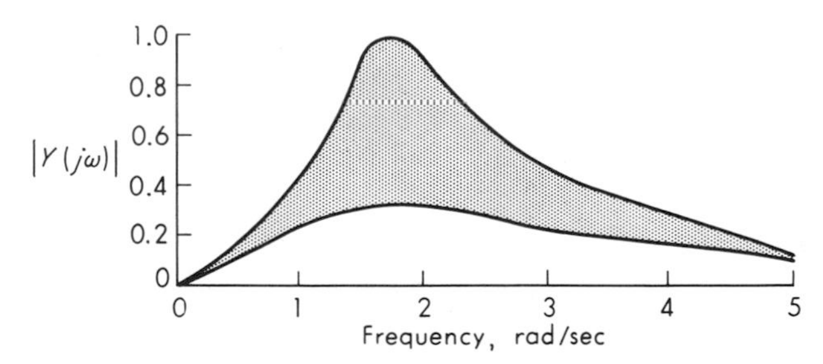

***Figure 2.11** Variation of the magnitude characteristic of a network function.*

where $A(p)$ and $B(p)$ are polynomials and x is an arbitrary parameter. Let p_j be a zero of $P(p)$, i.e., a pole of the network function. Then

$$P(p_j) = A(p_j) + xB(p_j) = 0 \tag{18}$$

Now let x take on an incremental change; i.e., let x become $x + \Delta x$. As a result there will be a corresponding change in p_j. If we replace p_j by $p_j + \Delta p_j$, (18) becomes

$$A(p_j + \Delta p_j) + (x + \Delta x)B(p_j + \Delta p_j) = 0 \tag{19}$$

The terms $A(p_j + \Delta p_j)$ and $B(p_j + \Delta p_j)$ may be evaluated as follows. Let

$$A(p) = a_1 + a_2p + a_3p^2 + a_4p^3 + \cdots \tag{20}$$

Then, substituting $p + \Delta p$ for p, we obtain

$$A(p + \Delta p) = a_1 + a_2(p + \Delta p) + a_3(p + \Delta p)^2 + a_4(p + \Delta p)^3 + \cdots \tag{21}$$

This may be rewritten as

$$\begin{aligned} A(p + \Delta p) = {} & a_1 + a_2p + a_3p^2 + a_4p^3 + \cdots + \Delta p(a_2 + 2a_3p \\ & + 3a_4p^2 + \cdots) + (\Delta p)^2(a_3 + 3a_4p + \cdots) + \cdots \end{aligned} \tag{22}$$

If we retain only first-order incremental terms, (22) may be written in the form

$$A(p + \Delta p) = A(p) + \Delta p\, A'(p) \tag{23}$$

where $A'(p) = dA(p)/dp$. Similarly, $B(p + \Delta p) = B(p) + \Delta p\, B'(p)$. Substituting these expressions into (19), we obtain

$$A(p_j) + \Delta p_j\, A'(p_j) + (x + \Delta x)[B(p_j) + \Delta p_j\, B'(p_j)] = 0 \tag{24}$$

Again retaining only first-order incremental terms, we obtain

$$\Delta x\, B(p_j) + \Delta p_j[A'(p_j) + xB'(p_j)] = \Delta x\, B(p_j) + \Delta p_j\, P'(p_j) = 0 \tag{25}$$

From (25) we see that

$$\frac{\Delta p_j}{\Delta x} = \frac{-B(p_j)}{P'(p_j)} \tag{26}$$

where

$$P'(p_j) = \left.\frac{dP(p)}{dp}\right|_{p=p_j} \tag{27}$$

In the limit as Δx approaches zero, the incrementals in (26) become differentials, and we may substitute in (16) to obtain a general expression for sensitivity. Thus,

$$S_x^{p_j} = \frac{dp_j}{dx/x} = \frac{-xB(p_j)}{P'(p_j)} \tag{28}$$

As an example of the determination of the root sensitivity, let us again consider the network shown in Fig. 2.7. The open-circuit voltage transfer function for this network for the indicated element values is

$$\frac{V_2}{V_1} = \frac{Q(p)}{P(p)} = \frac{K}{p^2 + (3 - K)p + 1} \tag{29}$$

Let us assume that the design or nominal value of K is 2. Then the roots of the polynomial $P(p)$ are $p_1 = -0.5 + j0.866$ and $p_2 = -0.5 - j0.866$. If we put $P(p)$ in the form of (17), we see that $A(p) = p^2 + 3p + 1$ and $B(p) = -p$. From (28) we may obtain the sensitivities for p_1 and p_2 as

$$S_K{}^{p_1} = 1 + j0.577$$
$$S_K{}^{p_2} = 1 - j0.577$$

From these sensitivities we see that if K changes from a nominal value of 2 to a value of 2.2, i.e., if $\Delta K = 0.2$, then $\Delta K/K = 0.1$, and $\Delta p_1 = 0.1 + j0.0577$ with $\Delta p_2 = 0.1 - j0.0577$. Thus, the poles of the voltage transfer function move toward the $j\omega$ axis and farther away from the real axis, the latter movement being a little more than half as great as the former.

As another example of determining root sensitivity consider the polynomial

$$P(p) = xp^2 + p(0.1x + 0.1) + 1.01 \tag{30}$$

Let x have a nominal value of unity. Then the roots of $P(p)$ are $p_1 = -0.1 + j1$ and $p_2 = -0.1 - j1$. If we put $P(p)$ in the form of (17), we see that $A(p) = 0.1p + 1.01$ and $B(p) = p^2 + 0.1p$. From (28) we may obtain the sensitivities

$$\begin{aligned} S_x{}^{p_1} &= 0.05 - j0.5 \\ S_x{}^{p_2} &= 0.05 + j0.5 \end{aligned} \tag{31}$$

From these sensitivities we see that if x changes from a nominal value of unity to a value of 1.1, i.e., if $\Delta x = 0.1$, then $\Delta p_1 = 0.005 - j0.05$, and $\Delta p_2 = 0.005 + j0.05$. Thus, in this case, the zeros of $P(p)$ move toward the $j\omega$ axis and also closer to the real axis, the latter movement being ten times as great as the former.

It should be noted that the sensitivity concepts as defined in this section are based on linear approximations to the actual root movement. As such, they are sometimes referred to as *first-order* sensitivities. Some authors have defined a second-order sensitivity function in order to gain additional information about the behavior of the roots.* The price that is paid for this additional information, however, is a high one in terms of the addi-

* J. J. Mikulski, "The Correlation between Classical and Pole-Zero Sensitivity," Ph.D. dissertation, University of Illinois, 1959.

tional difficulty in determining and using the sensitivity expression. Thus, applications of the concept of higher-order sensitivities are mostly confined to situations where digital computational techniques are utilized.

One other comment is significant with respect to the sensitivity defined in (28). It should be noted that if $P(p)$ has a nonsimple zero at p_j, then $P'(p_j)$ will also be zero. In this case [assuming that $B(p_j)$ is not zero] the sensitivity defined by (28) will be infinite. Thus, it is customary to refer to the sensitivity of multiple roots as being *infinite*.* This must not of course be construed to mean that the roots move an infinite distance for a finite change in the value of the parameter. Rather it means that the multiple root ceases to exist and is replaced by a set of simple roots. Because of the importance of the multiple-root case, a method of determining the movement of such roots with respect to parameter variations is presented in the following section.

2.4 *Some other root-sensitivity considerations*

In this section we shall extend the concept of root sensitivity developed in the previous section to include a treatment of the multiple-root case.† To do this, let us first examine in more detail the movement of the poles and zeros of a network function as a given parameter x is varied. Let the network function be $N(p,x)$. As discussed in Sec. 2.2, we assume that the function is bilinear in the parameter x. Thus, we may write

$$N(p,x) = \frac{Q(p,x)}{P(p,x)} = \frac{C(p) + xD(p)}{A(p) + xB(p)} \tag{32}$$

Now let us replace x by $x + \Delta x$. The poles of $N(p,x)$ will be determined by the roots of the equation

$$A(p) + (x + \Delta x)B(p) = 0 \tag{33}$$

If we define a function

$$F(p,x) = \frac{xB(p)}{P(p,x)} \tag{34}$$

we may write (33) in the form

$$1 + \frac{\Delta x}{x} F(p,x) = 0 \tag{35}$$

* F. F. Kuo, Pole-zero Sensitivity in Network Functions, *IRE Trans. Circuit Theory,* vol. CT-5, no. 4, pp. 372–373, Dec., 1958.

† Much of the material in this section is based on J. Mikulski, *op. cit.*

The form of (35) is such that it is amenable to a determination of the movement of its zeros [which are also the poles of $N(p,x)$] by root-locus techniques. Thus, with increasing Δx, the poles of $N(p,x)$ will move from their original locations [which are also the poles of $F(p,x)$] to the zeros of $B(p)$ [which are also the zeros of $F(p,x)$]. Now let the poles of $F(p,x)$ be p_j. Assuming that the numerator of $F(p,x)$ is lower in degree than the denominator, we may express this function as a partial-fraction expansion of the form

$$F(p,x) = \sum_j \frac{K_j}{p - p_j} \tag{36}$$

If we substitute the partial-fraction expansion of (36) into (35) and examine the behavior of the equation in the vicinity of the jth pole of $F(p,x)$, the jth term of the expansion will predominate. Thus we may write (35) in the form

$$1 + \frac{\Delta x}{x} \frac{K_j}{p_j' - p_j} = 0 \tag{37}$$

where p_j' is the value of p which satisfies the equation. As such it also represents the approximate new location of the jth pole of $N(p,x)$. Thus, we may write $p_j' - p_j = \Delta p_j$. Substituting this relation into (37), rearranging terms, and taking the limit as Δx approaches zero, we obtain an expression for the sensitivity of the jth pole of $N(p,x)$ as

$$S_x^{p_j} - \frac{dp_j}{dx/x} = -K_j \tag{38}$$

where K_j is the residue of $F(p,x)$ at its jth pole. In a similar fashion, if we define a function

$$G(p,x) = \frac{xD(p)}{Q(p)} \tag{39}$$

whose poles are z_i and make a partial-fraction expansion in terms of these poles [which are also the zeros of $N(p,x)$], we obtain

$$G(p,x) = \sum_i \frac{K_i}{p - z_i} \tag{40}$$

The sensitivity for the ith zero of $N(p,x)$ may then be shown to be

$$S_x^{z_i} = \frac{dz_i}{dx/x} = -K_i \tag{41}$$

where K_i is the residue of $G(p,x)$ at its ith pole. The sensitivities arrived at by the use of (38) and (41) will, of course, be the same as those arrived at by the use of (28).

The procedure outlined above may be extended to determine the change of root positions for the case where nonsimple roots are being considered. Suppose, for example, that $N(p,x)$ as defined in (32) has an nth-order pole p_1 together with m other simple poles. The partial-fraction expansion for $F(p,x)$ corresponding to that given in (36) will be

$$F(p,x) = \frac{K_{11}}{p - p_1} + \frac{K_{12}}{(p - p_1)^2} + \cdots + \frac{K_{1n}}{(p - p_1)^n} + \sum_{j=1}^{m} \frac{K_j}{p - p_j}$$

If we substitute this partial-fraction expansion into (35) and examine the behavior of the equation in the vicinity of p_1, we obtain

$$1 + \frac{\Delta x}{x}\left[\frac{K_{11}}{p_1' - p_1} + \frac{K_{12}}{(p_1' - p_1)^2} + \cdots + \frac{K_{1n}}{(p_1' - p_1)^n}\right] = 0$$

where p_1' is the value of p which satisfies the equation. If we make the substitution $p_1' - p_1 = \Delta p_1$ and multiply both members of the equation by $(\Delta p_1)^n$, we obtain

$$(\Delta p_1)^n + \frac{\Delta x}{x}\left[K_{11}(\Delta p_1)^{n-1} + K_{12}(\Delta p_1)^{n-2} + \cdots + K_{1n}\right] = 0 \quad (42)$$

From this equation we see that the nth-order root splits into n simple roots. The locations of these simple roots with respect to the nth-order root are given by the n values of Δp_1 found by solving (42). Thus we see that the "infinite" sensitivity of multiple poles discussed in the previous section actually implies that the multiple root splits into simple roots. It should be noted that the initial decomposition of the multiple roots can be determined by noting that for small values of Δp_1 the constant term will predominate over all of the other terms multiplied by $\Delta x/x$ in (42). Therefore, for this case we may write

$$\Delta p_1 = \left(\frac{-\Delta x}{x} K_{1n}\right)^{1/n}$$

Thus we see that initially the new n roots will be located equidistantly along the circumference of a circle centered at p_1.* Further changes of such roots may easily be explored by the techniques already described.

As an example of the sensitivity of such roots, consider the active *RC* circuit with a noninverting ideal voltage amplifier shown in Fig. 2.7. The open-circuit voltage transfer function for this circuit is

$$\frac{V_2}{V_1} = \frac{Q(p,K)}{P(p,K)} = \frac{K}{p^2 + (3 - K)p + 1}$$

* A. Papoulis, Displacement of the Zeros of the Impedance $Z(p)$ Due to Incremental Variations in the Network Elements, *Proc. IRE*, vol. 43, no. 1, pp. 79–82, Jan., 1955.

Assuming that K has a nominal value of unity, the polynomial $P(p,1) = p^2 + 2p + 1$. Thus it has a second-order zero at -1. Forming the function $F(p,K) = K\,B(p)/P(p,K)$, for $K = 1$ we obtain the partial-fraction expansion

$$F(p,1) = \frac{-1}{p+1} + \frac{1}{(p+1)^2}$$

If we define p_1 as the zero at -1, from (42) we see that in the limit

$$\Delta p_1 = \pm j\sqrt{\Delta K}$$

Thus, if we let $\Delta K = 0.01$, we see that the new roots of $P(p,1.01)$ are

$$\begin{aligned} p_{1a} &= -1 + j0.1 \\ p_{1b} &= -1 - j0.1 \end{aligned}$$

As another example of the sensitivity of multiple roots, consider the following polynomial with a parameter x:

$$P(p,x) = p^3 + 4p^2 + 5p + 2x$$

When $x = 1$, $P(p,1) = (p+1)^2(p+2)$. Thus the polynomial has a second-order zero at $p = -1$. Forming the function $F(p,x) = xB(p)/P(p,x)$ and making a partial-fraction expansion, we obtain, for the case when $x = 1$,

$$F(p,1) = \frac{-2}{p+1} + \frac{2}{(p+1)^2} + \frac{2}{p+2}$$

Let p_1 be the zero at -1. Then from (42) we obtain

$$(\Delta p_1)^2 - 2\Delta x\,\Delta p_1 + 2\Delta x = 0$$

This has the solution

$$\Delta p_1 = \Delta x \pm \sqrt{(\Delta x)^2 - 2\Delta x}$$

If we let $\Delta x = 0.01$, we obtain

$$\begin{aligned} p_{1a} &= -0.99 + j0.141 \\ p_{1b} &= -0.99 - j0.141 \end{aligned}$$

Thus, we see that a positive parameter variation splits the second-order zero into two complex conjugate zeros. The actual locations of these roots of the cubic for $x = 1.01$ are easily shown to be

$$\begin{aligned} p_{1a} &= -0.9903 + j0.1397 \\ p_{1b} &= -0.9903 - j0.1397 \end{aligned}$$

The agreement is seen to be quite good. Similarly, if we let $\Delta x = -0.01$, we obtain

$$p_{1a} = -1.152$$
$$p_{1b} = -0.868$$

We see that for this case the parameter variation splits the second-order zero into two real zeros. The actual locations of these zeros may be shown to be

$$p_{1a} = -1.1537$$
$$p_{1b} = -0.8671$$

Again, good agreement is obtained.

The form of the partial-fraction expansions given in (36) and (40) was based on the assumption that the degree of the numerator was less than the degree of the denominator for the functions $F(p,x)$ and $G(p,x)$ defined in (34) and (39). If the degrees of the numerator and denominator are the same for either of these functions, then in $N(p,x)$ the parameter x must appear as a multiplicative constant for the highest-degree term of the entire denominator or numerator, respectively. As such, it affects only the magnitude of $N(p,x)$ and does not affect the root positions. Thus, it need not be considered in determining the root sensitivities. Certain physical situations may arise, notably those involving coupled coils, where the degree of the numerator of $F(p,x)$ or $G(p,x)$ may be greater than the degree of the denominator. We shall not concern ourselves with these situations here.*

It should be pointed out that the development made in this section can also be used to relate root sensitivity to classical sensitivity. To see this, we need merely apply the definition of classical sensitivity given in (2) to the general network function given in (32). We obtain

$$S_x{}^N = \frac{xD(p)}{Q(p,x)} - \frac{xB(p)}{P(p,x)} = G(p,x) - F(p,x) \tag{43}$$

If we expand $F(p,x)$ and $G(p,x)$ in the form given in (36) and (40), respectively, and substitute the definitions of sensitivity given in (38) and (41), we obtain

$$S_x{}^N = \sum_j \frac{S_x{}^{p_j}}{p - p_j} - \sum_i \frac{S_x{}^{z_i}}{p - z_i} \tag{44}$$

Thus, we see that the classical sensitivity may be expressed as a weighted sum of the pole and zero sensitivities for a given network function.†

* A treatment of this case is given in J. Mikulski, *op. cit.*

† This was pointed out in a discussion by H. Ur of the paper by R. Y. Huang, The Sensitivity of the Poles of Linear Closed-loop Systems, *Trans. AIEE Applications and Industry*, no. 38, pp. 182–187, Sept., 1958.

2.5 The sensitivity matrix

In this section a method will be presented for making a complete sensitivity analysis for a network, i.e., determining the manner in which all of the parameters affect the network performance. Such information is of considerable importance in determining the relative tolerances within which various network components must be specified. A matrix format will be used for the presentation of the data.*

Let $P(p)$ be an arbitrary polynomial which we will use to represent the numerator or denominator polynomial of a network function. We may express $P(p)$ in the form

$$P(p) = a_1 + a_2p + a_3p^2 + \cdots + p^n \tag{45}$$

where, since we will be concerned with the roots of $P(p)$, we have assumed, without loss of generality, that the coefficient of the highest-degree term is unity. The coefficients a_i will, in general, be functions of all the parameters, i.e., the active and passive components, of the network. If we assume that there are m parameters x_j, we may write

$$a_i = f_i(x_1, \ldots, x_m) \tag{46}$$

Now assume that all the x_j take on incremental variations Δx_j. As a result there will be a corresponding variation Δa_i in the ith coefficient. If we replace all the x_j by $x_j + \Delta x_j$ and the a_i by $a_i + \Delta a_i$ in (46), we obtain (retaining only first-order terms)

$$\Delta a_i = \sum_{j=1}^{m} \frac{\partial}{\partial x_j} f_i(x_1, \ldots, x_m)\, \Delta x_j \tag{47}$$

Since there are n coefficients a_i, there will be n such equations. These may be written in matrix format by defining $\mathbf{\Delta a}$ as the n-row column matrix whose elements are the Δa_i, $\mathbf{\Delta x}$ as the m-row column matrix whose elements are the Δx_j, and $\mathbf{F}$ as an $n \times m$ matrix whose elements are defined by the relation

$$f_{ij} = \frac{\partial}{\partial x_j} f_i(x_1, \ldots, x_m) \tag{48}$$

Thus, the matrix equation relating changes in all the coefficients of $P(p)$ to changes in the network parameters may be written as

$$\mathbf{\Delta a} = \mathbf{F}\, \mathbf{\Delta x} \tag{49}$$

Now let us express the polynomial $P(p)$ in factored form. We shall assume that there are q pairs of complex conjugate roots among the n

* Much of the material in this section is based on the paper by L. P. Huelsman, Matrix Analysis of Network Sensitivities, *Proc. Nat. Electron. Conf.*, vol. 19, pp. 1–5, 1963.

roots of $P(p)$ and that the remaining roots are real. We may then represent the polynomial in the form

$$P(p) = \prod_{i=1}^{q} (p^2 + b_{2i-1}p + b_{2i}) \prod_{i=2q+1}^{n} (p + b_i) \tag{50}$$

The indexing in (50) is such as to specify n real numbers b_i. From the first $2q$ of these numbers we may readily obtain the real part and the magnitude of the complex-conjugate root locations. The last $n - 2q$ numbers give the locations of the real roots of $P(p)$. Thus, the factorization of $P(p)$ given in (50) provides all the pertinent information on root locations without requiring the use of complex quantities. This provides considerable simplification of computational procedures.

The coefficients of $P(p)$ as specified in (45) will now be related to the roots as specified by the b_i coefficients of (50). To do this, let us replace a_i by $a_i + \Delta a_i$ in (45). Similarly, in (50) let us replace b_i by $b_i + \Delta b_i$. Equating the two expressions and retaining only first-order terms, we obtain n expressions of the type

$$\Delta a_i = \sum_{j=1}^{n} d_{ij}\,\Delta b_j$$

where the d_{ij} are functions of the coefficients b_i. We may express these relations in matrix form as

$$\mathbf{\Delta a} = \mathbf{D}\,\mathbf{\Delta b} \tag{51}$$

where $\mathbf{\Delta a}$ is as previously defined, $\mathbf{D}$ is an $n \times n$ matrix with elements d_{ij}, and $\mathbf{\Delta b}$ is an n-row column matrix with elements Δb_i. We may combine (49) and (51) to obtain a relation between the parameter variations Δx_j and the root changes Δb_i. The result is

$$\mathbf{\Delta b} = \mathbf{D}^{-1}\mathbf{F}\,\mathbf{\Delta x} \tag{52}$$

Since normalized variations are generally of more interest than the actual variations, we may define the column matrix $\mathbf{\Delta b}^{(n)}$ whose elements are the normalized changes in the coefficients and the $n \times n$ matrix $\mathbf{B}$, a diagonal matrix, whose elements are the coefficients b_i. The normalizing relationship is given as

$$\mathbf{\Delta b} = \mathbf{B}\,\mathbf{\Delta b}^{(n)} \tag{53}$$

Similarly, let $\mathbf{\Delta x}^{(n)}$ be the column matrix whose elements are the normalized parameter changes, and let $\mathbf{X}$ be an $m \times m$ diagonal matrix whose elements are the parameters x_j. The normalizing relationship for the x_j is

$$\mathbf{\Delta x} = \mathbf{X}\,\mathbf{\Delta x}^{(n)} \tag{54}$$

Substituting (53) and (54) in (52), we obtain

$$\mathbf{\Delta b}^{(n)} = \mathbf{B}^{-1}\mathbf{D}^{-1}\mathbf{F}\mathbf{X}\,\mathbf{\Delta x}^{(n)} \tag{55}$$

Thus, we may define a *sensitivity matrix* **S**, where

$$\mathbf{S} = \mathbf{B}^{-1}\mathbf{D}^{-1}\mathbf{F}\mathbf{X} \tag{56}$$

which relates the normalized change in root locations (as specified by the coefficients b_i) to the normalized change in parameter variations. Thus, the elements of **S** are defined as

$$s_{ij} = \frac{\partial b_i / b_i}{\partial x_j / x_j} \tag{57}$$

As an example of the determination of the sensitivity matrix, let us consider the denominator polynomial of the voltage transfer function for the active RC circuit shown in Fig. 2.12. The polynomial may be written

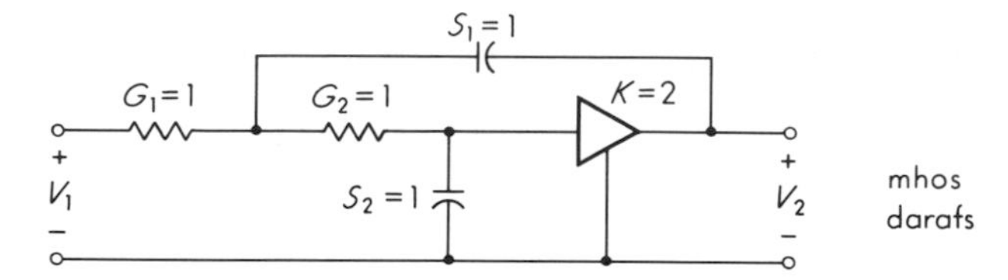

Figure 2.12 An active RC circuit.

in the form*

$$P(p) = p^2 + b_1 p + b_2 = p^2 + p[G_1S_1 + G_2S_1 + G_2S_2(1 - K)] + G_1G_2S_1S_2$$

Following the development given above we find the following expressions for the matrices of (56):

$$\mathbf{D} = \begin{bmatrix} 1 & 0 \\ 0 & 1 \end{bmatrix}$$

$$\mathbf{B} = \begin{bmatrix} b_1 & 0 \\ 0 & b_2 \end{bmatrix}$$

$$\mathbf{F} = \begin{bmatrix} S_1 & S_1 + S_2(1-K) & G_1 + G_2 & G_2(1-K) & -G_2S_2 \\ G_2S_1S_2 & G_1S_1S_2 & G_1G_2S_2 & G_1G_2S_1 & 0 \end{bmatrix}$$

$$\mathbf{X} = \begin{bmatrix} G_1 & & & & \\ & G_2 & & 0 & \\ & & S_1 & & \\ & 0 & & S_2 & \\ & & & & K \end{bmatrix}$$

* It will be convenient in this and future developments to use units of conductance (reciprocal resistance) and elastance (reciprocal capacitance). Thus, G_1 and G_2 represent the value of resistors 1 and 2 as given in mhos (reciprocal ohms). Similarly, S_1 and S_2 represent the values of capacitors 1 and 2 as given in darafs (reciprocal farads).

For the nominal element values given in the figure, $P(p) = p^2 + p + 1$. Thus, we find that the sensitivity matrix is given by the expression

$$\begin{bmatrix} b_1^{(n)} \\ b_2^{(n)} \end{bmatrix} = \begin{bmatrix} 1 & 0 & 2 & -1 & -2 \\ 1 & 1 & 1 & 1 & 0 \end{bmatrix} \begin{bmatrix} G_1^{(n)} \\ G_2^{(n)} \\ S_1^{(n)} \\ S_2^{(n)} \\ K^{(n)} \end{bmatrix}$$

As another example of the determination of the sensitivity matrix, consider the polynomial

$$P(p) = p^3 + p^2(5x_1 - x_2) + p(x_1x_2 + 2) + x_1x_2$$

Let the nominal values of the parameters be $x_1 = 1$ and $x_2 = 2$. For these values, $P(p)$ is seen to be

$$P(p) = p^3 + 3p^2 + 4p + 2 = (p^2 + 2p + 2)(p + 1)$$

For the general third-degree case, if we let $P(p)$ be of the form

$$P(p) = (p^2 + b_1p + b_2)(p + b_3) = a_1 + a_2p + a_3p^2 + p^3$$

then (51), which defines the matrix $\mathbf{D}$, may be shown to be

$$\begin{bmatrix} \Delta a_1 \\ \Delta a_2 \\ \Delta a_3 \end{bmatrix} = \begin{bmatrix} 0 & b_3 & b_2 \\ b_3 & 1 & b_1 \\ 1 & 0 & 1 \end{bmatrix} \begin{bmatrix} \Delta b_1 \\ \Delta b_2 \\ \Delta b_3 \end{bmatrix}$$

The matrix $\mathbf{D}^{-1}$ is then given by

$$\begin{bmatrix} \Delta b_1 \\ \Delta b_2 \\ \Delta b_3 \end{bmatrix} = \frac{1}{b_1b_3 - b_2 - b_3^2} \begin{bmatrix} 1 & -b_3 & b_1b_3 - b_2 \\ b_1 - b_3 & -b_2 & b_2b_3 \\ -1 & b_3 & -b_3^2 \end{bmatrix} \begin{bmatrix} \Delta a_1 \\ \Delta a_2 \\ \Delta a_3 \end{bmatrix}$$

For the given example, $b_1 = 2$, $b_2 = 2$, $b_3 = 1$, and we have

$$\mathbf{D}^{-1} = \begin{bmatrix} -1 & 1 & 0 \\ -1 & 2 & -2 \\ 1 & -1 & 1 \end{bmatrix}$$

The matrix $\mathbf{F}$ is easily seen to be

$$\mathbf{F} = \begin{bmatrix} 2 & 1 \\ 2 & 1 \\ 5 & -1 \end{bmatrix}$$

The matrices $\mathbf{B}$ of (53) and $\mathbf{X}$ of (54) are

$$\mathbf{B} = \begin{bmatrix} 2 & 0 & 0 \\ 0 & 2 & 0 \\ 0 & 0 & 1 \end{bmatrix} \qquad \mathbf{X} = \begin{bmatrix} 1 & 0 \\ 0 & 2 \end{bmatrix}$$

Forming the matrix product of (55), we obtain

$$\begin{bmatrix} \Delta b_1^{(n)} \\ \Delta b_2^{(n)} \\ \Delta b_3^{(n)} \end{bmatrix} = \begin{bmatrix} 0 & 0 \\ -4 & 3 \\ 5 & -2 \end{bmatrix} \begin{bmatrix} \Delta x_1^{(n)} \\ \Delta x_2^{(n)} \end{bmatrix}$$

Thus, we see that for this example the real part of the complex conjugate zeros, i.e., the coefficient b_1, is not affected (to a first-degree approximation) by changes in either of the parameters x_1 and x_2. We note also that these parameters have effects that are different in sign and magnitude on the magnitude of the complex-zero position (which is equal to $\sqrt{b_2}$) and the position of the negative-real root (which is $-b_3$). These conclusions are easily verified numerically. For example, if negative 1 percent changes are made separately in x_1 and x_2 and the actual roots of the resulting polynomial are determined, we find that the actual sensitivities are

$$\begin{bmatrix} \Delta b_1^{(n)} \\ \Delta b_2^{(n)} \\ \Delta b_3^{(n)} \end{bmatrix} = \begin{bmatrix} 0.185 & 0.064 \\ -3.796 & 3.064 \\ 4.63 & -2.17 \end{bmatrix} \begin{bmatrix} \Delta x_1^{(n)} \\ \Delta x_2^{(n)} \end{bmatrix}$$

These results, of course, are only correct for the stated change in the coefficients.

Now let us compare the actual changes of the coefficients with those predicted by the sensitivity matrix (with its first-order approximations). For example, from the theoretical sensitivity matrix we see that a negative 1 percent change in x_1 should produce a negative 5 percent change in the coefficient b_3 (assuming $\Delta x_2 = 0$). Thus, b_3 should change its value from 1.0 to 0.95. From the actual sensitivity figures given above, the value of b_3 that actually results from such a change is 0.9537. Comparing the two results, we see that they agree to within an accuracy of 0.39 percent. It is easily verified that all the other terms in the sensitivity matrix for this example yield even more accurate results than the above.

It should be noted that in some cases the matrix **D** may not have an inverse. For example, if multiple roots are present, then corresponding to these roots there must be a number of identical columns in **D**. Thus there will not be an inverse. In such a case, the variations of the coefficients a_i may be determined separately, and the root movements found by the method given in Sec. 2.4.

We may now derive some of the properties of the elements of the sensitivity matrix.

Property 1 *The sensitivity with respect to a reciprocal-valued element is the negative of the sensitivity with respect to the original element, that is,*

$$S_x^b = -S_{1/x}^b$$

where $S_x{}^b$ represents the s_{ij} element of the sensitivity matrix **S** *corresponding with coefficient b and parameter x.*

To see this, let $x' = 1/x$, then, for first-order effects

$$x' + \Delta x' = \frac{1}{x + \Delta x} \approx \frac{1}{x}\left(1 - \frac{\Delta x}{x}\right)$$

from which we see that

$$\Delta x' \approx -\frac{\Delta x}{x^2}$$

Substituting this relationship into the definition of $S_{x'}{}^b$ on an incremental basis, we obtain

$$S_{x'}{}^b = \frac{\Delta b}{\Delta x'}\frac{x'}{b} = \frac{\Delta b}{-\Delta x/x^2}\frac{1/x}{b} = -\frac{\Delta b}{\Delta x}\frac{x}{b} = -S_x{}^b$$

which, in the limit as the incrementals become differentials, proves the property. Thus, for example, we see that if the sensitivity coefficients s_{ij} have been determined for elements of conductance and elastance (reciprocal capacitance), the corresponding coefficients for elements of resistance and capacitance are simply the negative of the original sensitivities.

Property 2 *If a coefficient b has both a numerator n and a denominator d which are functions of some parameter, the sensitivity of b with respect to x may be written*

$$S_x{}^b = S_x{}^n - S_x{}^d$$

where $b = n/d$.

To see this, on an incremental basis we may define

$$S_x{}^b = \frac{\Delta b}{\Delta x}\frac{x}{b} = \left(\frac{\Delta n}{\Delta x}\frac{1}{d} - \frac{\Delta d}{\Delta x}\frac{n}{d^2}\right)\frac{x}{n/d}$$

Reducing the above, we obtain

$$S_x{}^b = \frac{\Delta n}{\Delta x}\frac{x}{n} - \frac{\Delta d}{\Delta x}\frac{x}{d} = S_x{}^n - S_x{}^d$$

This property is of value in determining the sensitivity matrix for polynomials in which the leading coefficient is not unity [since such polynomials must be reduced to the form shown in (45) by dividing all coefficients by the leading coefficient].

A case of special interest is the one in which $P(p)$ is of second degree; that is, $P(p) = p^2 + b_1p + b_2$. For this case $a_1 = b_1$ and $a_2 = b_2$. Thus the matrix **D** of (51) is simply the identity matrix, and b_1 and b_2 may be considered as the coefficients of $P(p)$. Now let us consider the form that the coefficients b_1 and b_2 may have. Because of the bilinear nature of the network functions, the dependence of a coefficient b_i on some parameter x_j may be expressed in the form

$$b_i = f_1(x_1, \ldots, x_{j-1}, x_{j+1}, \ldots, x_m) + x_j f_2(x_1, \ldots, x_{j-1}, x_{j+1}, \ldots, x_m) \quad (58)$$

where f_1 and f_2 are functions of any or all (or none) of the parameters *except* x_j. We may now specify three possible cases for the coefficients b_i and derive the resulting restrictions on the elements of the sensitivity matrix. The three cases are similar to those given for the classical sensitivity in Sec. 2.1. They define the following three properties:

Property 3 *If f_1 of (58) is zero, then, for the polynomial*

$$P(p) = p^2 + b_1 p + b_2$$

we may derive

$$s_{ij} = \frac{\partial b_i}{\partial x_j}\frac{x_j}{b_i} = 1$$

Thus we see that if the x_j parameter occurs as a multiplicative factor for the coefficients of second-degree polynomials, the resulting sensitivity is unity, and therefore independent of the value of the coefficient or the parameter.

Property 4 *If f_1 and the product $x_j f_2$ in (58) have the same polarity, we find that for the polynomial $P(p) = p^2 + b_1 p + b_2$,*

$$s_{ij} = \frac{\partial b_i}{\partial x_j}\frac{x_j}{b_i} = \frac{x_j f_2}{f_1 + x_j f_2}$$

Since the denominator of this sensitivity coefficient must always be greater than the numerator, we see that $|s_{ij}| < 1$ for this case. In most network situations of this type, f_1 and the product $x_j f_2$ will both be positive, in which case the sensitivity coefficient will also be positive.

Property 5 *If f_1 of (58) is positive but the product $x_j f_2$ is negative, we find that, for the polynomial $P(p) = p^2 + b_1 p + b_2$,*

$$s_{ij} = \frac{\partial b_i}{\partial x_j}\frac{x_j}{b_i} = \frac{-|x_j f_2|}{f_1 - |x_j f_2|}$$

In most network situations f_1 is also greater than $|x_j f_2|$. Thus in this case the coefficient will be negative. The magnitude of the coefficient is unrestricted. However, in Sec. 2.6 we shall see that there is a minimum value on its magnitude which is determined by the location of the zeros of the polynomial $P(p)$.

In succeeding chapters we shall discuss the realization of many network functions involving second-degree polynomials. In these chapters we shall see examples of properties 3, 4, and 5 given above.

One other interesting aspect of the sensitivity matrix for the second-degree polynomial is the relation between its elements and the classical sensitivity. For this case we have the following property:

Property 6 *If* $P(p) = p^2 + b_1 p + b_2$ *is the denominator of a network function* $N(p)$, *in which only the coefficient* b_1 *is a function of some parameter* x_j, *then*

$$S_{x_j}{}^N\,(j\sqrt{b_2}) = -s_{1j}$$

where $S_{x_j}{}^N\,(j\sqrt{b_2})$ *is the classical sensitivity evaluated at* $p = j\sqrt{b_2}$, *and* s_{1j} *is the element of the sensitivity matrix relating a change in* b_1 *to a change in* x_j.

The proof of the above property is easily seen by comparing (4) and (57). The negative sign results from the application of property 2 given above.

One other technique may be used to relate the changes in the coefficients a_j given in (45) to the changes in root locations. To see this, let us write $P(p)$ in the factored form

$$P(p) = \prod_{i=1}^{n} (p - p_i) \tag{59}$$

where the various p_i are the roots of $P(p)$ and may be real or complex. In the latter case, of course, they will occur in conjugate pairs. If we let the coefficients a_j of (45) take on incremental changes, i.e., if we replace a_j by $a_j + \Delta a_j$, then the resulting changes in the roots may be found by replacing the p_i of (59) by $p_i + \Delta p_i$. Equating the two perturbed equations and retaining only first-order incremental terms, we obtain*

$$-\sum_{i=1}^{n} \Delta p_i Q_i(p) = \sum_{j=1}^{n} \Delta a_j p^{j-1} \tag{60}$$

where

$$Q_i(p) = \frac{P(p)}{(p - p_i)} \tag{61}$$

If we now let $p = p_k$, the only nonzero term in the summation in the left member of (60) will be the kth one. Thus, we obtain

$$\Delta p_k = \frac{-1}{Q_k(p_k)} \sum_{j=1}^{n} \Delta a_j (p_k)^{j-1} \tag{62}$$

Thus we may define an n-row column matrix $\mathbf{\Delta p}$ with elements Δp_i, an

* G. Martinelli, On the Matrix Analysis of Network Sensitivities, *Proc. IEEE*, vol. 54, no. 1, pp. 72–73, Jan., 1966.

n-row column matrix $\mathbf{\Delta a}$ with elements Δa_j, and an $n \times n$ matrix $\mathbf{Q}$ whose elements are defined as

$$q_{ij} = \frac{\partial p_i}{\partial a_j} = \frac{-(p_i)^{j-1}}{Q_i(p_i)} \tag{63}$$

We see that

$$\mathbf{\Delta p} = \mathbf{Q}\,\mathbf{\Delta a} \tag{64}$$

An overall sensitivity formulation may now be expressed using the matrix $\mathbf{Q}$ from (64) and the matrices $\mathbf{F}$ and $\mathbf{X}$ defined in (49) and (54). Thus we may write

$$\mathbf{\Delta p} = \mathbf{QFX}\,\mathbf{\Delta x}^{(n)} \tag{65}$$

It should be noted that although this technique does not require matrix inversion, the computations, in general, will require the use of complex numbers and thus will be more complicated than those leading to the $\mathbf{S}$ matrix of (56).

As an example of this technique, let us consider the same example which was used earlier in this section. If we let $p_1 = -1 - j$, $p_2 = -1 + j$, and $p_3 = -1$, we obtain, applying the above techniques,

$$\begin{bmatrix} \Delta p_1 \\ \Delta p_2 \\ \Delta p_3 \end{bmatrix} = \begin{bmatrix} -4j & 3j \\ 4j & -3j \\ 5 & -2 \end{bmatrix} \begin{bmatrix} \Delta x_1^{(n)} \\ \Delta x_2^{(n)} \end{bmatrix}$$

A comparison of this with the previously determined sensitivity matrix readily verifies the validity of this approach.

2.6 *Polynomial decomposition—the difference case*

In the preceding sections of this chapter we have considered a network function $N(p,x)$ which is bilinear in its dependence on some parameter x. Thus, the numerator and denominator polynomials of $N(p,x)$ are linear in x. For such linear functions we have explored the sensitivity of the polynomial roots with respect to changes in the parameter x. In effect, we have made a sensitivity *analysis* of the network function. Our treatments in this and the following section will be quite different in nature. Here we will concern ourselves with the *synthesis* aspect; i.e., we shall be concerned with the manner in which a linear function can be formed from a given polynomial. Stated another way, we shall investigate the manner in which a given polynomial can be *decomposed* into the sum or difference of two other polynomials. It will be pointed out that such a decomposition can be optimized so as to minimize the sensitivity.

Let $P(p)$ be an arbitrary polynomial. Without loss of generality, since we are primarily concerned with the roots of $P(p)$, we may assume that the coefficient of the highest-degree term is unity. The linear dependence of such a polynomial on an arbitrary parameter x that was demonstrated in Sec. 2.2 permits us to write a general expression for the decomposition of $P(p)$ into two component polynomials $A(p)$ and $B(p)$. We obtain

$$P(p,x) = A(p) - xB(p) \tag{66}$$

We shall assume that the parameter x is positive and that the leading coefficients of $A(p)$ and $B(p)$ are positive (but not necessarily unity). We may also define a second general type of polynomial decomposition by the relation

$$P(p,x) = A(p) + xB(p) \tag{67}$$

In the first case we say that $P(p)$ is decomposed into the difference of two polynomials; in the second case, we say $P(p)$ is decomposed into the sum of two polynomials. We shall consider the case defined by (66) in this section. The case defined by (67) will be covered in the following section.

As an example of such a difference decomposition, consider the network shown in Fig. 2.7. For this network the open-circuit voltage transfer function is

$$\frac{V_2}{V_1} = \frac{Q(p,K)}{P(p,K)} = \frac{K}{p^2 + p(3 - K) + 1}$$

Thus, the denominator polynomial $P(p,K)$ may be written in the form given in (66), where $A(p) = p^2 + 3p + 1$, $B(p) = p$, and $x = K$.

Let $P(p)$ be a polynomial with only simple complex conjugate zeros. Let the zeros of $A(p)$ and $B(p)$ in (66) be restricted to the negative-real axis including the origin. Let the degree of $A(p)$ be equal to the degree of $P(p)$, and let the degree of $B(p)$ be equal to or 1 less than the degree of $P(p)$.* The zeros of $P(p,x)$ are determined by a root locus satisfying the equation

$$\frac{xB(p)}{A(p)} = 1 \tag{68}$$

It should be noted that this equation defines a 0° root locus rather than the more usual 180° locus. For such a locus we must have the alternation of the zeros of $A(p)$ and $B(p)$ shown in Fig. 2.13, where the zero closest to

* There are, of course, several other decomposition cases that can be studied based on different restrictions on the perimssible location of the zeros of $P(p)$, $A(p)$, and $B(p)$. The case defined here is the one most frequently encountered in the study of active *RC* networks. A discussion of sensitivity considerations for some cases with complex conjugate zeros of $A(p)$ and $B(p)$ may be found in L. P. Huelsman, Active RC Synthesis with Prescribed Sensitivities, *Proc. Nat. Electron. Conf.*, vol. 16, pp. 412–426, 1960. See also, S. S. Hakim, Synthesis of *RC* Active Filters with Prescribed Pole Sensitivity, *Proc. IEE*, vol. 112, no. 12, pp. 2235–2242, Dec., 1965.

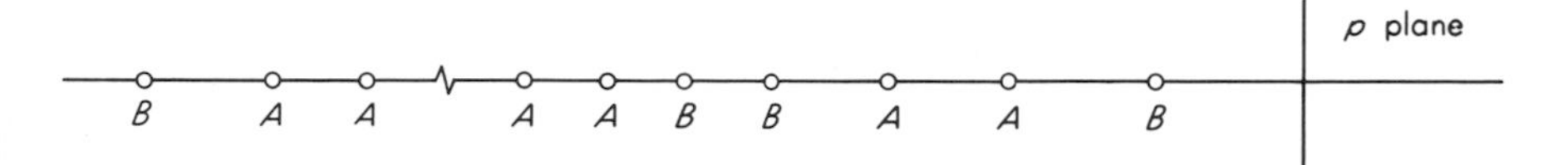

***Figure 2.13** Alternation of the zeros of $A(p)$ and $B(p)$ for the difference decomposition of (66).*

the origin (it may also lie at the origin) is a zero of $B(p)$. The zero closest to infinity (it may also lie at infinity) must also belong to $B(p)$.*

For a given $P(p)$ a unique decomposition exists such that the magnitude of the sensitivities of all the roots of $P(p,x)$ are minimized with respect to variations in the parameter x. Such a decomposition is considered optimum and is referred to as a *Horowitz decomposition*.† For this optimum decomposition, $B(p)$ has a simple zero at the origin and at infinity. All the other zeros of $A(p)$ and $B(p)$ are of the second order. The relative positions of the zeros are shown in Fig. 2.14. In Appendix C a proof of the optimal-

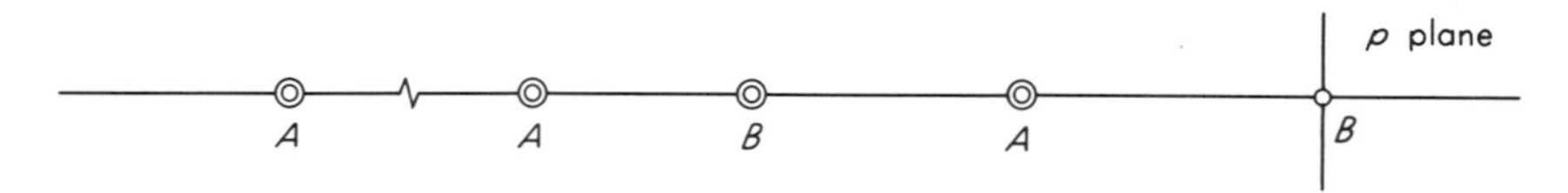

***Figure 2.14** Alternation of the zeros of $A(p)$ and $B(p)$ for an optimum difference decomposition.*

ity of this decomposition is given. Here we shall describe the procedure for accomplishing the decomposition.

The locations of the zeros of $A(p)$ and $B(p)$ may be found by the following procedure:‡

1. Determine the roots of the polynomial $P(p^2)$, that is, the polynomial formed by replacing p with p^2. Let $F(p)$ contain the left-half-plane roots of $P(p^2)$. $F(p)$ is obviously Hurwitz and is sometimes referred to as

* The interpretation of a "zero at infinity" is that the degree of $B(p)$ is 1 less than the degree of $P(p)$.

† The optimum nature of the decomposition [and a method for determining the zeros of $A(p)$ and $B(p)$] was originally demonstrated for the magnitude of the classical sensitivity (evaluated for $p = j\omega$) by I. M. Horowitz in the paper, Optimization of Negative-impedance Conversion Methods of Active *RC* synthesis, *IRE Trans. Circuit Theory,* vol. CT-6, no. 3, pp. 290–303, Sept., 1959. The fact that the magnitudes of the root sensitivities were also minimized was pointed out by D. A. Calahan in the paper, Notes on the Horowitz Optimization Procedure, *IRE Trans. Circuit Theory,* vol. CT-7, no. 3, pp. 352–354, Sept., 1960.

‡ D. A. Calahan, *op. cit.*

the *associated Hurwitz polynomial of* $P(p)$. Let $F(-p)$ contain the right-half-plane roots of $P(p^2)$. Thus we obtain

$$P(p^2) = F(p)F(-p) \tag{69}$$

2. Let $F(p) = a(p^2) + pb(p^2)$, where $a(p^2)$ is the even part of $F(p)$ and $pb(p^2)$ is the odd part. Then $F(-p) = a(p^2) - pb(p^2)$, and from (69) we have

$$P(p^2) = a^2(p^2) - p^2b^2(p^2) \tag{70}$$

3. The decomposition is found by substituting p for p^2 in (70). We obtain

$$P(p) = a^2(p) - pb^2(p) \tag{71}$$

Thus we see that we may define $A(p) = a^2(p)$ and $xB(p) = pb^2(p)$ to yield a decomposition of $P(p)$ into the form of $P(p,x)$ given in (66).

The process may be illustrated by the following example. Let

$$P(p) = p^2 + 6p + 25$$

Then

$$P(p^2) = p^4 + 6p^2 + 25 = (p^2 + 2p + 5)(p^2 - 2p + 5)$$

For $F(p)$ we choose the left-half-plane zeros of $P(p^2)$. We obtain

$$F(p) = p^2 + 2p + 5 = (p^2 + 5) + 2p$$

Thus, $a(p^2) = p^2 + 5$, and $b(p^2) = 2$. From (70) we see that

$$P(p^2) = (p^2 + 5)^2 - p^2(4)$$

Thus, we obtain the optimum decomposition

$$P(p) = (p + 5)^2 - 4p$$

If the nominal value of x is unity, we may write

$$P(p,x) = (p + 5)^2 - x(4p)$$

It is easily seen that this is equal to the original polynomial.

As a second example, one which will be useful in our studies of specific realizations, consider the general normalized second-degree function

$$P(p) = p^2 + kp + 1$$

where $k < 2$. The above procedure may be applied to show that the optimum decomposition for this function is*

$$P(p) = (p + 1)^2 - p(2 - k)$$

* A tabulation of the decompositions for several common polynomials with Butterworth and Chebyshev characteristics may be found in S. S. Hakim, *RC* Active Filters Using Amplifiers as Active Elements, *Proc. IEE*, vol. 112, no. 5, pp. 901–912, May, 1965.

Let us assume that the nominal value of x is unity. Thus the optimum decomposition of $P(p,x)$ is

$$P(p,x) = (p + 1)^2 - xp(2 - k)$$

For this case, we may compute the sensitivity

$$S_x^k = \frac{\partial k}{\partial x}\frac{x}{k} = -\frac{2}{k} + 1 \tag{72}$$

If this polynomial is the denominator polynomial of a function of the form $N(p) = Hp/(p^2 + kp + 1)$, then, since the Q of the function is $1/k$, we see that the optimum sensitivity may be expressed in terms of the Q as $-2Q + 1$. It should be readily apparent that for high-Q networks, even in the optimal case, the sensitivity will be large. Since Q is always greater than $\frac{1}{2}$, we see that the optimum sensitivity is always negative. As pointed out in Sec. 2.5, property 6, the above result can be considered as defining an element of the sensitivity matrix, or if it is multiplied by -1, it gives the minimum value of the classical sensitivity, assuming none of the other coefficients of the network function are functions of k.

An additional property of the optimum decomposition for $P(p)$ given in (71) should be noted. Let $P(p)$ be the denominator polynomial of some network function $N(p)$. Thus, we may write

$$N(p) = \frac{Q(p)}{P(p)} = \frac{Q(p)}{a^2(p) - pb^2(p)} \tag{73}$$

If we divide numerator and denominator by the polynomial $pa(p)b(p)$,

$$N(p) = \frac{Q(p)/pa(p)b(p)}{a(p)/pb(p) - b(p)/a(p)} \tag{74}$$

Since $a(p^2)$ and $pb(p^2)$ are the even and odd parts of the Hurwitz polynomial $F(p)$, their ratio is an LC driving-point impedance (or admittance) function. Such a function may be related to an RC driving-point function by the relation*

$$Z_{RC}(p) = \frac{1}{s} Z_{LC}(s)$$

under the transformation $p = s^2$. Thus, we see that

$$\frac{1}{s} Z_{LC}(s) = \frac{1}{s}\left[\frac{a(s^2)}{sb(s^2)}\right] = \frac{a(p)}{pb(p)} = Z_{RC}(p) \tag{75}$$

* For a discussion of such transformations see any book on modern network synthesis, for example, M. E. Van Valkenburg, "Introduction to Modern Network Synthesis," chap. 6, John Wiley & Sons, Inc., New York, 1960.

We conclude that the first term in the denominator of (74) is a passive RC driving-point impedance. Similarly, we may write

$$\frac{1}{s} Z_{LC}(s) = \frac{1}{s}\left[\frac{sb(s^2)}{a(s^2)}\right] = \frac{b(p)}{a(p)} = Z_{RC}(p) \tag{76}$$

Thus, we conclude that the denominator of (74) is composed of the difference of two passive RC driving-point impedance functions.

Now let us divide the numerator and denominator of (73) by the polynomial $a(p)b(p)$. We obtain

$$N(p) = \frac{Q(p)/a(p)b(p)}{a(p)/b(p) - pb(p)/a(p)} \tag{77}$$

On an admittance basis, where $p = s^2$, it is known that

$$Y_{RC}(p) = sY_{LC}(s) \tag{78}$$

If we apply this relationship to the LC immittances defined by the ratio of the polynomials $a(p^2)$ and $pb(p^2)$, we see that

$$sY_{LC}(s) = s\left[\frac{a(s^2)}{sb(s^2)}\right] = \frac{a(p)}{b(p)} = Y_{RC}(p) \tag{79}$$

and

$$sY_{LC}(s) = s\left[\frac{sb(s^2)}{a(s^2)}\right] = \frac{pb(p)}{a(p)} = Y_{RC}(p) \tag{80}$$

In this case, the denominator of $N(p)$ has been expressed in (77) as the difference of two passive RC driving-point admittance functions. We shall see applications of these cases in the realization techniques to be discussed in the following chapters.

As a simple example of such an application, consider the realization of the open-circuit voltage transfer function

$$\frac{V_2}{V_1} = \frac{-p}{p^2 + p + 1}$$

If the denominator is optimally decomposed and the function is put in the form of (77), we obtain

$$\frac{V_2}{V_1} = \frac{-p/(p+1)}{(p+1) - p/(p+1)}$$

A network realization for this transfer function is shown in Fig. 2.15, where the block labeled "NIC" is a negative-immittance converter. This device multiplies an admittance by $-K$, where K is the "gain" of NIC. Thus, for $K = 1$, the circuit realization is optimally insensitive to changes in the gain of the NIC. A more detailed treatment of NICs will be given in Chap. 4.

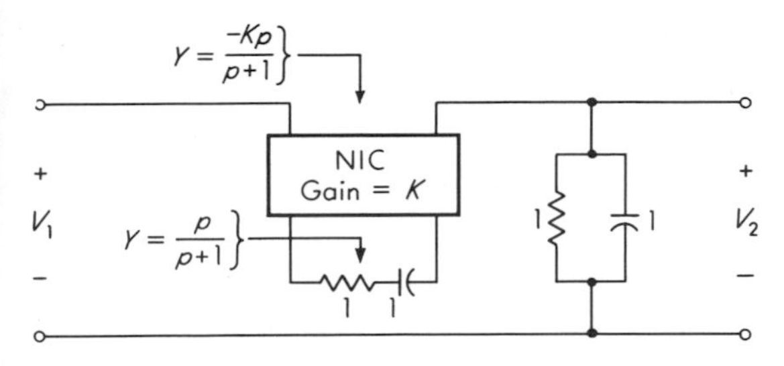

Figure 2.15 A network realization using an NIC.

2.7 Polynomial decomposition—the sum case

In the last section, the decomposition of a polynomial into the *difference* of two polynomials was discussed. In this section we shall discuss the decomposition of a polynomial into the *sum* of two polynomials. We shall treat this decomposition for the same restrictions on the original polynomial and the resulting component polynomials that were imposed in the previous section.

Let $P(p)$ be a polynomial with simple complex conjugate zeros. Let this polynomial be decomposed into the sum of two polynomials as indicated in (67), where the zeros of $A(p)$ and $B(p)$ are restricted to the negative-real axis (including the origin) and where x is an arbitrary positive parameter. Let the degree of $A(p)$ be equal to the degree of $P(p)$, and let the degree of $B(p)$ be equal to or be 1 or 2 less than the degree of $P(p)$. The zeros of $P(p,x)$ are determined by a root locus satisfying the equation

$$\frac{xB(p)}{A(p)} = -1 \tag{81}$$

Thus, we see that the zeros follow a conventional 180° root locus. Such a locus must have the alternation of the zeros of $A(p)$ and $B(p)$ shown in Fig. 2.16, where the zero closest to the origin (it may also lie at the origin) is a zero of $A(p)$. The two zeros closest to infinity (either or both of them may also lie at infinity) must belong to $B(p)$.*

* Since a summation of polynomials is defined in this case, it is possible to interchange the designations $A(p)$ and $B(p)$ in the above discussion.

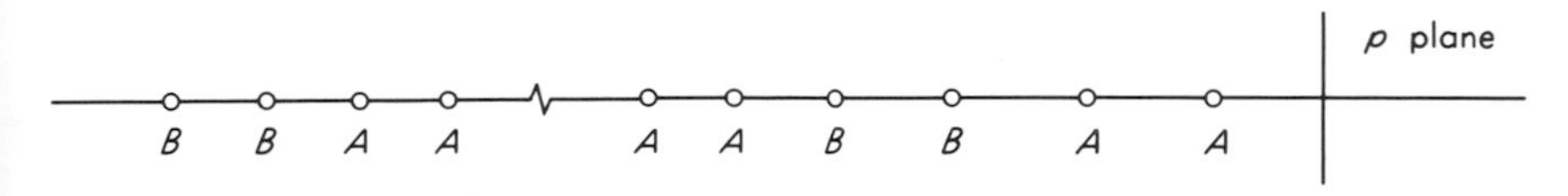

Figure 2.16 Alternation of the zeros of $A(p)$ and $B(p)$ for the sum decomposition of (67).

Now let us assume that $P(p)$ is of degree n and that its leading coefficient is unity. We may express it in the factored form

$$P(p) = \prod_{i=1}^{n/2} (p + p_i)(p + \bar{p}_i) \tag{82}$$

where the zeros of $P(p)$ are located at $-p_i$ and $-\bar{p}_i$. If we define the quantities p_i as having positive imaginary parts, we may define the angles arg p_i as shown in Fig. 2.17. If these arguments satisfy the inequality

$$\sum_{i=1}^{n/2} \arg p_i \leq \frac{\pi}{2} \tag{83}$$

then a unique decomposition of $P(p)$ is possible in the form of (67). The component polynomials $A(p)$ and $B(p)$ will have the form

$$\begin{aligned} A(p) &= \prod_{i=1}^{n/2} (p + a_i)^2 \\ B(p) &= b_0 \prod_{i=1}^{n/2-1} (p + b_i)^2 \end{aligned} \tag{84}$$

where the a_i and b_i are real and nonnegative. Thus, the zeros of $A(p)$ and $B(p)$ shown in Fig. 2.16 will all be of the second order, and the two zeros of $B(p)$ shown at the left will be missing. Such a decomposition is optimum

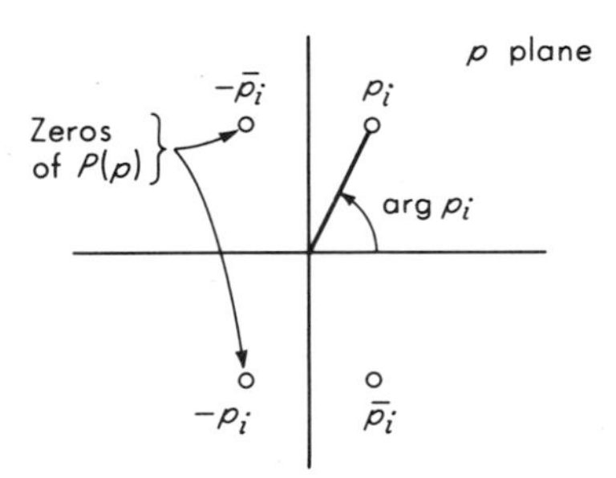

Figure 2.17 Definition of arg p_i.

in the sense that it will provide the minimum magnitudes of root sensitivities for $P(p)$ that are possible with a decomposition of the type of (67). The locations of the zeros of $A(p)$ and $B(p)$ of (84) may be found by the following procedure:*

* A description of this decomposition as well as a proof of the condition of inequality of (83) is given by D. A. Calahan in the article: Restrictions on the Natural Frequencies of an *RC-RL* Network, *J. Franklin Inst.*, vol. 272, no. 2, pp. 112–133, Aug., 1961. The article also considers the case where $P(p)$ has negative-real zeros. In that case, for m negative-real

1. Let the terms p_i all have a positive imaginary part. Now form a product of the factors $p + p_i$. This product will have a real part and an imaginary part and may be written in the form

$$\prod_{i=1}^{n/2} (p + p_i) = R(p) + jQ(p) \tag{85}$$

2. Make the identifications

$$\begin{aligned} A(p) &= R^2(p) \\ xB(p) &= Q^2(p) \end{aligned} \tag{86}$$

Substitution of the equations of (86) into (67) provides the optimum decomposition.

As an example of this technique, consider the polynomial

$$P(p) = p^2 + 2ap + 1 = (p + a + j\sqrt{1 - a^2})(p + a - j\sqrt{1 - a^2}) \qquad a < 1$$

For this case $p_1 = a + j\sqrt{1 - a^2}$. If we apply the angle criterion of (83), we see that decomposition is possible only if a is nonnegative, i.e., if the zeros of $P(p)$ are in the left half-plane or on the $j\omega$ axis. Proceeding as in (85), we obtain

$$R(p) + jQ(p) = p + p_1 = (p + a) + j\sqrt{1 - a^2}$$

Thus, from the relations of (86), the desired decomposition is

$$P(p) = (p + a)^2 + (1 - a^2)$$

For the case where x has a nominal value of unity we may write

$$P(p,x) = (p + a)^2 + x(1 - a^2)$$

To further illustrate the technique, let us consider a second example, involving two pairs of complex conjugate zeros. Let

$$\begin{aligned} P(p) &= (p^2 + 4p + 5)(p^2 + 8p + 25) \\ &= (p + 2 + j1)(p + 2 - j1)(p + 4 + j3)(p + 4 - j3) \end{aligned}$$

In this case we may let $p_1 = 2 + j1$ and $p_2 = 4 + j3$. Then, arg $p_1 = 26.6°$

---

zeros the optimum decomposition has the form $A(p) \prod_{i=1}^{m} (p + \sigma_i) + B(p) \prod_{i=1}^{m} (p + \sigma_i)$, where $A(p)$ and $B(p)$ are the polynomials resulting from the decomposition of the complex conjugate zeros of the original polynomial by the process described above. The proof follows the general form of argument given in Appendix C of this text.

and $\arg p_2 = 36.9°$, and from (83) we know that the specified decomposition exists. Proceeding as in (85), we obtain

$$\begin{aligned} R(p) + jQ(p) &= (p + 2 + j1)(p + 4 + j3) \\ &= (p + 1)(p + 5) + j4(p + 2.5) \end{aligned}$$

Thus, the desired decomposition, assuming a nominal value of unity for x, is

$$P(p,x) = (p + 1)^2(p + 5)^2 + 16x(p + 2.5)^2$$

One other form may be obtained for the decomposition of a polynomial $P(p)$ with simple complex conjugate zeros into the sum of two polynomials with negative-real zeros. Let $P(p)$ again be expressed in the manner of (82). If the quantities p_i satisfy the inequality

$$\sum_{i=1}^{n/2} \arg p_i < \frac{\pi}{2} \tag{87}$$

then a *nonunique* decomposition of the type given in (67) is possible where $A(p)$ and $B(p)$ have the form*

$$\begin{aligned} A(p) &= a_0 \prod_{i=1}^{n/2} (p + a_i)^2 \\ B(p) &= b_0 \prod_{i=1}^{n/2} (p + b_i)^2 \end{aligned} \tag{88}$$

This decomposition will also be optimum; i.e., it will produce the same minimum magnitude of root sensitivities as was produced by the decomposition described earlier in this section.

For the case in which $P(p)$ is of second degree, the decompositions are easily found. Let

$$P(p) = (p + \sigma + j\omega)(p + \sigma - j\omega) \tag{89}$$

From (87) we see that σ must be positive and nonzero. For this case, the decomposition will be of the form

$$P(p) = a_0(p + a)^2 + b_0(p + b)^2 \tag{90}$$

where all constants are nonnegative. Since $p = -\sigma - j\omega$ is a zero of $P(p)$, we see that

$$a_0(p + a)^2 + b_0(p + b)^2 \Big|_{p=-\sigma-j\omega} = 0$$

The above equation must be satisfied in both phase and magnitude.

* D. A. Calahan, Sensitivity Minimization in Active *RC* Synthesis, *IRE Trans. Circuit Theory*, vol. CT-9, no. 1, pp. 38–42, March, 1962.

Therefore, we see that

$$\arg(p+a) - \arg(p+b)\Big|_{p=-\sigma-j\omega} = \frac{\pi}{2}$$

We may solve the preceding equation trigonometrically to obtain the relation

$$\frac{(\omega^2+\sigma^2)-\sigma a}{\sigma - a} = b \tag{91}$$

Therefore, for $P(p)$ of the second degree we may choose a value of a and find the correct value of b, subject to the constraint that both a and b must be nonnegative. Once a and b have been chosen to satisfy (91), the values of a_0 and b_0 are easily computed.

As an example, consider

$$P(p) = p^2 + 1.2p + 1 = (p + 0.6 + j0.8)(p + 0.6 - j0.8)$$

Inserting the values $\sigma = 0.6$ and $\omega = 0.8$ into (91) and choosing a value $a = 0.2$, we obtain $b = 2.2$. Equating coefficients, we find that $a_0 = 0.8$ and $b_0 = 0.2$. Thus, we obtain the decomposition

$$P(p,x) = 0.8(p+0.2)^2 + 0.2x(p+2.2)^2$$

where it is assumed that the nominal value of x is unity. Other decompositions may be easily obtained by choosing other values for a.

It should be noted that although the decompositions discussed in this section all provide the same optimum value of the magnitude of the root sensitivity, the real and imaginary parts of the sensitivity may be expected to be considerably different for different decompositions. It should also be noted that if the sum decomposition described in this section is possible, it will always produce a lower magnitude of sensitivity than the difference case discussed in the previous section.

The optimum sum decompositions given in this section may be related to passive RC driving-point immittances in a manner similar to that used for the optimum difference decompositions of the preceding section. Let $P(p)$ be the denominator polynomial of some network function $N(p)$ which has numerator $Q(p)$. If $P(p)$ is optimally decomposed, $N(p)$ may be written in the form

$$N(p) = \frac{Q(p)}{a_0 a^2(p) + b_0 b^2(p)} \tag{92}$$

where $a(p) = \pi(p + a_i)^2$ and $b(p) = \pi(p + b_i)^2$ and the zeros of $a(p)$ and $b(p)$ alternate on the real axis. If we divide the numerator and the denominator of $N(p)$ by $a(p)b(p)$, we obtain

$$N(p) = \frac{Q(p)/a(p)b(p)}{a_0 a(p)/b(p) + b_0 b(p)/a(p)} \tag{93}$$

It is easily seen (see problems) that the term $a_0a(p)/b(p)$ is realizable as a passive RC driving-point *admittance* function, whereas the term $b_0b(p)/a(p)$ is realizable as a passive RC driving-point *impedance* function. Thus, we see that either of the decompositions of this section may be used to decompose the denominator of a network function into the sum of a passive RC driving-point impedance and a passive RC driving-point admittance. We shall find an application of this decomposition in a later chapter.

As a simple example of such an application, consider the realization of the open-circuit voltage transfer function

$$\frac{V_2}{V_1} = \frac{3/4}{p^2 + p + 1}$$

If the denominator is optimally decomposed and the function is put in the form of (93), we obtain

$$\frac{V_2}{V_1} = \frac{3/4/(p + 1/2)}{p + 1/2 + 3/4/(p + 1/2)}$$

A network realization for this transfer function is shown in Fig. 2.18, where the block labeled "Gyrator" has the property that it inverts a given immittance and multiplies it by a constant K. Thus, for $K = 1$, the circuit realization is optimally insensitive to changes in the value of K. A more detailed treatment of gyrators will be given in Chap. 5.

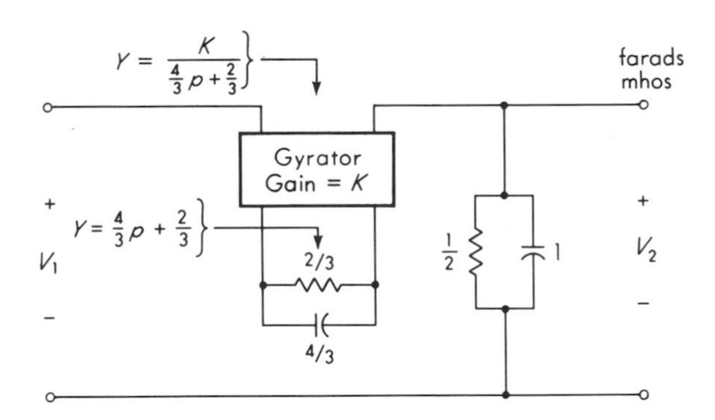

Figure 2.18 A network realization using a gyrator.

2.8 *The second-degree case*

Sensitivity considerations that occur in the synthesis of active RC networks frequently preclude the use of a single network stage for the realization of polynomials of higher than second degree. As an example of this

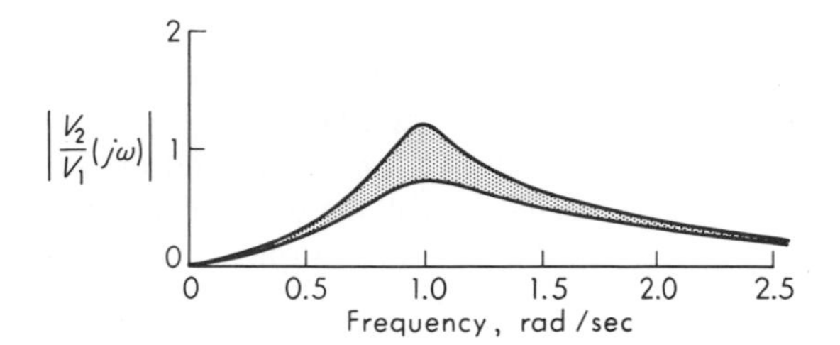

Figure 2.19 ***Variation of the magnitude characteristic for two cascaded second-degree realizations.***

statement, consider the realization of the voltage transfer function

$$\frac{V_2}{V_1} = \frac{p^2}{(p^2 + p + 1)^2} = \frac{p^2}{p^4 + 2p^3 + 3p^2 + 2p + 1}$$

If we realize the function

$$\frac{V_2}{V_1} = \frac{p}{p^2 + p + 1}$$

by an active *RC* network using a single NIC (negative-immittance converter) and cascade it with another identical realization, the variation of the overall transfer-function magnitude for ± 10 percent changes of both NIC gains is as shown in Fig. 2.19 (techniques for accomplishing such a realization will be discussed in Chap. 4). On the other hand, if we realize the entire function by means of a single NIC, the variation of the transfer function magnitude [using an optimum decomposition (see Sec. 2.6)] for ± 10 percent changes in the NIC gain is as shown in Fig. 2.20. Comparing

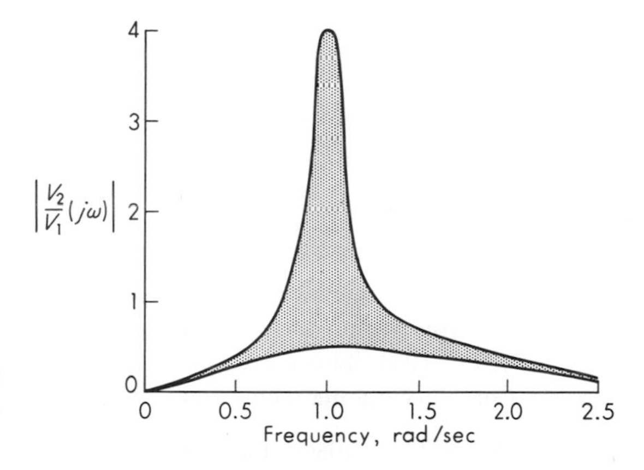

Figure 2.20 ***Variation of the magnitude characteristic for a single fourth-degree realization.***

the two figures, we see that the sensitivity for the single-NIC realization is more than ten times greater than the sensitivity for the two-NIC realization. Thus, it is appropriate to consider the polynomial decompositions introduced in the last two sections in more detail for the second-degree case. In this section we shall consider the general problem of the decomposition of a polynomial consisting of a single pair of complex conjugate zeros into the sum or difference of two polynomials.

Let $P(p)$ be a polynomial of the second degree, having a leading coefficient of unity magnitude, whose zeros are complex. We shall define a general decomposition of the form

$$P(p) = a_0A(p) + Kb_0B(p) \tag{94}$$

where $A(p)$ and $B(p)$ are polynomials of the zero, first, or second degree with a leading coefficient of unity, and a_0, b_0, and K are positive- or negative-valued real constants. In most cases, $A(p)$ and $B(p)$ will be polynomials associated with the driving-point or transfer immittances of passive RC networks, a_0 and b_0 will be overall constants pertaining to these immittance functions, and K will be the gain of some active element. $A(p)$ and $B(p)$ will each have one of the following forms:

Form 1: $(p + \alpha)^2 + \beta^2$
Form 2: $(p + \sigma_1)(p + \sigma_2)$
Form 3: $p + \sigma$
Form 4: 1

The zeros of (94) are determined by the root locus satisfying the equation

$$\frac{Kb_0B(p)}{a_0A(p)} = -1 \tag{95}$$

Two different situations arise, depending on the relative signs of a_0, b_0, and K. The first of these occurs when a_0 and the product Kb_0 have the same sign; the second occurs when they have opposite signs. A given choice of signs and a given choice of the form of $A(p)$ and $B(p)$ will determine a root-locus configuration on which the zeros of $P(p)$ must lie. When a_0 and the product Kb_0 have the same sign, this will be a 180° locus. When they have opposite signs, it will be a 0° locus. If we consider a_0 and b_0 as fixed, the movement of the zeros of $P(p)$ along the root locus will be determined by the value of K.

It is easily shown that there are 13 cases which may produce complex conjugate zeros in the polynomial $P(p)$ of (94). These are shown together with their root loci in Table 2.1.* For convenience the constant K' has

* L. P. Huelsman, Stability Criteria for Active *RC* Synthesis Techniques, *Proc. Nat. Electron. Conf.*, vol. 20, pp. 731–736, 1964.

Table 2.1 Polynomial decompositions for the second-degree case

Case	Sign of a_0 and Kb_0	Form of $A(p)$	Form of $B(p)$
1	Same	1	1
2	Same	2	1
3	Same	3	1
4	Same	4	1
5	Same	2	2
6	Same	3	2
7	Same	2	4
8	Opposite	1	1
9	Opposite	1	2
10	Opposite	1	3
11	Opposite	1	4
12	Opposite	2	2
13	Opposite	2	3

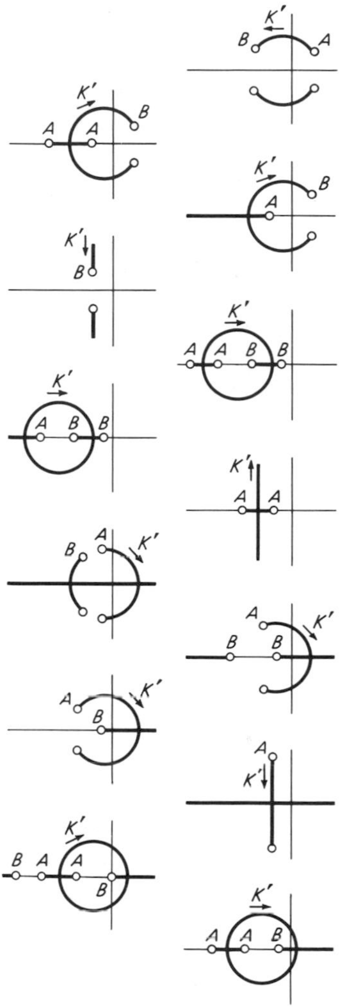

Form 1: $(p+\alpha)^2+\beta^2$ Form 2: $(p+\sigma_1)(p+\sigma_2)$
Form 3: $(p+\sigma)$ Form 4: 1

been used to indicate direction on the root loci, where

$$K' = \frac{Kb_0}{a_0} \tag{96}$$

For the second-degree case, all the root loci will be circles or straight lines, as indicated in the table. The configurations may, of course, be displaced along the real axis without changing the basic shape of a particular configuration. It should be noted that another set of seven cases similar to cases 1 to 7 will result if the zeros of $A(p)$ and $B(p)$ are interchanged. The only significant modification of the cases shown will be that the direction of increasing K' is reversed. For cases 8 to 13, the case shown is for the condition that a_0 is positive. If a_0 is negative, the designations $A(p)$ and $B(p)$ and the direction of increasing K' must be reversed.

The various cases of polynomial decomposition shown in Table 2.1 will have greatly differing sensitivities. Some qualitative information on these sensitivities may be determined by considering the manner in which the zeros of (94) move as K' of (96) varies. Let p_j be a zero of $P(p)$. If K' changes by an incremental amount $\Delta K'$, then p_j must also change by an incremental amount Δp_j. From (94) we see that*

$$|A(p_j + \Delta p_j)| = |K' + \Delta K'|\,|B(p_j + \Delta p_j)| \tag{97}$$

Thus, the magnitude of Δp_j will be minimized if $|A(p_j + \Delta p_j)|$ changes more rapidly along the portion of the root locus in the vicinity of p_j than $|B(p_j + \Delta p_j)|$ does. This implies that as the root locus approaches the zeros of either $A(p)$ or $B(p)$, the sensitivity decreases. Similarly, any portion of a root locus in which the magnitudes of $A(p)$ and $B(p)$ change very slowly can be expected to have a large sensitivity.

In order to illustrate the various decompositions given in Table 2.1 a decomposition of the polynomial $P(p) = p^2 + 0.2p + 1.01$ has been made for the 13 cases shown in the table. The sensitivities have been evaluated for the root located at $-0.1 + j1$. The results are shown in Table 2.2. It should be noted that case 5 includes as a special subcase the situation in which the optimum decomposition of the second type considered in Sec. 2.7 is achieved. For this subcase, the zeros of $A(p)$ and $B(p)$ shown in Table 2.1 are of the second order. Similarly, when the zeros of $A(p)$ in case 7 are coincident, this case includes the optimum decomposition of the first type considered in Sec. 2.7. Finally, case 13 includes the situation in which the optimum difference decomposition discussed in Sec. 2.6 is realized. For such a decomposition, the zeros of $A(p)$ are

* L. P. Huelsman, Active *RC* Synthesis with Prescribed Sensitivities, *Proc. Nat. Electron. Conf.*, vol. 16, pp. 412–426, 1960.

Table 2.2 Sensitivities for $P(p) = p^2 + 0.2p + 1.01$

Case	$a_0A(p)$	Zeros of $A(p)$	$b_0B(p)$	Zeros of $B(p)$	S_k^p	$\lvert S_k^p \rvert$
1	$0.5(p^2 + 0.1p + 1.12)$	$-0.05 \pm j1.058$	$0.5(p^2 + 0.3p + 0.9)$	$-0.15 \pm j0.936$	$-0.025 + j0.03$	0.039
2	$0.112(p^2 + p + 0.0625)$	$-0.067, -0.933$	$0.888(p^2 + 0.1p + 1.13)$	$-0.05 \pm j1.062$	$0.044 + j0.058$	0.073
3	$0.1p$	$0, \infty$	$p^2 + 0.1p + 1.01$	$-0.05 \pm j1.003$	$0.05 + j0.005$	0.0502
4	0.098	∞, ∞	$p^2 + 0.2p + 0.912$	$-0.1 \pm j0.95$	$-j0.049$	0.049
5	$0.991p^2$	$0, 0$	$0.00925(p + 8)(p + 13.65)$	$-8, -13.65$	$-0.099 + j0.491$	0.501
6	$0.1(p + 10.1)$	$-10.1, \infty$	$p(p + 0.1)$	$0, -0.1$	$0.05 - j0.5$	0.502
7	1.01	∞, ∞	$p(p + 0.2)$	$0, -0.2$	$-j0.505$	0.505
8	$2(p^2 + 0.4p + 1.25)$	$-0.2 \pm j1.1$	$p^2 + 0.6p + 1.49$	$-0.3 \pm j1.83$	$0.2 - j0.22$	0.297
9	$1.5(p^2 + 2.2p + 3.21)$	$-1.1 \pm j1.414$	$0.5(p^2 + 6.7p + 8.16)$	$-1.6, -5.1$	$1.625 - j1.625$	2.3
10	$p^2 + 2.2p + 2.01$	$-1.1 \pm j0.739$	$2(p + 0.5)$	$-0.5, \infty$	$1 - j0.4$	1.076
11	$p^2 + 0.2p + 3$	$-0.1 \pm j1.73$	2	∞, ∞	$-j1$	1.0
12	$2.5(p + 0.2)(p + 2.02)$	$-0.2, -2.02$	$1.5p(p + 3.53)$	$0, -3.53$	$2.5 + j1.007$	2.69
13	$(p + 0.2)(p + 5.05)$	$-0.2, -5.05$	$5.05p$	$0, \infty$	$2.52 + j0.252$	2.53
			Optimum decompositions			
5	$0.9901p^2$	$0, 0$	$0.0099(p + 10.1)^2$	$-10.1, -10.1$	$-0.099 + j0.49$	0.5
7	$(p + 0.1)^2$	$-0.1, -0.1$	1.0	∞, ∞	$j0.5$	0.5
13	$(p + 1.005)^2$	$-1.005, -1.005$	$1.81p$	$0, \infty$	$0.905 + j0.0905$	0.91

coincident, and the zero of $B(p)$ occurs at the origin. A study of Table 2.2 illustrates the following points:

1. Decompositions into the sum of two component polynomials (as shown in cases 1 to 7), in general, have lower sensitivities than decompositions into the difference of two polynomials (as shown in cases 8 to 13). This is especially true when only negative-real zeros are permitted in the component polynomials.
2. The two types of optimum decomposition for the sum case described in Sec. 2.7 and shown as case 5 and case 7 may have different complex values of sensitivity, although they will have the same magnitude.
3. If complex zeros are permitted in the component polynomials, the sensitivity may be reduced below the optimum value (which is based on polynomials with real zeros only).
4. The use of the optimum decomposition may not affect the sensitivity of the sum case to an appreciable extent. Its use in the difference case is of considerably more importance.

As an example of the use of the various cases shown in Table 2.1 to classify a given active RC network consider the one shown in Fig. 2.7. The voltage transfer function for this network is

$$\frac{V_2}{V_1} = \frac{K}{p^2 + 3p + 1 - Kp}$$

If we compare the denominator polynomial of this transfer function with the decomposition given in (94), we see that $a_0 = 1$, $A(p) = p^2 + 3p + 1$, $b_0 = -1$, and $B(p) = p$. The decomposition is thus of the type shown as case 13 in Table 2.1 (assuming that K is positive). We shall see many other applications of these cases in the chapters that follow.

2.9 *Conclusion*

The material on sensitivity and polynomial decomposition that has been introduced in this chapter will form a theoretical basis for the study of the various realization techniques to be presented in the chapters that follow. These techniques will be classified according to the type of active device that is used in their realizations. The bilinear nature of the realizations with respect to the gain of the active element will be emphasized. Thus, we can use the conclusions of our sensitivity studies in evaluating different realizations to provide factual information on some of the relative advantages and disadvantages of these realizations. Similarly, the studies of polynomial decomposition, especially the 13 classes of decomposition introduced for the second-degree case, can be used to categorize the various types of realizations. We shall see that realizations which use quite different types of active devices may actually produce their network functions by comparable polynomial decompositions. Finally, it will be shown that the optimization techniques described in this chapter may be applied to many of the realization schemes to provide an improvement in the performance of the overall network over that which might have been achieved without the benefit of the optimization. It should be noted that the optimization techniques minimize the *magnitude* of the sensitivity. In some network applications it may be more desirable to minimize the real or the imaginary part of the sensitivity. For such a criterion, the optimum decompositions given in this chapter are, of course, not always the best choice. We shall consider this subject further in connection with our discussion of gyrators in Chap. 5.

PROBLEMS

2.1 Find the classical sensitivity $S_x{}^N$ for the function $N(p,x)$ given below. Assume that x has a nominal value of unity. Plot the real and imaginary parts of the sensitivity for $p = j\omega$.

$$N(p,x) = \frac{p}{p^2 + p + 3x}$$

2.2 Find the multiparameter sensitivity $\mathbf{S}^N$ for the function $N(p,x_1,x_2)$ given below. Assume that x_1 and x_2 have nominal values of unity. Evaluate the sensitivity at $p = j2$ and $p = j\sqrt{3}$.

$$N(p,x_1,x_2) = \frac{p}{p^2 + x_1 p + 3x_2}$$

2.3 Prove the relation

$$S_K{}^N = -S_{1/K}^N$$

2.4 Find the short-circuit current transfer function I_2/I_1 for the network shown in Fig. P2.4 in terms of the cofactors of the nodal admittance matrix of the network.

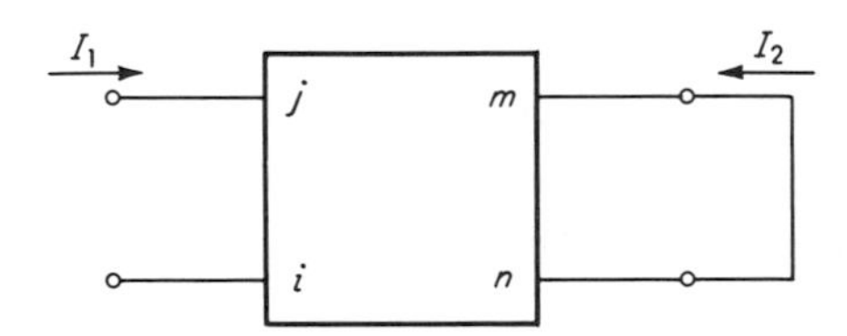

Figure P2.4

2.5 Prove that the network functions of an arbitrary network are bilinear with respect to the gain R of a current-controlled voltage source imbedded in the network.

2.6 Some authors have defined a root sensitivity $S_x^{p_i} = (dp_i/dx)(x/p_i)$. Comment on the meaning of such a sensitivity.

2.7 If a polynomial with only simple roots can be written in the form $P(p) = A(p) + xB(p)$, find an expression for the change in root positions that takes first- *and second*-order incremental changes of x into account.

2.8 For the polynomial $P(p,x) = p^3 + 3p^2 + 3p + x$, where x has a nominal value of unity, find the change in the root positions when x changes to a value of 1.01. Do the same for the case in which x changes to a value of 0.99.

2.9 For the network function $N(p,x)$ given below (where x has a nominal value of unity), show that the classical sensitivity may be expressed as a weighted sum of the root sensitivities

$$N(p,x) = \frac{p + 2x}{p^2 + 4p + 3x}$$

2.10 Find the sensitivity matrix for the following polynomial:

$$P(p,x_1,x_2) = p^3 + p^2(x_1 + x_2) + 4p(x_1 - x_2) + x_1x_2$$

where the nominal value of x_1 is 1, and the nominal value of x_2 is 2.

2.11 For the polynomial given in Prob. 2.10, find the complex sensitivity matrix **QFX** defined by (65).

2.12 Find the optimum difference decomposition for the polynomial $P(p)$ which follows (assume $4b > a^2$):

$$P(p) = p^2 + ap + b$$

2.13 Find the optimum difference decomposition for the polynomial $P(p)$ which follows:

$$P(p) = (p^2 + 2p + 2)(p^2 + p + 1)$$

2.14 Show that the denominator of the network function $N(p)$ which follows may be decomposed into the difference of two passive RC driving-point impedance functions by an optimum decomposition:

$$N(p) = \frac{Hp}{p^2 + ap + b}$$

2.15 Show that the denominator of the network function $N(p)$ given in Prob. 2.14 may be decomposed into the difference of two passive RC driving-point admittances by an optimum decomposition.

2.16 Find an optimum sum decomposition of the type given in (84) for the following polynomial:

$$P(p) = p^2 + ap + b$$

2.17 Find two different types of optimum sum decompositions for the following polynomial:

$$P(p) = (p^2 + 2p + 2)(p^2 + 4p + 5)$$

2.18 Show that the denominator of the network function $N(p)$ given in Prob. 2.14 may be decomposed into the sum of a passive RC driving-point impedance and a passive RC driving-point admittance by an optimum decomposition.

2.19 Determine the cases in Table 2.1 in which the zeros of $A(p)$ and $B(p)$ may be interchanged without changing the positive leading coefficient of $P(p)$, where $P(p) = a_0A(p) + Kb_0B(p)$.

2.20 Find the case from Table 2.1 which applies to the active RC realization shown in Fig. P2.20, where the movement along the root locus is a function of the gain r of the controlled source.*

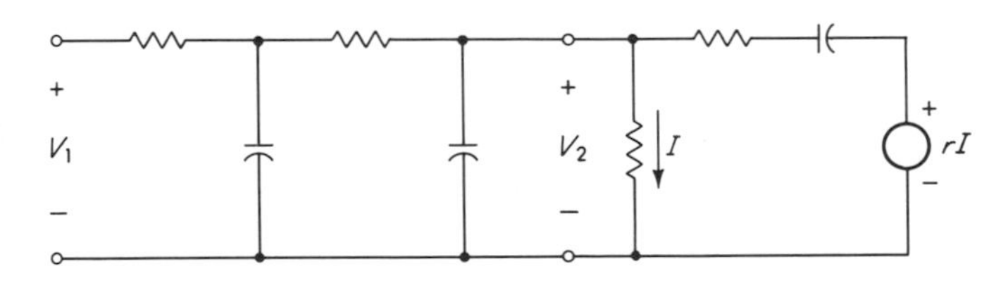

Figure P2.20

2.21 Find the case from Table 2.1 which applies to the active RC realization shown in Fig. P2.21, where the movement along the root locus is a function of the gain α of the transistor.†

* This circuit is from E. S. Kuh, Transfer Function Synthesis of Active RC Networks, *IRE Trans. Circuit Theory*, vol. CT-7, Special supplement, pp. 3–7, Aug., 1960.

† This circuit is from B. R. Myers, Transistor-RC Network Synthesis, *IRE WESCON Record*, pt. 2, pp. 65–74, 1959.

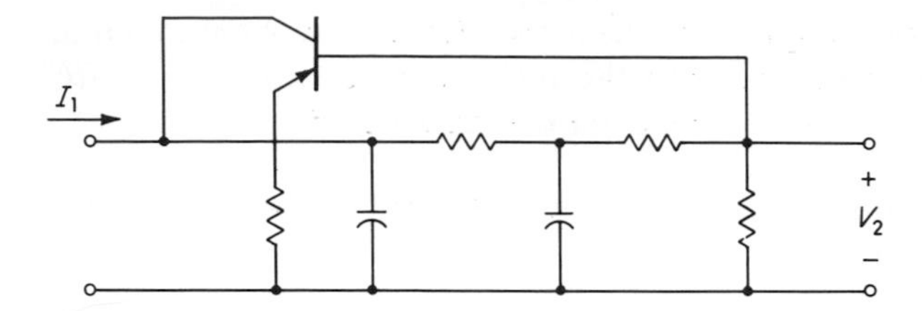

Figure P2.21

2.22 Prove that the root loci for all of the cases shown in Table 2.1 are straight lines or circles.

2.23 Find an expression for the elements of a matrix $\mathbf{M}$ which will relate $\mathbf{\Delta b}^{(n)}$ of (55) and $\mathbf{\Delta p}$ of (65).

2.24 Prove that the decomposition given in the denominator of (93) (see Sec. 2.7) represents the sum of an RC driving-point admittance and an RC driving-point impedance.

Chapter 3 *Controlled-source realizations*

Starting with this chapter, we shall turn our attention to the subject of active *RC* circuit realizations. Each of the following chapters will treat realizations by means of a different active device. In this chapter we shall consider the subject of realizations that use controlled sources. The sufficiency of a single controlled source in connection with a passive *RC* network for the realization of an arbitrary transfer function has been demonstrated.*

We have already seen some examples of realizations using controlled sources. For example, the circuit shown in Fig. 1.7 is an active *RC* realization using a voltage-controlled voltage source (indicated by the triangle in the figure) of gain K to realize a network magnitude characteristic which possesses a "resonant hump," as shown in Fig. 1.2. Here we shall investigate both the theoretical and practical aspects of controlled-source realizations. Thus, in Sec. 3.1 we shall discuss the general theoretical considerations that result when a controlled source is added to a passive network. In Secs. 3.2 through 3.4, we shall discuss the use of controlled sources to realize low-pass, high-pass, and bandpass transfer functions, considering the use of both inverting and noninverting sources and presenting detailed examples illustrating the application of the concepts. In Sec. 3.5 we present a realization technique for transfer functions with transmission zeros on the $j\omega$ axis, and in Sec. 3.6 we discuss a general realization technique for transfer functions of any complexity. Some means of realizing the controlled source itself are given in Sec. 3.7. Finally, in Sec. 3.8, we present detailed realization techniques, complete with design formulas and numerical examples, for three circuits which

* This sufficiency was established for the realization of an arbitrary driving-point function by B. K. Kinariwala, Synthesis of Active *RC* Networks, *Bell System Tech. J.*, vol. 38, pp. 1269–1316, Sept., 1959. The article also discusses the extension of the results to transfer-function realizations.

have frequent application, namely, the second-degree low-pass, high-pass, and bandpass voltage transfer functions.

3.1 *The general theory of controlled-source realizations*

There are four basic types of controlled sources. These are the voltage-controlled voltage source (VCVS), the current-controlled voltage source (ICVS), the voltage-controlled current source (VCIS), and the current-controlled current source (ICIS). Considered as ideal active elements, voltage-controlled sources are considered to have infinite input impedance, and current-controlled sources to have zero input impedance. Similarly, voltage sources are considered to have zero output impedance, and current sources to have infinite output impedance. A schematic representation and a representative set of two-port network parameters for each of these sources is shown in Fig. 3.1.* It should be noted that each of the sources has a constant associated with it. This is usually referred to as the

* For a definition of the various types of network parameters and a discussion of their properties see L. P. Huelsman, "Circuits, Matrices, and Linear Vector Spaces," chap. 3, McGraw-Hill Book Company, New York, 1963.

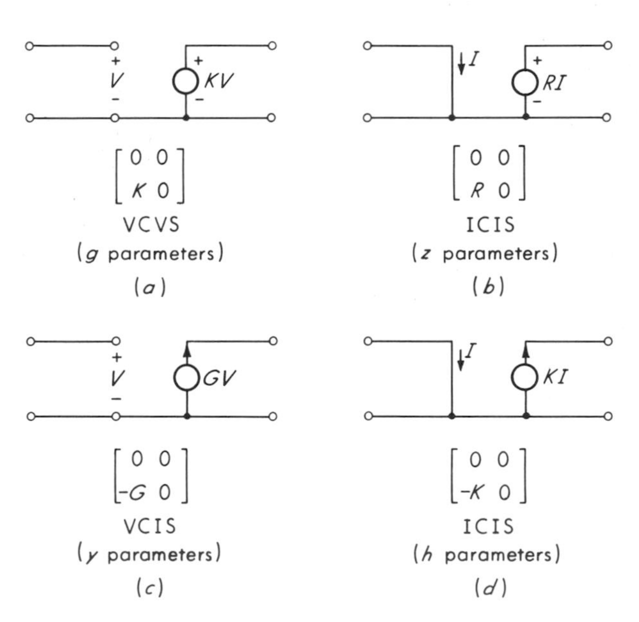

***Figure 3.1** The four basic types of ideal controlled sources.*

"gain" of the source. For the VCVS and the ICIS, the constant is dimensionless. For the ICVS it has the dimensions of impedance; for the VCIS it has the dimensions of admittance. Any nonideal behavior connected with such sources may be represented as parasitic elements which may be absorbed in the accompanying networks.

As an introduction to the study of controlled-source realizations, let us consider the effect of embedding a VCVS in an arbitrary passive RC network. Consider a four-port network defined by its y parameters. Let port 1 be the input port and port 2 be the output port, and let a VCVS be connected between ports 3 and 4 as shown in Fig. 3.2. The circuit may be

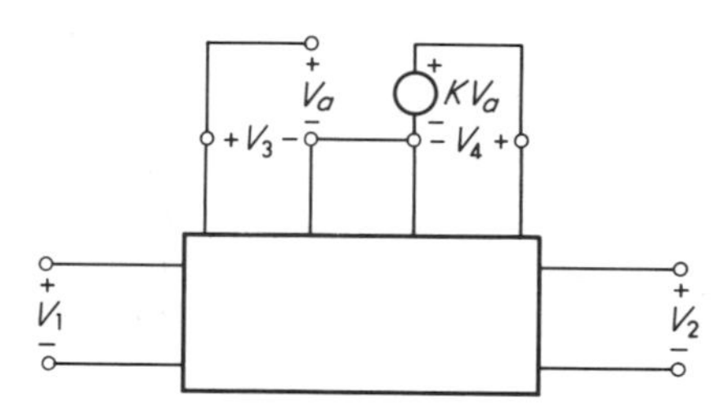

Figure 3.2 A passive four-port network and a VCVS.

analyzed to obtain the open-circuit voltage transfer function in terms of the gain K of the VCVS and the y parameters of the passive network.* We obtain

$$\frac{V_2}{V_1} = \frac{y_{21}(y_{33} + Ky_{34}) - y_{31}(y_{23} + Ky_{24})}{y_{32}(y_{23} + Ky_{24}) - y_{22}(y_{33} + Ky_{34})} \tag{1}$$

From this equation, we note that a subtraction of terms appears in both the numerator and denominator. Thus, there are possibilities for applying the difference polynomial decomposition techniques introduced in the preceding chapter.

A slightly less general configuration, but one which is more applicable to actual practice, may be defined by taking the output of the controlled source as the output port of the network. The advantage of this method is that the output impedance of the network will now be the output impedance of the VCVS, which is zero. Thus, the network may be cascaded with other networks to permit the realization of higher-order transfer functions without interaction occurring between the networks. For this configuration, we may consider a passive RC three-port network defined by its y parameters and a VCVS with gain K, interconnected as shown

* A general procedure for making such an analysis was given by A. Nathan, Matrix Analysis of Constrained Networks, *Inst. Elec. Eng. (England)*, Monograph No. 399E, pp. 98–105, Sept., 1960.

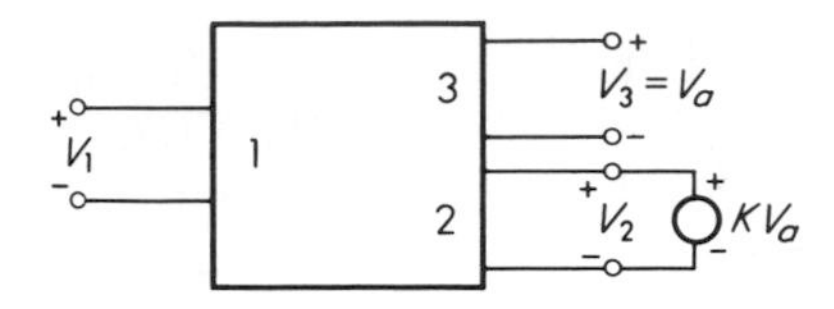

***Figure 3.3** A passive three-port network and a VCVS.*

in Fig. 3.3. For this configuration, the open-circuit voltage transfer function is

$$\frac{V_2}{V_1} = \frac{-Ky_{31}}{y_{33} + Ky_{32}} \tag{2}$$

It should be noted that the network function defined by (2) is bilinear in K, the gain of the VCVS. Thus, the sensitivity of any of the roots with respect to K falls under the general class defined in the last chapter.

The zeros of the voltage transfer function defined in (2) are determined by the zeros of y_{31}.* It is shown in Appendix B that the zeros of a passive RC transfer admittance can be located anywhere on the complex-frequency plane. Thus, the zeros of the voltage transfer function are unrestricted. From (2) we see that the denominator of the voltage transfer function is expressed in terms of two component polynomials, i.e., the numerators of y_{33} and Ky_{32}. Thus, we may apply the polynomial decomposition techniques presented in the last chapter. If the numerator of y_{33} is written in the form $a_0\Pi(p + \sigma_i)$, then a_0 can only be positive. Similarly, if y_{32} is written in the form $b_0\Pi(p + p_i)$, then b_0 can only be negative.† The constant K may be positive or negative. Thus, in the denominator of (2), we may encounter either the sum or the difference case of polynomial decomposition. In addition, although the zeros of y_{33} will be on the real axis, the zeros of y_{32} may be anywhere on the complex-frequency plane. Thus, a considerable variety of decompositions is possible.

Similar considerations hold true for the case in which other types of controlled sources are combined with arbitrary passive RC networks. For example, consider an ICVS connected to a three-port network as shown in Fig. 3.4. The open-circuit voltage transfer function for this configuration is

$$\frac{V_2}{V_1} = \frac{-Ry_{31}}{1 + Ry_{32}} \tag{3}$$

It is easily seen that the network function is bilinear in R, the gain of the

* It will be assumed that all the y parameters shown in (2) have the same denominator, i.e., that there are no private poles. The extension to the case where this is not true is easily made.

† It is possible to realize a y_{32} in which the constant b_0 is positive, but this requires the use of networks which do not have a common ground. These are usually not desirable in practical realizations.

ICVS, and that polynomial decomposition techniques similar to those described for the case of the VCVS apply.

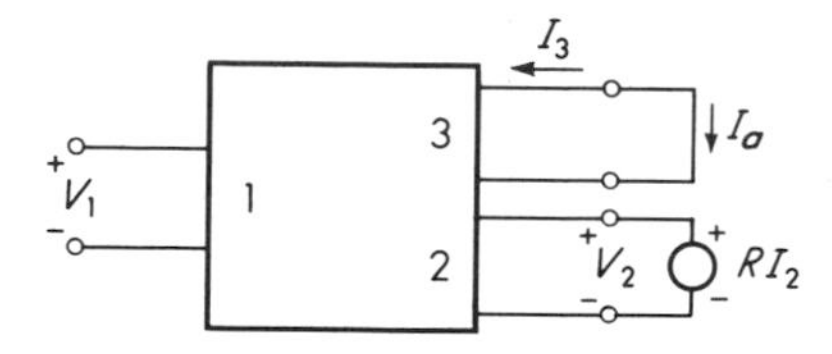

***Figure 3.4** A passive three-port network and an ICVS.*

In dealing with current sources, it is more appropriate, in terms of possible applications, to consider short-circuit current transfer functions.

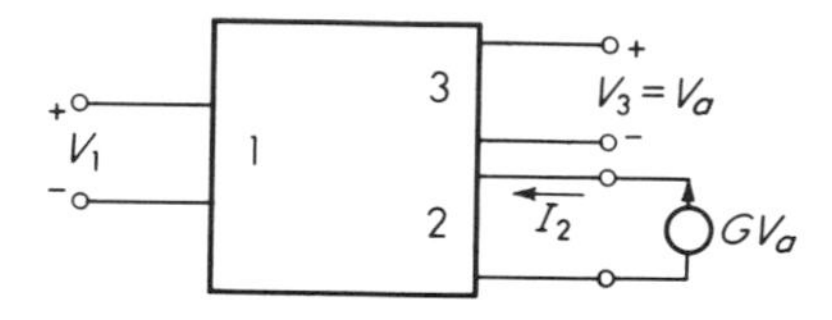

***Figure 3.5** A passive three-port network and a VCIS.*

Thus, if a VCIS is connected to a three-port passive network as shown in Fig. 3.5, the short-circuit current transfer function is given as

$$\frac{I_2}{I_1} = \frac{Gz_{31}}{1 - Gz_{32}} \tag{4}$$

where the z_{ij} are the z parameters of the three-port network, and G is the gain of the VCIS. Note that the function is bilinear in G. Similarly, if an ICIS is connected to a passive RC network as indicated in Fig. 3.6, the

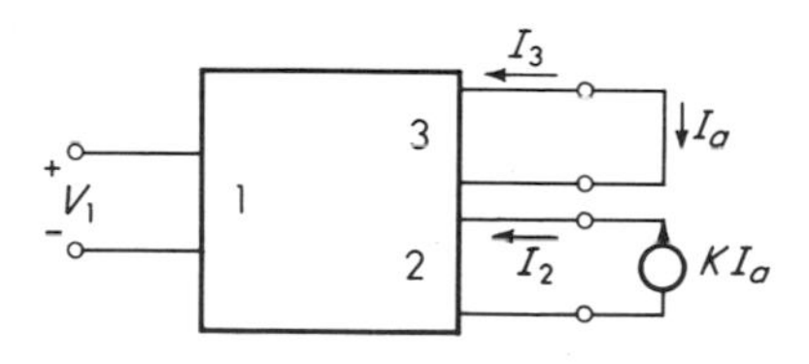

***Figure 3.6** A passive three-port network and an ICIS.*

short-circuit current transfer function is

$$\frac{I_2}{I_1} = \frac{Kz_{31}}{z_{33} - Kz_{32}} \tag{5}$$

where K is the gain of the ICIS.

In this section we have defined the four basic types of controlled sources. An investigation of the most practical means of embedding these sources in a passive RC network has shown that the resulting transfer functions are bilinear in the gain of the sources and that the denominator polynomials are in a form which may readily be linked to the polynomial decomposition methods described in the last chapter. In the following sections we shall investigate realization techniques for this class of active RC networks in more detail and also investigate realizations for some of the more practical controlled sources.

3.2 *The realization of low-pass functions*

In this section we will discuss the realization of low-pass network functions using ideal controlled sources. The general form of an all-pole low-pass network function is

$$N(p) = \frac{H}{p^n + b_1 p + \cdots + b_{n-1} p + b_n} \tag{6}$$

The coefficients b_i are positive and may be chosen so as to satisfy some suitable approximation criteria. For example, if a maximally-flat-magnitude characteristic is desired, they must be selected so as to make the function have a Butterworth response. Similarly, if an equal-ripple-magnitude characteristic is desired, the coefficients should be chosen so that the denominator contains a Chebyshev polynomial.* The constant H may be considered as a gain constant. It is easily seen that the low-frequency or passband gain of the function is equal to H/b_n. The steepness of the cutoff outside the passband is determined by the location and number of the poles of the function.

If the general low-pass network function given in (6) is compared with the various transfer functions and circuit configurations given in Sec. 3.1, it is apparent that the numerator of the network function of (6) is determined by the numerator of the transfer immittance from port 1 to port 3 of the passive network used in connection with the controlled source. Thus we see that a purely resistive path must exist between the input port of the network and the input port of the controlled source. Similarly, if the denominator of (6) is compared with the denominators of the transfer functions given in Sec. 3.1, we see that it is necessary to decompose the denominator polynomial of (6) into the sum or difference of two polyno-

* The details of determining the coefficients b_i in (6) for a desired approximation criteria may be found in any modern book on network synthesis. For example, see M. E. Van Valkenburg, "Introduction to Modern Network Synthesis," chap. 13, John Wiley & Sons, Inc., New York, 1960. A more detailed treatment is given in D. A. Calahan, "Modern Network Synthesis," vol. 1, Hayden Publishing Company, New York, 1964.

mials, one of which represents the zeros of a passive *RC* driving-point immittance, the other of which must have the zeros of a passive *RC* transfer immittance. Thus we may apply the techniques discussed in Chap. 2. It should be noted that, in general, network structures which realize complex-conjugate or even negative-real zeros of a transfer immittance introduce considerable network complexity. Therefore, in practice we shall restrict our transfer immittances to those producing zeros at the origin or at infinity. There are several decomposition possibilities, and obviously the number of possible decompositions increases rapidly as the degree of the denominator polynomial increases. We shall therefore restrict our detailed discussion to the second-degree case for the sake of both brevity and practicality. In addition, we shall consider only the realization of open-circuit voltage transfer functions using an ideal VCVS. This case has considerable practical application. Moreover, an extension of the results determined for it may easily be made for the cases where other transfer functions are desired or where other types of controlled sources must be used.

As an illustration of the realization of a low-pass network function, we shall consider the following second-degree open-circuit voltage transfer function:

$$\frac{V_2}{V_1} = \frac{H}{p^2 + b_1 p + b_2} \tag{7}$$

The gain in the passband is H/b_2. Depending on the network configuration and the characteristics of the controlled source, H may be positive or negative.

Let us assume that this function is to be realized by the network configuration shown in Fig. 3.3 using an ideal VCVS. Thus, we may compare the low-pass voltage transfer function given above with the voltage transfer function given in (2).

Referring to Table 2.1 and comparing the cases shown there with the denominator of (2), we see that all the cases except cases 5, 6, 7, 12, and 13 are eliminated by the requirement of network simplicity which precludes the use of complex-conjugate zeros in the transfer admittance. Some of the eliminated cases also represent unrealizable situations with respect to the y parameters of the passive *RC* network. Of those remaining case 5 is difficult to realize with a simple passive *RC* network structure and therefore will not be discussed. Case 6 and case 12 require negative-real zeros of transmission for the y_{32} parameter and therefore require a more complicated network than some of the other realizations. Thus, although some of the other cases are realizable, we shall confine our investigation of possible decompositions to the remaining cases 7 and 13.

To see how case 7 applies, we may make the following identifications:

$$y_{31} = \frac{-h_0}{p+\sigma_0} \qquad y_{32} = \frac{-b_0}{p+\sigma_0}$$
$$y_{33} = \frac{a_0(p+\sigma_1)(p+\sigma_2)}{p+\sigma_0} \tag{8}$$

where a_0, b_0, h_0, σ_1, σ_2, and σ_0 are positive-real constants. Substituting these relations into (2) and canceling the common factor $p + \sigma_0$, we obtain

$$\frac{V_2}{V_1} = \frac{Kh_0}{a_0(p+\sigma_1)(p+\sigma_2) - Kb_0} \tag{9}$$

Obviously, case 7 will only apply for negative values of K. In this case, we may write (9) in the form

$$\frac{V_2}{V_1} = \frac{-|K|h_0}{a_0(p+\sigma_1)(p+\sigma_2) + |K|b_0} \tag{10}$$

A network configuration in which the passive RC network has the y parameters of the general form given in (8) is shown in Fig. 3.7. For this

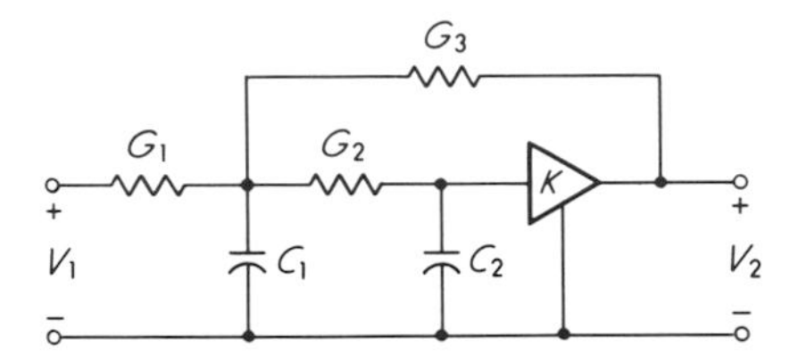

***Figure 3.7** A low-pass network with $K < 0$.*

network the voltage transfer function is given explicitly in terms of the elements as

$$\frac{V_2}{V_1} = \frac{-|K|G_1G_2S_1S_2}{p^2 + p[S_1(G_1+G_2+G_3) + S_2G_2] + G_2S_1S_2(G_1+G_3+|K|G_3)} \tag{11}$$

where the S_i are values of reciprocal capacitance. The following properties may be noted with respect to this transfer function:

1. It is bilinear with respect to the gain K and with respect to the passive elements.
2. The decomposition of the denominator with respect to K is a sum decomposition. The optimization described in Sec. 2.7 for this type of decomposition cannot be applied, however, since it would require that $\sigma_1 = \sigma_2$ in (8), and the resulting y parameters would not be realizable by a passive RC network.

3. Since the denominator decomposition is of the type illustrated as case 7 of Table 2.1, the realization is stable for all values of K. When K is varied, the imaginary part of the poles changes, but the real part remains constant.

4. The low-frequency (passband) gain is $-|K|G_1/(G_1 + G_3 + |K|G_3)$. Thus, the constant H in (7) is negative.

The following comments apply to the elements of the sensitivity matrix that will result for this realization:

1. The sensitivities for the b_1 coefficient of (7) will all be positive and less than unity (see Sec. 2.5, property 4).

2. The sensitivities for the b_2 coefficient of (7) with respect to the elements G_2, S_1, and S_2 will be unity. With respect to the elements G_1, G_3, and the gain $|K|$, they will be positive and less than unity (see Sec. 2.5, properties 3 and 4).

The above conclusions are easily verified in the following example:

Example 3.1 As an example of the use of the network shown in Fig. 3.7 to realize a low-pass network function, consider the maximally-flat-magnitude frequency-normalized voltage transfer function

$$\frac{V_2}{V_1} = \frac{-10}{p^2 + \sqrt{2}p + 1}$$

If we equate the coefficients of this transfer function with the coefficients of (11), a set of nonlinear equations results. A solution to these equations may be found fairly easily by trial and error. One such solution results in the following element values:

$$\begin{aligned} G_1 &= 2.5 \text{ mhos} & S_1 &= 0.25 \text{ daraf} \\ G_2 &= 0.592 \text{ mho} & S_2 &= 1.02 \text{ darafs} \\ G_3 &= 0.15 \text{ mho} & K &= -26.5 \end{aligned}$$

We may apply the techniques of Sec. 2.5 to determine a sensitivity matrix for this realization. In terms of the coefficients given in the denominator of (7) we obtain

$$\begin{bmatrix} \Delta b_1^{(n)} \\ \Delta b_2^{(n)} \end{bmatrix} = \begin{bmatrix} 0.442 & 0.531 & 0.026 & 0.573 & 0.427 & 0 \\ 0.377 & 1.0 & 0.622 & 1.0 & 1.0 & 0.6 \end{bmatrix} \begin{bmatrix} \Delta G_1^{(n)} \\ \Delta G_2^{(n)} \\ \Delta G_3^{(n)} \\ \Delta S_1^{(n)} \\ \Delta S_2^{(n)} \\ \Delta |K|^{(n)} \end{bmatrix}$$

Let us now consider the application of case 13 of Table 2.1 to the realization of a low-pass network function. If we make the identifications

$$y_{31} = \frac{-h_0}{p + \sigma_0} \qquad y_{32} = \frac{-b_0 p}{p + \sigma_0}$$
$$y_{33} = \frac{a_0(p + \sigma_1)(p + \sigma_2)}{p + \sigma_0} \tag{12}$$

where a_0, b_0, h_0, σ_1, σ_2, and σ_0 are positive constants, a positive value of K will provide the desired decomposition. The voltage transfer function in terms of the y parameters of (12) is

$$\frac{V_2}{V_1} = \frac{Kh_0}{a_0(p + \sigma_1)(p + \sigma_2) - Kpb_0} \tag{13}$$

A network configuration for this case is shown in Fig. 3.8.

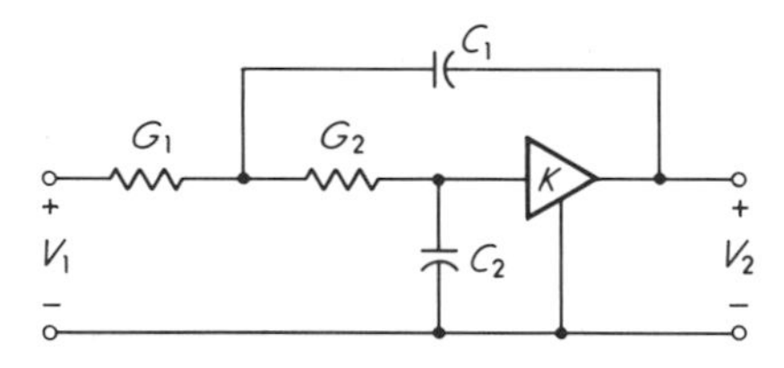

Figure 3.8 A low-pass network with $K > 0$.

For this network the voltage transfer function is*

$$\frac{V_2}{V_1} = \frac{KG_1G_2S_1S_2}{p^2 + p(G_1S_1 + G_2S_1 + G_2S_2 - KG_2S_2) + G_1G_2S_1S_2} \tag{14}$$

where the S_i are values of reciprocal capacitance. The following properties may be noted with respect to this transfer function:

1. It is bilinear with respect to the gain K and with respect to the passive elements.
2. The decomposition of the denominator with respect to K is a difference decomposition. The optimization described in Sec. 2.6 for this type of decomposition, however, cannot be applied.
3. Since the denominator decomposition is of the type shown as case 13 in Table 2.1, the realization may go unstable for large changes in K.
4. The low-frequency (passband) gain is K. Thus, the constant H of (7) is positive.
5. The coefficient of the first-degree term in the denominator of (14) is a function of K. Therefore, if K is varied, the frequency characteristics of

* The network configurations shown in Figs. 3.7 and 3.8 are also shown as circuits 1 and 2 by R. P. Sallen and E. L. Key, A Practical Method of Designing *RC* Active Filters, *IRE Trans. Circuit Theory,* vol. CT-2, no. 1, pp. 74–85, March, 1955.

the network will be changed. We shall see in Sec. 3.7 that it is possible to realize the VCVS in such a manner as to eliminate this dependence.

The following comments apply to the elements of the sensitivity matrix that results for this realization:

1. The sensitivity for the b_1 coefficient of (7) with respect to K will be negative and greater in magnitude than $2Q - 1$, where $Q = \sqrt{b_2}/b_1$ (see Sec. 2.6).
2. The sensitivities for the b_2 coefficient of (7) with respect to the elements G_1, G_2, S_1, and S_2 will be unity (see property 3, Sec. 2.5).

The above conclusions are easily verified by an example.

Example 3.2 As an example of the use of the network shown in Fig. 3.8 to realize a low-pass function, consider the frequency-normalized voltage transfer function with a maximally-flat-magnitude characteristic

$$\frac{V_2}{V_1} = \frac{10}{p^2 + \sqrt{2}p + 1}$$

A suitable choice of element values may be found by equating the coefficients of the above function with those of (14). We obtain

$$G_1 = 1.0 \text{ mho} \qquad S_1 = 2.504 \text{ darafs}$$
$$G_2 = 1.0 \text{ mho} \qquad S_2 = 1/2.504 \text{ daraf}$$
$$K = 10$$

We may now apply the techniques discussed in Sec. 2.5 to obtain the following sensitivity matrix for the network in terms of the coefficients of (7):

$$\begin{bmatrix} \Delta b_1^{(n)} \\ \Delta b_2^{(n)} \end{bmatrix} = \begin{bmatrix} 1.77 & -0.768 & 3.54 & -2.54 & -2.82 \\ 1.0 & 1.0 & 1.0 & 1.0 & 0 \end{bmatrix} \begin{bmatrix} \Delta G_1^{(n)} \\ \Delta G_2^{(n)} \\ \Delta S_1^{(n)} \\ \Delta S_2^{(n)} \\ \Delta K^{(n)} \end{bmatrix}$$

Note that the sensitivity of the coefficient b_1 with respect to K is -2.82. In Sec. 2.6 it was shown that the optimum sensitivity that is obtainable for a difference decomposition of this type is $-2Q + 1$, which for this example is -0.414.

Although both of the network configurations described in this section are capable of realizing low-pass voltage transfer functions of the type given in (7), practical experience has shown that the configuration given in Fig. 3.8 has several practical advantages from the standpoint of economy of network elements and ease of adjustment. A comparison of the elements of the sensitivity matrices given in Examples 3.1 and 3.2 will illustrate the fact that this realization has higher sensitivities than the configuration shown in Fig. 3.7. The magnitudes of these sensitivities, however, are still quite reasonable. In addition, the fact that the realization shown in Fig. 3.8 can be implemented with a VCVS of considerably lower gain than the one in Fig. 3.7 is frequently an advantage. Because of its frequent application, a detailed design procedure for the realization of low-pass network functions with the configuration shown in Fig. 3.8 is given in Sec. 3.8 as circuit 1.

3.3 *The realization of high-pass functions*

In this section we will discuss the realization of high-pass network functions by means of active *RC* circuits using ideal controlled sources as the active elements. The general form of the high-pass network function which has all its zeros at the origin is

$$N(p) = \frac{Hp^n}{p^n + b_1p^{n-1} + \cdots + b_{n-1}p + b_n} \tag{15}$$

The same criteria that were discussed for the denominator of the low-pass function in (6) apply to the denominator of (15) since the two functions are related by the frequency transformation $s = \omega_0/p$, where s is the low-pass complex-frequency variable, p is the high-pass complex-frequency variable, and ω_0 is the frequency around which the transformation is made. The constant H is a gain constant, giving the value of the high-frequency or passband gain of the function.

If the numerator of the general high-pass function given in (15) is compared with the various transfer functions and circuit configurations given in Sec. 3.1, we see that the signal path from the input port of the network (port 1) to the input port of the controlled source (port 3 of the network) must have n transmission zeros at the origin of the complex-frequency plane. Thus, this path must encounter n capacitors in such a way as to provide these zeros. The realization of the denominator is accomplished by the same decomposition process which was discussed for the low-pass case.

As an illustration of a high-pass network function, we shall consider the realization of a second-degree open-circuit voltage transfer function. This has the form

$$\frac{V_2}{V_1} = \frac{Hp^2}{p^2 + b_1p + b_2} \tag{16}$$

where H is a real constant specifying the gain in the passband. Depending on the network configuration and the characteristics of the controlled source, H may be positive or negative. We shall investigate the use of the configuration shown in Fig. 3.3, using a VCVS to realize the voltage transfer function. Thus we may compare (16) with (2) as given for the general case. The decomposition of the denominator of (16) will be restricted by the requirement that the zeros of y_{32} of (2) be located only at the origin or infinity. This will simplify the network configuration. Considerations similar to those made for the low-pass case show that cases 5 and 13 from Table 2.1 apply to the denominator decomposition for this function.

To see how case 5 applies, we may make the following identifications:

$$y_{31} = \frac{-h_0p^2}{p+\sigma_0} \qquad y_{32} = \frac{-b_0p^2}{p+\sigma_0}$$
$$y_{33} = \frac{a_0(p+\sigma_1)(p+\sigma_2)}{p+\sigma_0} \tag{17}$$

where a_0, b_0, h_0, σ_1, σ_2, and σ_0 are real positive constants. Substituting these relations into (2), we see that this case will only apply if K is negative, i.e., if an inverting VCVS is used. For such a VCVS, the voltage transfer function will have the form

$$\frac{V_2}{V_1} = \frac{-|K|h_0p^2}{a_0(p+\sigma_1)(p+\sigma_2)+|K|b_0p^2} \tag{18}$$

A network configuration in which the passive RC network has y parameters of the form given in (17) is shown in Fig. 3.9. For this network the

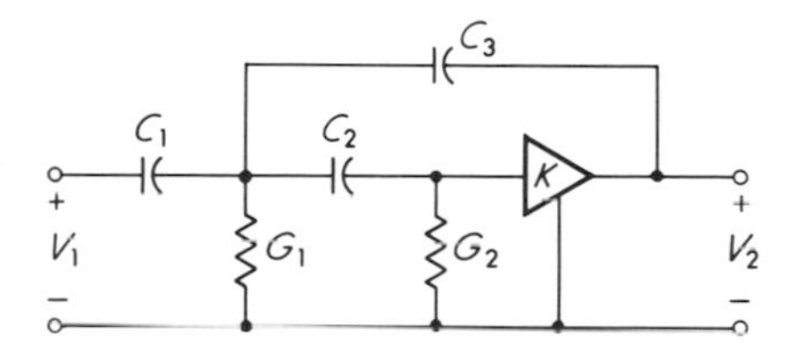

Figure 3.9 A high-pass network with $K < 0$.

voltage transfer function may be written*

$$\frac{V_2}{V_1} = \frac{-|K|p^2C_1C_2R_1R_2}{p^2R_1R_2C_2(C_1+C_3+|K|C_3)+p[R_2C_2+R_1(C_1+C_2+C_3)]+1} \tag{19}$$

* For this network realization, a simpler form for the voltage transfer function is obtained by writing the function in terms of elements of resistance and capacitance rather than the reciprocal elements of conductance and elastance. In future developments, we shall continue to choose the type of units which lead to the simpler expression for the transfer function.

The following properties may be noted with respect to this transfer function:

1. It is bilinear with respect to the gain K and with respect to the passive elements.
2. The decomposition of the denominator with respect to $|K|$ is a sum decomposition. The optimization described in Sec. 2.7 for this type of decomposition, however, cannot be applied.
3. Since the denominator decomposition is of the type illustrated as case 5 of Table 2.1, the realization is stable for all values of K.
4. The high-frequency (passband) gain is $-|K|C_1/(C_1 + C_3 + |K|C_3)$. Thus, the constant H in (16) is negative.

In analyzing the sensitivity of the network function we note that the denominator of (19) is of the general form

$$D(p) = b_0'p^2 + b_1'p + 1 \tag{20}$$

where b_0' and b_1' are functions of the active and passive elements. In order to study the sensitivity of the roots of this denominator we may write it in a form similar to that given in the denominator of (16). Thus, we obtain

$$D(p) = b_0'\left(p^2 + \frac{b_1'}{b_0'}p + \frac{1}{b_0'}\right) = b_0'(p^2 + b_1p + b_2) \tag{21}$$

Considering only first-order effects, from property 2 of Sec. 2.5 we see that

$$\begin{aligned} S_x^{b_1} &= S_x^{b_1'} - S_x^{b_0'} \\ S_x^{b_2} &= -S_x^{b_0'} \end{aligned} \tag{22}$$

where x is any parameter. Thus, we may determine the sensitivities for b_0' and b_1' of (20) in terms of the elements R_1, R_2, C_1, C_2, C_3, and $|K|$ given in (19) and directly relate these to the sensitivities for b_1 and b_2 of (16).

The following comments apply to the elements of the sensitivity matrix for this realization as determined by the above procedure:

1. The sensitivities for the coefficients b_0' and b_1' of (20) will all be positive and less than or equal to unity (see property 4, Sec. 2.5). Thus, from (22), the magnitude of the sensitivities for the b_1 coefficient will be less than or equal to unity.
2. The sensitivities for the b_2 coefficient with respect to the elements R_1, R_2, and C_2 will be -1; with respect to the elements C_1, C_3, and the gain $|K|$, they will be negative and less than unity in magnitude (see properties 3 and 4, Sec. 2.5).

The above conclusions are easily verified by an example.

Example 3.3 As an example of the use of the network shown in Fig. 3.9 to realize a high-pass function, consider the maximally-flat-magnitude frequency-normalized voltage transfer function

$$\frac{V_2}{V_1} = \frac{-10p^2}{p^2 + \sqrt{2}p + 1}$$

If we equate the coefficients of this transfer function with the coefficients of (19), a set of nonlinear equations results. One solution, found by trial and error, results in the following element values:

$$\begin{aligned} C_1 &= 2.5 \text{ farads} & R_1 &= 0.25 \text{ ohm} \\ C_2 &= 0.5916 \text{ farad} & R_2 &= 1.02 \text{ ohms} \\ C_3 &= 0.15 \text{ farad} & K &= -26.5 \end{aligned}$$

In terms of the coefficients of (20) (using the techniques of Sec. 2.5) we find the following sensitivity matrix:

$$\begin{bmatrix} \Delta b_0'^{(n)} \\ \Delta b_1'^{(n)} \end{bmatrix} = \begin{bmatrix} 1.0 & 1.0 & 0.378 & 1.0 & 0.623 & 0.599 \\ 0.572 & 0.426 & 0.441 & 0.532 & 0.026 & 0 \end{bmatrix} \begin{bmatrix} \Delta R_1{}^{(n)} \\ \Delta R_2{}^{(n)} \\ \Delta C_1{}^{(n)} \\ \Delta C_2{}^{(n)} \\ \Delta C_3{}^{(n)} \\ \Delta |K|^{(n)} \end{bmatrix}$$

If we apply the relations of (22), we may determine the sensitivities in terms of the coefficients in the denominator of (16). The sensitivities are given by the matrix

$$\begin{bmatrix} \Delta b_1{}^{(n)} \\ \Delta b_2{}^{(n)} \end{bmatrix}$$

$$= \begin{bmatrix} -0.428 & -0.574 & 0.063 & -0.468 & -0.597 & -0.599 \\ -1.0 & -1.0 & -0.378 & -1.0 & -0.623 & -0.599 \end{bmatrix} \begin{bmatrix} \Delta R_1{}^{(n)} \\ \Delta R_2{}^{(n)} \\ \Delta C_1{}^{(n)} \\ \Delta C_2{}^{(n)} \\ \Delta C_3{}^{(n)} \\ \Delta |K|^{(n)} \end{bmatrix}$$

Let us now consider the application of case 13 of Table 2.1 to the realization of a high-pass network function. We may make the identifications

$$y_{31} = \frac{-h_0 p^2}{p + \sigma_0} \qquad y_{32} = \frac{-b_0 p}{p + \sigma_0}$$
$$y_{33} = \frac{a_0(p + \sigma_1)(p + \sigma_2)}{p + \sigma_0} \tag{23}$$

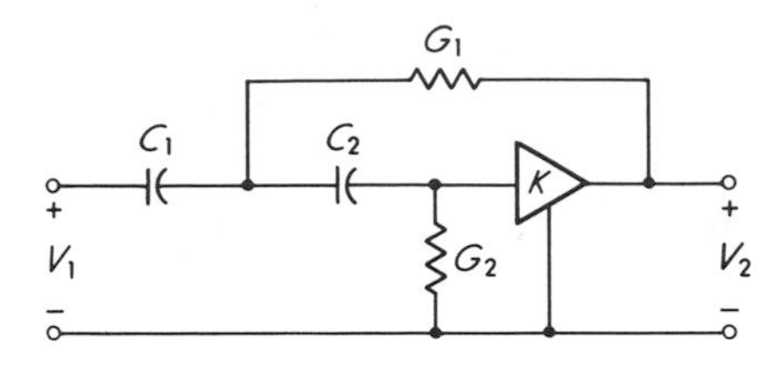

Figure 3.10 A high-pass network with $K > 0$.

where a_0, b_0, h_0, σ_1, σ_2, and σ_0 are real and positive. For this case, a positive value of K must be used; i.e., the VCVS must be noninverting. The voltage transfer function for the y parameters given in (23) is

$$\frac{V_2}{V_1} = \frac{Kh_0p^2}{a_0(p + \sigma_1)(p + \sigma_2) - Kpb_0} \tag{24}$$

A network configuration for this case is shown in Fig. 3.10. For this network the voltage transfer function is*

$$\frac{V_2}{V_1} = \frac{Kp^2}{p^2 + p(G_1S_1 + G_2S_2 + G_2S_1 - KG_1S_1) + G_1G_2S_1S_2} \tag{25}$$

The following properties may be noted with respect to this transfer function:

1. It is bilinear with respect to the gain K and with respect to the passive elements.
2. The decomposition of the denominator with respect to K is a difference decomposition. The optimization described in Sec. 2.6 for this type of decomposition, however, cannot be applied.
3. Since the denominator decomposition is of the type shown as case 13 of Table 2.1, the realization may go unstable for large changes of K.
4. The high-frequency (passband) gain is K. Thus, the constant H of (16) is positive.
5. The coefficient of the first-degree term in the denominator of (25) is a function of K. Therefore, if K is varied, the frequency characteristics of the network will also be changed. We shall see in Sec. 3.7 that it is possible to realize the VCVS in such a manner as to eliminate this dependence.

The following comments apply to the elements of the sensitivity matrix that results for this realization:

1. The sensitivity for the b_1 coefficient of (16) with respect to K will be negative and greater in magnitude than $2Q - 1$, where $Q = \sqrt{b_2}/b_1$ (see Sec. 2.6).

* The network configurations shown in Figs. 3.9 and 3.10 are also shown as circuits 4 and 3 in Sallen and Key, *op. cit.*

2. The sensitivities for the b_2 coefficient of (16) with respect to the elements G_1, G_2, S_1, and S_2 will be unity (see property 3, Sec. 2.5).

The above conclusions are easily verified by an example.

Example 3.4 As an example of the use of the network shown in Fig. 3.10 to realize a high-pass function by the decomposition shown as case 13 of Table 2.1, consider the maximally-flat-magnitude voltage transfer function

$$\frac{V_2}{V_1} = \frac{10p^2}{p^2 + \sqrt{2}\,p + 1}$$

If we equate the coefficients of this function with those of (25), one solution yields the following element values:

$$\begin{aligned} G_1 &= 1/2.504 \text{ mho} \qquad & C_1 &= 1.0 \text{ farad} \\ G_2 &= 2.504 \text{ mhos} \qquad & C_2 &= 1.0 \text{ farad} \end{aligned}$$
$$K = 10$$

In terms of the coefficients of (16) we find the following sensitivity matrix:

$$\begin{bmatrix} \Delta b_1^{(n)} \\ \Delta b_2^{(n)} \end{bmatrix} = \begin{bmatrix} -2.54 & 3.54 & -0.768 & 1.77 & -2.82 \\ 1.0 & 1.0 & 1.0 & 1.0 & 0 \end{bmatrix} \begin{bmatrix} \Delta G_1^{(n)} \\ \Delta G_2^{(n)} \\ \Delta S_1^{(n)} \\ \Delta S_2^{(n)} \\ \Delta K^{(n)} \end{bmatrix}$$

Although both of the network configurations described in this section are capable of realizing high-pass transfer functions of the type given in (16), practical experience has indicated that the configuration shown in Fig. 3.10 (case 13) is usually the more useful one. This circuit has properties similar to those enumerated in Sec. 3.2 for the low-pass circuit shown in Fig. 3.8. The values of the network elements may be found by simultaneously equating the coefficients of (16) and (25). The resulting set of equations is nonlinear, but solutions are easily found. Such a set of solutions, together with design information for the circuit, is given in Sec. 3.8 as circuit 2.

3.4 *The realization of bandpass functions*

In this section we will discuss the realization of bandpass network functions by means of active *RC* circuits using ideal controlled sources as the active elements. The general form of the type of bandpass network function to be discussed here is

$$N(p) = \frac{Hp^m}{p^n + b_1p^{n-1} + \cdots + b_{n-1}p + b_n} \tag{26}$$

where m is less than n. For this class of network functions, n, the degree of the denominator polynomial is even, and all the poles are usually complex. From (26) we see that there are m zeros at the origin. Thus, there are also $m - n$ zeros located at infinity. Frequently m is chosen equal to $n/2$. H is a gain constant which may be plus or minus depending on the specific network configuration. In the general case, no simple rule exists for determining the bandpass gain in terms of the constant H and the locations of the zeros of the denominator.

If we compare the general form of the bandpass network function given in (26) with the network configurations and general equations given in Sec. 3.1 for the various controlled-source realizations, we see that the feedback path provided from the input of the network to the input of the controlled source must produce the m transmission zeros at the origin. Thus, the path must encounter m capacitors in such a way as to provide these zeros. The poles of the network function, as in the low-pass and high-pass cases, will be the result of a polynomial decomposition process.

In the bandpass-network case, most useful network functions are required to be of the high-Q type, i.e., functions with their poles located relatively close to the $j\omega$ axis. For such functions, relatively small movements of the poles will produce instability; therefore, the sensitivity problem for such realizations must be carefully studied. It is generally found that the higher the degree of the function that is realized, the larger will be the sensitivities. Thus, it is common to restrict the application of active RC techniques to the realization of bandpass network functions of only the second degree.

As an example of a bandpass network function, we shall consider an open-circuit voltage transfer function with a single pair of complex-conjugate poles. The function may be written in the form

$$\frac{V_2}{V_1} = \frac{Hp}{p^2 + b_1p + b_2} \tag{27}$$

where H may be positive or negative. A criterion of interest for such a network is the gain in the passband. This is usually specified as the gain under conditions of sinusoidal excitation at the resonant frequency. In the second-degree case given in (27) the passband gain is equal to H/b_1.

When we examine the decomposition classes given in Table 2.1 with respect to their applicability to the realization of the bandpass network function, we find that more of the classes may be applied than was possible in the low-pass or high-pass cases. This is possible under similar restraints of the avoidance of undue network complexity. First of all, let us consider case 5. We may make the following identifications:

$$y_{31} = \frac{-h_0 p}{p + \sigma_0} \qquad y_{32} = \frac{-b_0 p^2}{p + \sigma_0}$$
$$y_{33} = \frac{a_0(p + \sigma_1)(p + \sigma_2)}{p + \sigma_0} \tag{28}$$

where a_0, b_0, h_0, σ_1, σ_2, and σ_0 are real and positive. A negative value of K provides the desired decomposition and leads to a voltage transfer function of the form

$$\frac{V_2}{V_1} = \frac{-h_0 p|K|}{a_0(p + \sigma_1)(p + \sigma_2) + |K|b_0 p^2} \tag{29}$$

A network configuration for this case is shown in Fig. 3.11. For this net-

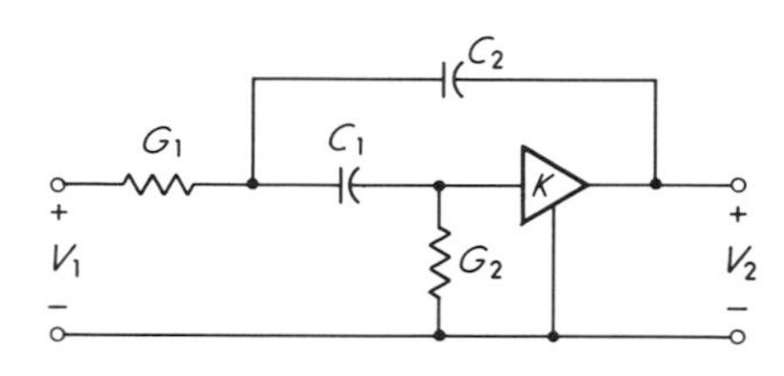

Figure 3.11 A bandpass network with K < 0.

work the voltage transfer function is

$$\frac{V_2}{V_1} = \frac{-p|K|R_2C_1}{p^2(1 + |K|)C_1C_2R_1R_2 + p(R_2C_1 + R_1C_2 + R_1C_1) + 1} \tag{30}$$

The following properties may be noted with respect to this transfer function:

1. It is bilinear with respect to the gain K and with respect to the passive elements.
2. The decomposition of the denominator with respect to K is a sum decomposition. The optimization described in Sec. 2.7 for this type of decomposition, however, cannot be applied.
3. Since the denominator decomposition is of the type illustrated as case 5 of Table 2.1, the realization is stable for all values of K.
4. The gain at resonance is $-|K|R_2C_1/(R_2C_1 + R_1C_2 + R_1C_1)$. Thus, the constant H of (27) is negative.

In determining the elements of the sensitivity matrix for the denominator of the network function of (30) we may note that the denominator has the form given in (20) and (21). Thus, we may use the relations of (22) to determine the sensitivities. The following comments apply:

1. The magnitude of the sensitivities for the b_1 coefficient of (27) will be less than or equal to unity.

2. The sensitivities for the b_2 coefficient with respect to the elements R_1, R_2, C_1, and C_2 will be -1; with respect to the gain $|K|$, the sensitivity will be negative and less than unity in magnitude (see properties 3 and 4 of Sec. 2.5).

The above conclusions are easily verified by an example.

Example 3.5 As an example of the use of the network shown in Fig. 3.11 to realize a bandpass function by means of the decomposition shown as case 5 of Table 2.1, consider the frequency-normalized function

$$\frac{V_2}{V_1} = \frac{Hp}{p^2 + 0.1p + 1}$$

If we equate the coefficients of this transfer function with the coefficients of (30), we find as a suitable choice of element values the following:

$$R_1 = 1/21.0 \text{ ohm} \qquad C_1 = 0.1 \text{ farad}$$
$$R_2 = 1/2.1 \text{ ohm} \qquad C_2 = 1.0 \text{ farad}$$
$$K = -440$$

In terms of the coefficients of (27), we find the following sensitivity matrix:

$$\begin{bmatrix} \Delta b_1^{(n)} \\ \Delta b_2^{(n)} \end{bmatrix} = \begin{bmatrix} -0.475 & -0.523 & -0.475 & -0.523 & -0.997 \\ -1.0 & -1.0 & -1.0 & -1.0 & -0.997 \end{bmatrix} \begin{bmatrix} \Delta R_1^{(n)} \\ \Delta R_2^{(n)} \\ \Delta C_1^{(n)} \\ \Delta C_2^{(n)} \\ \Delta |K|^{(n)} \end{bmatrix}$$

For this realization, the constant H of (27) is approximately -21. Thus, the gain in the passband is about -210.

Another realization related to the one described above may be found by interchanging the elements of resistance and capacitance. For such a transformation, the transfer admittance y_{32} will have zeros at infinity rather than at the origin. The form of the other parameters in (28) remains the same. Thus, the result has the decomposition shown in case 7 of Table 2.1. For the required negative value of K we obtain the voltage transfer function

$$\frac{V_2}{V_1} = \frac{-h_0 p|K|}{a_0(p + \sigma_1)(p + \sigma_2) + |K|b_0} \tag{31}$$

A network configuration which realizes this case is shown in Fig. 3.12. The

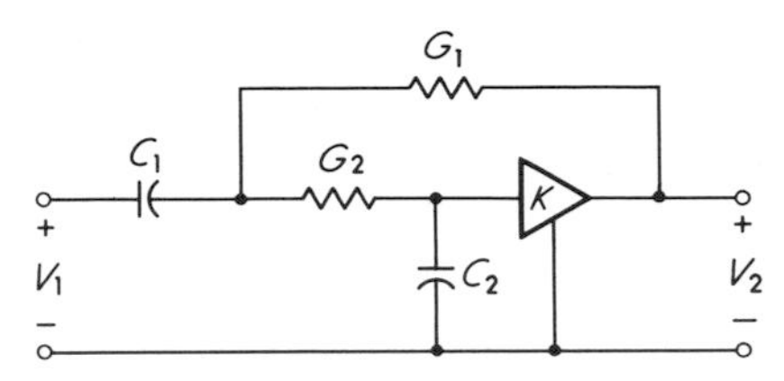

Figure 3.12 A bandpass network with K < 0.

interchange of resistive and capacitive element locations with Fig. 3.11 is easily noted. The voltage transfer function may be shown to be

$$\frac{V_2}{V_1} = \frac{-p|K|G_2S_2}{p^2 + p(G_1S_1 + G_2S_1 + G_2S_2) + G_1G_2S_1S_2(1 + |K|)} \tag{32}$$

The following properties may be noted with respect to this transfer function:

1. It is bilinear with respect to the gain K and with respect to the passive elements.
2. The decomposition of the denominator with respect to K is a sum decomposition. The optimization described in Sec. 2.7 for this type of decomposition, however, cannot be applied.
3. Since the denominator decomposition is of the type shown as case 7 of Table 2.1, the realization is stable for all values of K.
4. The gain at resonance is $-|K|G_2S_2/(G_1S_1 + G_2S_1 + G_2S_2)$. Thus the constant H of (27) is negative.
5. Changes in K vary the resonant frequency while keeping the bandwidth constant.

The following comments apply to the elements of the sensitivity matrix that will result for this realization:

1. The sensitivities for the b_1 coefficient of (27) will all be positive and less than unity (see property 4, Sec. 2.5).
2. The sensitivities for the b_2 coefficient with respect to the elements G_1, G_2, S_1, and S_2 will be unity; with respect to the gain $|K|$, the sensitivity will be positive but less than unity (see properties 3 and 4, Sec. 2.5).

The above conclusions are easily verified by an example.

Example 3.6 As an example of the use of the network shown in Fig. 3.12 to realize a bandpass function by means of the decomposition shown as case 7 of Table 2.1, consider the frequency-normalized function

$$\frac{V_2}{V_1} = \frac{Hp}{p^2 + 0.1p + 1}$$

If we equate the coefficients of this transfer function with the coefficients of (32), we find, as a suitable choice of element values, the following:

$$G_1 = 0.476 \text{ mho} \qquad S_1 = 0.1 \text{ daraf}$$
$$G_2 = 0.0476 \text{ mho} \qquad S_2 = 1.0 \text{ daraf}$$
$$K = -440$$

In terms of the coefficients of (27), we find the following sensitivity matrix:

$$\begin{bmatrix} \Delta b_1^{(n)} \\ \Delta b_2^{(n)} \end{bmatrix} = \begin{bmatrix} 0.475 & 0.523 & 0.523 & 0.475 & 0 \\ 1.0 & 1.0 & 1.0 & 1.0 & 0.997 \end{bmatrix} \begin{bmatrix} \Delta G_1^{(n)} \\ \Delta G_2^{(n)} \\ \Delta S_1^{(n)} \\ \Delta S_2^{(n)} \\ \Delta |K|^{(n)} \end{bmatrix}$$

For this realization the constant H of (27) is approximately -21. Thus, the gain in the passband is about -210.

Now let us apply case 13 of Table 2.1 to the realization of the bandpass function of (27). We shall make the identifications

$$y_{31} = \frac{-h_0 p}{p + \sigma_0} \qquad y_{32} = \frac{-b_0 p}{p + \sigma_0}$$
$$y_{33} = \frac{a_0(p + \sigma_1)(p + \sigma_2)}{p + \sigma_0} \tag{33}$$

where a_0, b_0, h_0, σ_1, σ_2, and σ_0 are real and positive. A positive value of K is required for the decomposition. The resulting voltage transfer function will have the form

$$\frac{V_2}{V_1} = \frac{p h_0 K}{a_0(p + \sigma_1)(p + \sigma_2) - b_0 K p} \tag{34}$$

A network realization for this case is shown in Fig. 3.13. For this circuit

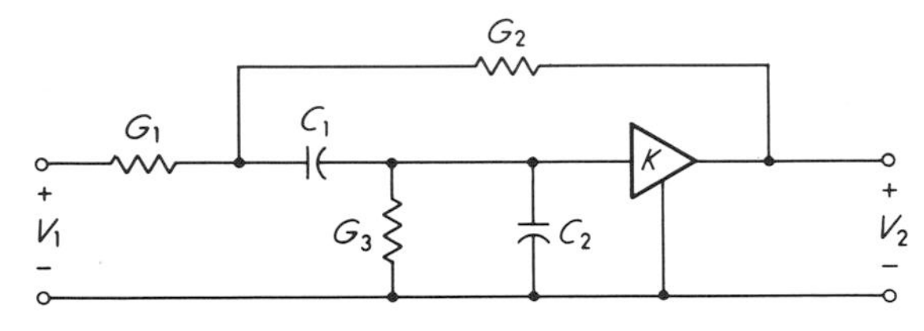

Figure 3.13 A bandpass network with $K > 0$.

the voltage transfer function may be shown to be

$$\frac{V_2}{V_1} = \frac{pKG_1S_2}{p^2 + p(G_3S_2 + G_1S_1 + G_2S_1 + G_1S_2 + G_2S_2 - KG_2S_2) + G_3(G_1 + G_2)S_1S_2} \tag{35}$$

The following properties may be noted with respect to this transfer function:

1. It is bilinear with respect to the gain K and with respect to the passive elements.
2. The decomposition of the denominator with respect to K is a difference decomposition. The optimization described in Sec. 2.6 for this type of decomposition, however, cannot be applied.
3. Since the denominator decomposition is of the type shown as case 13 of Table 2.1, changes in the gain may make the realization unstable. Thus, the sensitivity problem becomes of considerable import, especially for high-Q realizations.
4. The gain at resonance is $KG_1S_2/(G_3S_2 + G_1S_1 + G_2S_1 + G_1S_2 + G_2S_2 - KG_2S_2)$ where K is positive. Thus, the constant H of (27) is positive.
5. Since, in the denominator, only the first-degree coefficient is a function of K, changes in K will vary the bandwidth without appreciably affecting the resonant frequency of the network function.

The following comments apply to the elements of the sensitivity matrix that will result for this realization:

1. The sensitivity for the b_1 coefficient of (27) with respect to the gain K will be negative and greater in magnitude than $2Q - 1$, where

$$Q = \sqrt{b_2}/b_1$$

(see Sec. 2.6).

2. The sensitivities for the b_2 coefficient of (27) with respect to the elements G_3, S_1, and S_2 will be unity; with respect to the elements G_1 and G_2 the sensitivities will be less than unity (see properties 3 and 4, Sec. 2.5).

The above conclusions are easily verified by an example.

Example 3.7 As an example of the use of the network shown in Fig. 3.13 to realize a bandpass function by means of the decomposition shown as case 13 of Table 2.1, consider the frequency-normalized function

$$\frac{V_2}{V_1} = \frac{Hp}{p^2 + 0.1p + 1}$$

If we equate the coefficients of this transfer function with the coefficients of (35), we find, as a suitable choice of element values, the following:

$$\begin{aligned} G_1 &= 1.0 \text{ mho} & S_1 &= 0.5 \text{ daraf} \\ G_2 &= 3.0 \text{ mhos} & S_2 &= 1.0 \text{ daraf} \\ G_3 &= 0.5 \text{ mho} & K &= 2.133 \end{aligned}$$

In terms of the coefficients of (27), we find the following sensitivity matrix:

$$\begin{bmatrix} \Delta b_1^{(n)} \\ \Delta b_2^{(n)} \end{bmatrix} = \begin{bmatrix} 15 & -19 & 5 & 20 & -19 & -64 \\ 0.25 & 0.75 & 1.0 & 1.0 & 1.0 & 0 \end{bmatrix} \begin{bmatrix} \Delta G_1^{(n)} \\ \Delta G_2^{(n)} \\ \Delta G_3^{(n)} \\ \Delta S_1^{(n)} \\ \Delta S_2^{(n)} \\ \Delta K^{(n)} \end{bmatrix}$$

For this realization the constant H of (27) is 2.133. Thus, the gain in the passband is 21.33.

It should be noted that the sensitivities for the coefficient b_1 in Example 3.7 are considerably larger than those encountered for the same network function in Examples 3.5 and 3.6. This is especially true for the sensitivity with respect to the gain K. From the discussion of Sec. 2.6, we know that the minimum magnitude which is possible for this sensitivity is 19. Although this optimum value cannot be obtained in this realization, we might logically suspect that we could come closer to it by a "better" choice of element values than those given above. The element values, however, are the result of a trial-and-error solution of a set of nonlinear equations. Thus, any attempts to impose additional constraints adds considerable additional mathematical complexity to the solution. As a result, circuits based on a decomposition of the type shown in case 13 of Table 2.1 are limited to low-Q bandpass realizations. In later chapters of this text we shall investigate circuits which are more suitable to the higher-Q cases.

Another realization based on a case 13 decomposition of the denominator of a bandpass function may be formed by interchanging the locations of the resistors and capacitors in Fig. 3.13. The resulting parameters also have the form given in (33). Thus, the realization will still have the decomposition indicated by case 13. The circuit, however, has the disadvantage of requiring three capacitors rather than the two shown in the circuit in Fig. 3.13. Another disadvantage is that such a transformed circuit would have a series capacitance in the input rather than the series

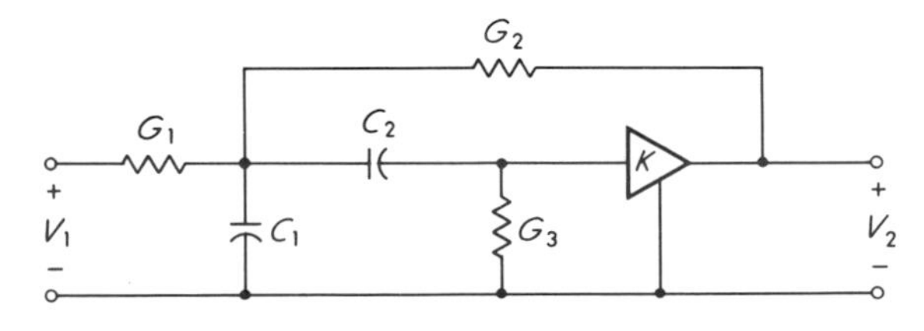

Figure 3.14 A bandpass network with $K > 0$.

resistance shown in Fig. 3.13. Thus, the circuit is of less practical importance, and it will not be discussed further.

Another application of case 13 may be made with the circuit shown in Fig. 3.14.* For this circuit the voltage transfer function in terms of the indicated elements is

$$\frac{V_2}{V_1} = \frac{pKG_1S_1}{p^2 + p(G_1S_1 + G_2S_1 + G_3S_2 + G_3S_1 - KG_2S_1) + G_3S_1S_2(G_1 + G_2)} \tag{36}$$

The properties of this network function and the comments concerning the elements of the sensitivity matrix are the same as those made for the network shown in Fig. 3.13, with the transfer function given in (35), except that the passband gain is $KG_1S_1/(G_1S_1 + G_2S_1 + G_3S_2 + G_3S_1 - KG_2S_1)$. An example of this realization follows.

Example 3.8 As an example of the use of the network shown in Fig. 3.14 to realize a bandpass function by means of the decomposition of case 13 of Table 2.1, consider the frequency-normalized transfer function

$$\frac{V_2}{V_1} = \frac{Hp}{p^2 + 0.1p + 1}$$

If we equate the coefficients of this transfer function with those of (36), we find, as a suitable choice of element values, the following:

$$\begin{aligned} G_1 &= 1.0 \text{ mho} & S_1 &= 1.0 \text{ daraf} \\ G_2 &= 3.0 \text{ mhos} & S_2 &= 0.5 \text{ daraf} \\ G_3 &= 0.5 \text{ mho} & K &= 1.55 \end{aligned}$$

In terms of the coefficients of (27), we find the following sensitivity matrix:

$$\begin{bmatrix} \Delta b_1^{(n)} \\ \Delta b_2^{(n)} \end{bmatrix} = \begin{bmatrix} 10.0 & -16.5 & 7.5 & -1.5 & 2.5 & -46.5 \\ 0.25 & 0.75 & 1.0 & 1.0 & 1.0 & 0 \end{bmatrix} \begin{bmatrix} \Delta G_1^{(n)} \\ \Delta G_2^{(n)} \\ \Delta G_3^{(n)} \\ \Delta S_1^{(n)} \\ \Delta S_2^{(n)} \\ \Delta K^{(n)} \end{bmatrix}$$

For this realization, the constant H of (27) is 1.55. Thus, the gain in the passband is 15.5.

As was the case for the circuit given in Fig. 3.13, a transformed alternate realization for the circuit given in Fig. 3.14 is possible; however, it is of less practical importance and will not be discussed further.

* The circuits shown in Figs. 3.11, 3.12, 3.13, and 3.14 are similar to the circuits 5, 7, 9, and 6, respectively, by Sallen and Key, *op. cit.*

A realization using the decomposition listed as case 12 in Table 2.1 may also be developed for the bandpass voltage transfer function of (27). For this case we may make the identifications

$$y_{31} = \frac{-h_0 p}{p + \sigma_0} \qquad y_{32} = -b_0(p + \sigma_a)$$
$$y_{33} = \frac{a_0(p + \sigma_1)(p + \sigma_2)}{p + \sigma_0} \tag{37}$$

where a_0, b_0, h_0, σ_1, σ_2, and σ_0 are real and positive and where $\sigma_1 < \sigma_0 < \sigma_2$ and $\sigma_1 < \sigma_a < \sigma_2$. The voltage transfer function for a positive value of K is

$$\frac{V_2}{V_1} = \frac{Kh_0 p}{a_0(p + \sigma_1)(p + \sigma_2) - b_0 K(p + \sigma_a)(p + \sigma_0)} \tag{38}$$

A network configuration which realizes this case is shown in Fig. 3.15.

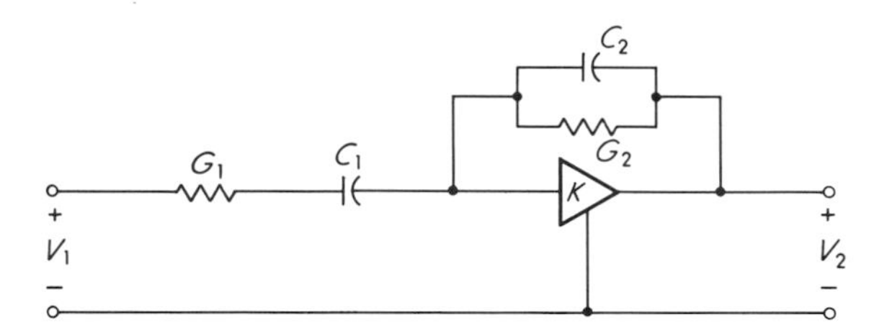

Figure 3.15 A bandpass network with $K > 0$.

The voltage transfer function in terms of the element values shown in this figure is

$$\frac{V_2}{V_1} = \frac{pKG_1C_1}{p^2C_1C_2(1 - K) + p[(G_2C_1 + G_1C_2)(1 - K) + G_1C_1] + G_1G_2(1-K)} \tag{39}$$

The following properties may be noted with respect to this realization:

1. It is bilinear with respect to the gain K and with respect to the passive elements.
2. The decomposition of the denominator with respect to K is a difference decomposition. Since it is of the type shown in case 12, however, it cannot be optimized by the methods of Sec. 2.6.
3. The two negative-real zeros in the left member of the denominator of (38) form the polynomial B in case 12 of Table 2.1. Similarly, the two

negative-real zeros in the right member form the polynomial A. Thus the direction of movement on the root locus for increasing K (the gain of the VCVS) is opposite to that shown for K' in the table. Such a realization is said to be conditionally stable, since lowering the gain K produces instability. For this network K must be greater than the quantity $(G_1C_1 + G_1C_2 + G_2C_1)/(G_1C_2 + G_2C_1)$ for stability.

4. The gain at resonance is $KG_1C_1/[(G_2C_1 + G_1C_2)(1 - K) + G_1C_1]$. Because of the limitation on the minimum value of gain given in (3) above, the denominator of the above quantity will be negative. Thus, the constant H given in (27) is negative.

In analyzing the sensitivity of the network function, we note that the denominator of (39) is of the general form $D(p) = b_0'p^2 + b_1'p + b_2'$, where b_0', b_1', and b_2' are functions of the active and passive elements. In a manner similar to that done for (20) in Sec. 3.3, the sensitivities for the coefficients b_1 and b_2 of (27) are easily found in terms of the sensitivities for b_0', b_1', and b_2' by the relations (see also property 2, Sec. 2.5)

$$\begin{aligned} S_x^{b_1} &= S_x^{b_1'} - S_x^{b_0'} \\ S_x^{b_2} &= S_x^{b_2'} - S_x^{b_0'} \end{aligned}$$

An example of this realization follows.

Example 3.9 As an example of the use of the network shown in Fig. 3.15 to realize a bandpass function by means of the decomposition of case 12 of Table 2.1, consider the frequency-normalized transfer function

$$\frac{V_2}{V_1} = \frac{Hp}{p^2 + 0.1p + 1}$$

If we equate the coefficients of this transfer function with those of (39), we find, as a suitable choice of element values, the following:

$$\begin{aligned} G_1 &= 1.0 \text{ mho} \qquad & C_1 &= 1.0 \text{ farad} \\ G_2 &= 1.0 \text{ mho} \qquad & C_2 &= 1.0 \text{ farad} \end{aligned}$$
$$K = 1.526$$

In terms of the coefficients of (27), we find the following sensitivity matrix

$$\begin{bmatrix} \Delta b_1^{(n)} \\ \Delta b_2^{(n)} \end{bmatrix} = \begin{bmatrix} -9.0 & -10.0 & -10.0 & 9.0 & 55.1 \\ 1.0 & 1.0 & -1.0 & -1.0 & 0 \end{bmatrix} \begin{bmatrix} \Delta G_1^{(n)} \\ \Delta G_2^{(n)} \\ \Delta C_1^{(n)} \\ \Delta C_2^{(n)} \\ \Delta K^{(n)} \end{bmatrix}$$

For this realization the constant H of (27) is -2.9. Thus, the gain in the passband is -29.

Although all of the network configurations described in this section are capable of realizing bandpass transfer functions of the type given in (27), practical experience has shown that the configuration shown in Fig. 3.13 has many practical advantages. First of all, it does not require a high value of gain. Thus, stabilizing the gain in the VCVS is simplified. To some extent this advantage compensates for the higher sensitivities of this realization when compared with the inverting realizations shown in Figs. 3.11 and 3.12. Second, the fact that in the denominator the gain K appears only in the first-degree term makes the final adjustment of the Q of the network function relatively easy. Third, since some of the sensitivities are negative, the information presented by the sensitivity matrix for this realization may be used in the practical design of the network to improve the actual sensitivities. For example, if it is experimentally determined that the gain of the VCVS decreases with temperature, the use of a resistor with a decrease of conductance with temperature that is approximately four times as great (on a percentage basis) for G_1 may be used to cancel the effect of such a change on the coefficient b_1. Other possibilities for sensitivity cancellation exist. For example, if the percentage change of the values of the two capacitors due to temperature or other effects is very nearly the same, the net effect on the coefficient b_1 is minimized. Fourth, parasitic input elements associated with the VCVS are easily absorbed in the elements S_2 and G_3. It should be noted, however, that this circuit will usually only be suitable for moderate values of Q. In succeeding chapters realizations more appropriate to the realization of very high-Q circuits will be discussed. For convenience, a detailed design procedure for the realization of bandpass circuits with the configuration shown in Fig. 3.13 is given in Sec. 3.8 as circuit 3.

3.5 *The realization of functions with $j\omega$-axis zeros*

In the preceding section, the realization of bandpass network functions was discussed. This type of network function, in addition to providing transmission of a band of frequencies, provides high rejection to signals at zero and infinite frequencies. In some applications it is more desirable to concentrate the rejection capabilities of the network function at some other frequencies. Thus we desire the realization of network functions of the type

$$N(p) = \frac{H \prod_i (p^2 + \omega_i^2)}{p^n + b_1 p^{n-1} + \cdots + b_{n-1} p + b_n} \tag{40}$$

One of the pairs of zeros in the network function given above may, of course, be located at zero and infinity to provide rejection at those frequencies as well. Because of the importance of these types of network functions, a method of realizing them will be presented in this section.*

As a specific example of the type of network function described above, let us consider the frequency-normalized open-circuit voltage transfer function

$$\frac{V_2}{V_1} = \frac{H(p^2 + b)}{p^2 + ap + 1} \tag{41}$$

Comparing this function with the general form given in (2), we see that a passive RC network is required whose transfer admittance from ports 1 to 3 has zeros on the $j\omega$ axis. There are several network configurations which may be used to realize such network functions. The one which will be described here may be characterized as a *parallel-ladder realization.* Although it has the disadvantage of additional network elements over some of the other realizations, this configuration has been found to give reliable results with low sensitivity figures.†

The ladder-network configuration which will be used to produce the transmission zeros on the $j\omega$ axis is shown in Fig. 3.16. The element values

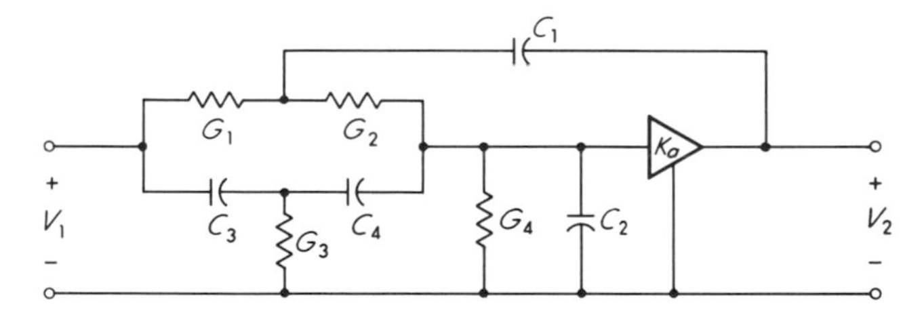

***Figure 3.16** A bandpass network with jω-axis zeros.*

may be expressed in terms of the coefficients a and b in (41), where b is the square of the frequency (expressed in radians per second) at which the

* Design formulas for the realization of complex conjugate transmission zeros not restricted to the $j\omega$ axis with a VCVS as the active element are given by N. Balabanian and B. Patel, Active Realization of Complex Zeros, *IEEE Trans. Circuit Theory,* vol. CT-10, no. 2, pp. 299–300, June, 1963.

† W. J. Kerwin and L. P. Huelsman, The Design of High Performance Active *RC* Band-pass Filters, *IEEE Intern. Conv. Record,* vol. 14, part 10, pp. 74–80, March, 1966. This configuration may also be used to realize elliptic function filters. See W. J. Kerwin, An Active *RC* Elliptic Function Filter, *IEEE Region Six Conf. Record,* vol. 2, pp. 647–654, April, 1966.

desired zeros are located. The relations are

$$\begin{aligned} G_1 &= \frac{3b}{b+1} & C_1 &= \frac{4.5b}{b+1} \\ G_2 &= \frac{1.5b}{b+1} & C_2 &= \frac{b}{b+1} \\ G_3 &= \frac{4.5}{b+1} & C_3 &= \frac{3}{b+1} \\ G_4 &= \frac{1}{b+1} & C_4 &= \frac{1.5}{b+1} \\ K_a &= \frac{(2.5-a)(b+1)}{1.5b} \end{aligned} \tag{42}$$

For this choice of element values, the y parameters have the following form:

$$-y_{31} = \frac{h_0(p^2+b)}{p+1} \qquad -y_{32} = \frac{b_0 p}{p+1} \qquad y_{33} = \frac{p^2+2.5p+1}{p+1} \tag{43}$$

where h_0 and b_0 are functions of b. Thus, from (2) we see that the voltage transfer function has the form

$$\frac{V_2}{V_1} = \frac{K_a h_0(p^2+b)}{p^2+2.5p+1-K_a b_0 p} \tag{44}$$

From (42) we see that K_a will be a positive constant and therefore that the denominator decomposition is of the type given in Table 2.1 as case 13. The constant H of (41) may be shown to be

$$H = \frac{2.5-a}{1.5b} \tag{45}$$

It should be noted that it is possible to use the passive elements shown in Fig. 3.16 in a slightly different configuration to form the voltage transfer function of (41). The configuration is shown in Fig. 3.17. For the element values given in (42), the y parameters will again have the form given in (43). Only the constant b_0 will be changed. This will necessitate a different value of controlled-source gain in the final realization. The gain is referred

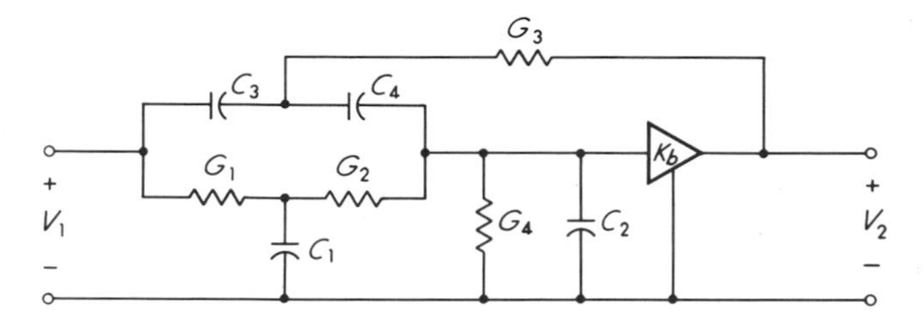

Figure 3.17 A bandpass network with jω-axis zeros.

to as K_b in Fig. 3.17. It may be shown that for the choice of element values of (42) the gain of the VCVS in this case is

$$K_b = \frac{(2.5 - a)(1 + b)}{2.5} \tag{46}$$

The overall gain constant H of (41) is also changed in this case. It is given by the expression

$$H = \frac{2.5 - a}{1.5} \tag{47}$$

Thus, the designer may make a choice between the two realizations given in Figs. 3.16 and 3.17, based on more closely approaching the desired gain for the overall network function. An example follows.

Example 3.10 As an example of the realization of a network function of the type described in this section, consider the function

$$\frac{V_2}{V_1} = \frac{H(p^2 + 2)}{p^2 + 0.1p + 1}$$

Comparing this function with the one given in (41) we see that $a = 0.1$, $b = 2$. Substituting these values in the relations of (42), we obtain the element values

$$\begin{aligned} G_1 &= 2 \text{ mhos} & C_1 &= 3 \text{ farads} \\ G_2 &= 1 \text{ mho} & C_2 &= 2/3 \text{ farad} \\ G_3 &= 3/2 \text{ mho} & C_3 &= 1 \text{ farad} \\ G_4 &= 1/3 \text{ mho} & C_4 &= 1/2 \text{ farad} \end{aligned}$$
$$K_a = 2.4$$

The realization is of the type shown in Fig. 3.16. The constant H has a value of 0.8. If we apply the techniques of Sec. 2.5, assuming that the denominator of (41) is written in the form $p^2 + b_1p + b_2$, we obtain the following sensitivity matrix (for convenience a tabular form has been used):

	$\Delta G_1^{(n)}$	$\Delta G_2^{(n)}$	$\Delta G_3^{(n)}$	$\Delta G_4^{(n)}$	$\Delta C_1^{(n)}$	$\Delta C_2^{(n)}$	$\Delta C_3^{(n)}$	$\Delta C_4^{(n)}$	$\Delta K^{(n)}$
$\Delta b_1^{(n)}$	7.25	−10.3	0.787	3.37	−10.8	6.02	−0.642	4.53	−24
$\Delta b_2^{(n)}$	0.947	0.807	−0.088	0.337	−1.08	−0.669	−0.052	−0.195	0

A realization may also be made in the form given in Fig. 3.17. For such a realization, the passive element values remain the same. However, a gain of 4.8 is required for the VCVS, and the gain constant H has a value of 1.6.

3.6 *A general realization technique*

In this section we shall describe a synthesis technique which may easily be applied to the realization of an arbitrary network function. Although it has the disadvantage of requiring two VCVSs, it has the advantage that the determination of the values of the network components is quite simple.

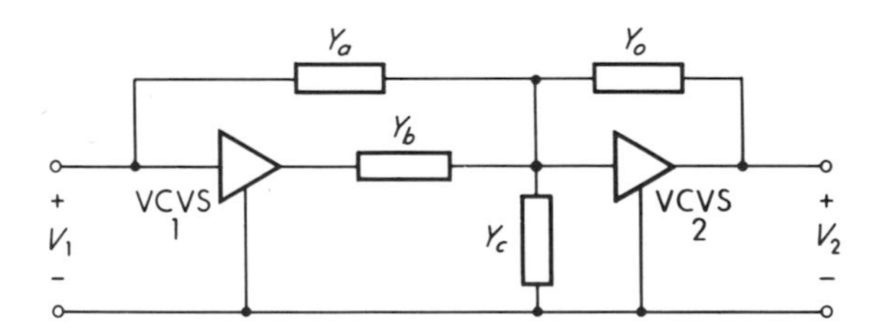

Figure 3.18 A general VCVS realization technique.

The circuit used in this approach is shown in Fig. 3.18. The source indicated as VCVS 1 is an inverting one, and it may be considered to have a gain of $-K_1$, where K_1 is a positive constant normally set equal to unity. The source indicated as VCVS 2 is a noninverting one, and it may be considered to have a gain K_2, where K_2 is a positive constant normally set equal to 2.0. The circuit may be readily analyzed to determine the open-circuit voltage transfer function V_2/V_1 in terms of the gains K_1 and K_2, and the admittances Y_a, Y_b, Y_c, Y_d, and Y_0. We obtain

$$\frac{V_2}{V_1} = \frac{K_2(Y_a - K_1 Y_b)}{(Y_0 + Y_a + Y_b + Y_c) - K_2 Y_0}$$

As is to be expected, the network function is bilinear in K_1 and K_2. For the case in which $K_1 = 1$, $K_2 = 2$, and $Y_0 = Y_a + Y_b + Y_d$, the voltage transfer function given above simplifies to

$$\frac{V_2}{V_1} = \frac{2(Y_a - Y_b)}{Y_c - Y_d} \tag{48}$$

Now let us consider the realization of a voltage transfer function of the form

$$\frac{V_2}{V_1} = \frac{N(p)}{D(p)}$$

If we divide the numerator and denominator by a polynomial $Q(p)$ consisting only of distinct negative-real zeros and of degree 1 less than the degree of $N(p)$ or $D(p)$ (whichever is greater), we may make partial-fraction expansions of the numerator and denominator as follows:

$$\frac{V_2}{V_1} = \frac{N(p)/Q(p)}{D(p)/Q(p)} = \frac{k_\infty^{(n)}p + k_0^{(n)} + \sum_i k_i^{(n)}p/(p + \sigma_i)}{K_\infty^{(d)}p + k_0^{(d)} + \sum_i k_i^{(d)}p/(p + \sigma_i)} \tag{49}$$

The various k's in (49) may be positive or negative (or zero). The two-terminal admittances shown in Fig. 3.18 may now be determined by equating positive and negative terms in the numerator and denominator of (48) and (49) Thus we set $2Y_a$ equal to the positive terms in the expansion of $N(p)/Q(p)$, etc.*

Although this realization technique is general, it usually requires a fairly large number of network elements since Y_a and Y_b must be realized twice. In addition, it cannot be used to provide an optimum decomposition. An example follows.

Example 3.11 As an example of the use of the circuit shown in Fig. 3.18 to realize a network function, consider the frequency normalized all-pass voltage transfer function

$$\frac{V_2}{V_1} = \frac{(p-1)^2}{(p+1)^2} = \frac{p^2 - 2p + 1}{p^2 + 2p + 1} = \frac{Q(p)}{p^2 + b_1 p + b_2}$$

* R. J. A. Paul, Active Network Synthesis Using One-port *RC* Networks, *Proc. IEE*, vol. 113, no. 1, pp. 83–86, Jan., 1966.

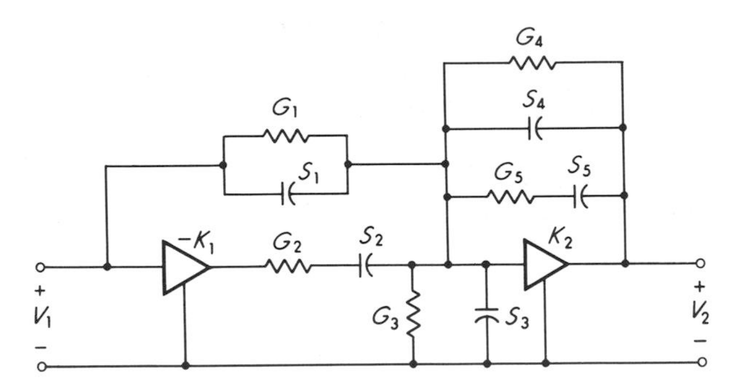

Figure 3.19 An example of a general VCVS realization technique.

From (48) and (49) we obtain

$$Y_a = \tfrac{1}{2}(p+1) \qquad Y_c = p + 1$$
$$Y_b = \frac{2p}{p+1} \qquad Y_d = 0$$

This specifies the element configuration shown in Fig. 3.19, where

$$\begin{aligned} G_1 &= 0.5 \text{ mho} & S_1 &= 2.0 \text{ darafs} \\ G_2 &= 2.0 \text{ mhos} & S_2 &= 0.5 \text{ daraf} \\ G_3 &= 1.0 \text{ mho} & S_3 &= 1.0 \text{ daraf} \\ G_4 &= 0.5 \text{ mho} & S_4 &= 2.0 \text{ darafs} \\ G_5 &= 2.0 \text{ mhos} & S_5 &= 0.5 \text{ daraf} \\ K_1 &= -1 & K_2 &= 2 \end{aligned}$$

3.7 *Circuit realizations for controlled sources*

The realization techniques described in the preceding sections of this chapter are based on the use of ideal VCVSs. It is possible to realize such controlled sources both from solid-state and thermionic devices. A detailed treatment of these techniques is beyond the scope of this book. However, for completeness, some representative methods of realizing such sources are presented in this chapter.

One realization scheme for the VCVS involves the use of an operational amplifier. Such an amplifier may be described as a voltage-controlled voltage source of high input impedance, low output impedance, and very high gain. Because of their wide usage in analog computers and other circuit applications, the design of such amplifiers has been highly developed. For high-quality units, in typical applications, the effective input impedance may be in the order of hundreds of megohms, whereas the output impedance may be fractions of an ohm. Such amplifiers may be used to simulate inverting or noninverting VCVSs of the type that are required for the realizations described in this chapter.

A symbolic representation for a differential-input operational amplifier is given in Fig. 3.20. The "minus" terminal is usually referred to as the *inverting input terminal*, and the "plus" terminal is called the *noninverting* terminal. The current into these terminals is assumed to be zero. The voltage at the output terminal is proportional to the difference between

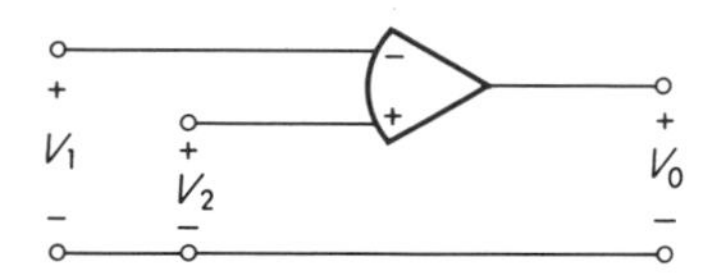

Figure 3.20 Circuit symbol for an operational amplifier.

the voltages applied to the two input terminals. Thus, for the variables defined in the figure we may write

$$V_0 = K(V_2 - V_1)$$

where K is the open-loop gain of the operational amplifier. Gains of 100,000 are not uncommon. In circuit applications, one of the effects of such gain is to drive the voltage difference $V_2 - V_1$ to zero. This effect is frequently useful in analyzing operational amplifier circuits.*

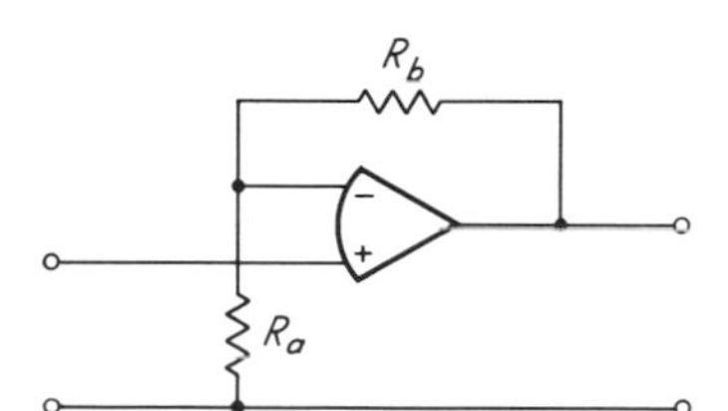

Figure 3.21 A noninverting VCVS.

A noninverting VCVS may be realized with an operational amplifier using the configuration shown in Fig. 3.21. This circuit represents a VCVS

* A very readable treatment of the characteristics and applications of operational amplifiers may be found in the book, "Handbook of Operational Amplifier Applications," published by the Burr-Brown Research Corporation, Tucson, Arizona, 1963.

of the type shown in Fig. 3.1*a* with a gain of K, where

$$K = \frac{R_a + R_b}{R_a}$$

Thus, we see that this circuit can only be used for gains greater than unity. For the general network configuration shown in Fig. 3.3, the voltage transfer function of (2) becomes

$$\frac{V_2}{V_1} = \frac{-[(R_a + R_b)/R_a]y_{31}}{y_{33} + [(R_a + R_b)/R_a]y_{32}} \tag{50}$$

Now let us consider attaching terminal 2 of the passive network to the junction of the resistors R_a and R_b rather than to the output of the operational amplifier. The configuration is shown in Fig. 3.22. If we

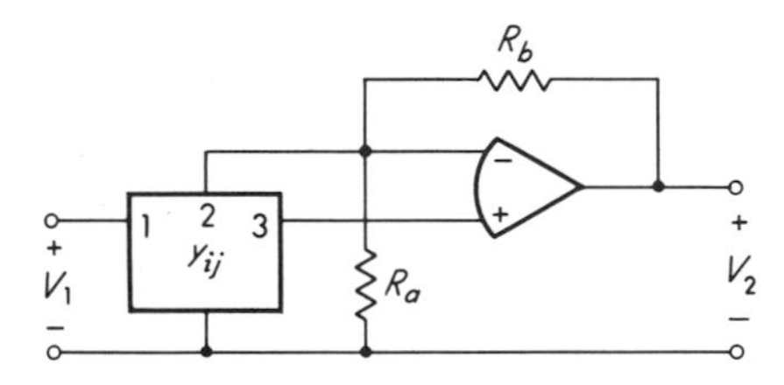

***Figure 3.22** A general noninverting network configuration.*

assume that the impedance levels in the passive network and the impedance levels of the resistors R_a and R_b are so chosen that the passive network does not appreciably load the resistor feedback network, the effect is to multiply y_{32} by the factor $R_a/(R_a + R_b)$. Under these conditions (50) becomes

$$\frac{V_2}{V_1} = \frac{-[(R_a + R_b)/R_a]y_{31}}{y_{33} + y_{32}} \tag{51}$$

Thus, the denominator polynomial of the network function becomes independent of the gain of the VCVS. Such an approach is useful in low-pass and high-pass configurations since it permits adjustment of the gain

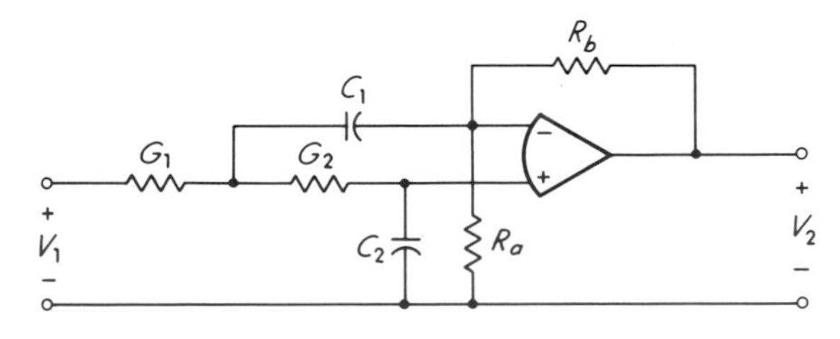

***Figure 3.23** An operational amplifier low-pass network.*

in the passband without changing the frequency characteristics of the network. For example, the low-pass configuration shown in Fig. 3.8 may be modified to that shown in Fig. 3.23. Under the stated assumptions, the voltage transfer function for this circuit is

$$\frac{V_2}{V_1} = \frac{KG_1G_2}{p^2C_1C_2 + p(G_1C_2 + G_2C_2) + G_1G_2} \tag{52}$$

Similarly, the high-pass configuration shown in Fig. 3.10 may be modified to that shown in Fig. 3.24. The voltage transfer function is

$$\frac{V_2}{V_1} = \frac{p^2KC_1C_2}{p^2C_1C_2 + p(C_1G_2 + C_2G_2) + G_1G_2} \tag{53}$$

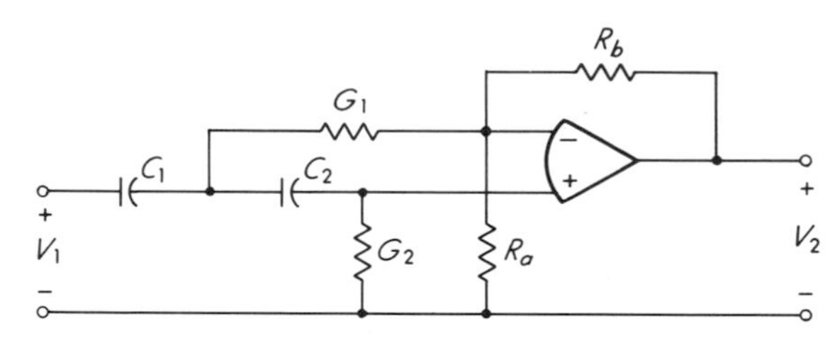

***Figure 3.24** An operational amplifier high-pass network.*

This approach is not generally applicable where poles close to the $j\omega$ axis are desired.

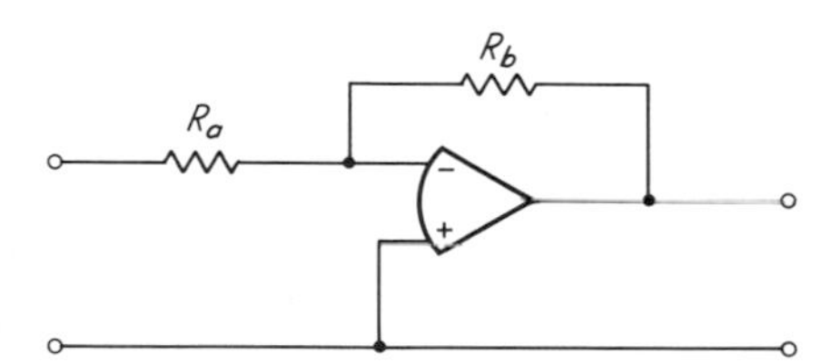

***Figure 3.25** An inverting VCVS.*

The operational amplifier may also be used to realize an inverting VCVS. The circuit is shown in Fig. 3.25. For this circuit the gain may be seen to be

$$K = \frac{-R_b}{R_a} \tag{54}$$

Since the input impedance of this circuit is determined by the value of R_a, high values are usually required for the feedback resistors. Such a VCVS may be used in the various circuit configurations requiring a negative value of K presented in the earlier sections of this chapter.*

The second method which may be applied to the realization of a VCVS is the direct design of a solid-state (or thermionic) circuit with the desired properties. As a representative example of such a realization, consider the circuit shown in Fig. 3.26. The biasing elements have been deleted from this circuit for convenience.† If we assume an idealized model for the

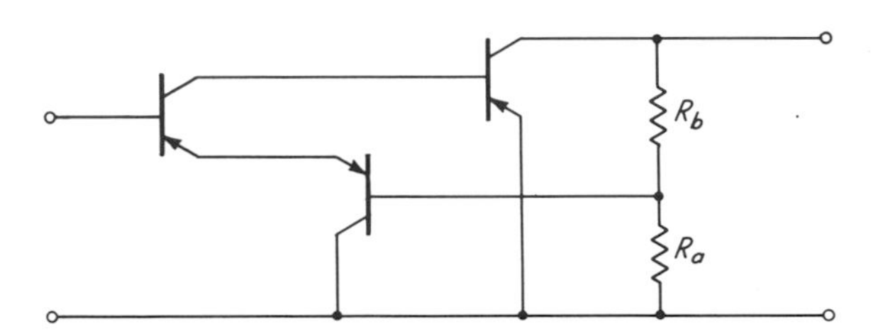

Figure 3.26 A noninverting VCVS.

transistors and further assume that all alphas are equal, routine circuit analysis shows that the voltage transfer function is

$$\frac{V_2}{V_1} = \frac{\alpha^2}{2\alpha - 1} \frac{R_a + R_b}{R_a} \tag{55}$$

In the limit as the alphas of the transistors approach unity, we see that the voltage transfer function is specified completely by the resistors R_a and R_b. A similar analysis may be used to verify the low output impedance of this circuit. Thus, this circuit may be used as a noninverting VCVS in the network realizations given in the previous sections. A detailed schematic of this same amplifier is shown in Fig. 3.27. The open-loop gain is better than 1500, the input impedance is of the order of 100 kilohms, and the output impedance is approximately 20 ohms. In addition, both the input and the output are at zero dc potential. Thus it is possible to cascade realizations using this amplifier without the need for coupling capacitors. A miniaturized hybrid form of this amplifier has been constructed in a package 8 mm on a side.‡

* For some other realizations using operational amplifiers, see A. S. Morse, The Use of Operational Amplifiers in Active Network Theory, *Proc. Nat. Electron. Conf.*, vol. 20, pp. 748–752, 1964.

† The details of this circuit and a discussion of its performance are given in W. J. Kerwin and L. P. Huelsman, *op. cit.*

‡ W. J. Kerwin, *op. cit.* Several other realizations for VCVSs and ICISs may be found in S. S. Hakim, *RC* Active Filters Using Amplifiers as Active Elements, *Proc. IEE*, vol. 112, no. 5, pp. 901–912, May, 1965.

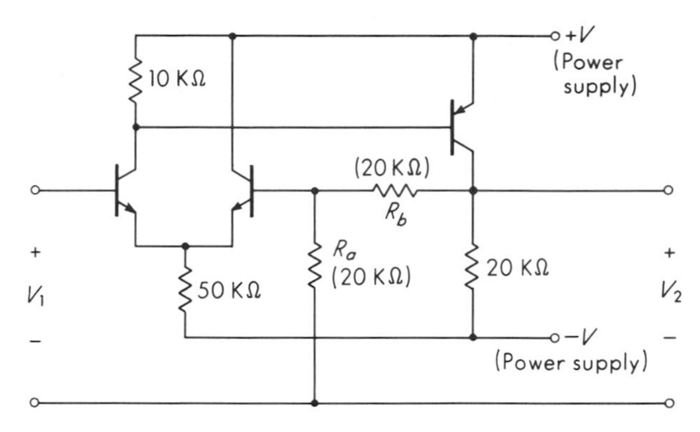

Figure 3.27 Complete schematic for the noninverting VCVS shown in Fig. 3.26.

3.8 *Realization procedures and design information*

In this chapter we have considered the use of a controlled source as the active element for the realization of network functions. In the following pages, design information and actual numerical examples of circuit realizations for second-degree low-pass, high-pass, and bandpass network functions are given. These are titled, respectively, circuits 1, 2, and 3. The network function which is realized in each case is an open-circuit voltage transfer function. The controlled source which is used is a voltage-controlled voltage source (VCVS). In order to make the circuits realistic, an actual realization for the source using an operational amplifier is shown. Other realizations for controlled sources have been discussed earlier in this chapter. In each circuit, a general design procedure is described in terms of the elements shown in the schematic. In addition, a specific numerical example is given illustrating the application of the design procedure. It should be noted that in all these circuits the impedance normalization constant is free to be chosen. Thus, in all of the design procedures there will be one step in which some element is set to a convenient value. Once this value is chosen, the correct normalization is achieved for all the remaining elements. It should be noted that the examples described in these circuit diagrams have actually been constructed and tested. Thus, the frequency-response curves indicated are those found by actual measurement.*

* The circuit diagrams and the design information given in these diagrams are reproduced through the permission of the copyright owner, the Burr-Brown Research Corporation of Tucson, Arizona, from their publication, "Handbook of Operational Amplifier *RC* Networks."

Circuit 1 Design procedure for the realization of a second-degree low-pass voltage transfer function using an operational amplifier realization for a voltage-controlled voltage source.

General circuit schematic

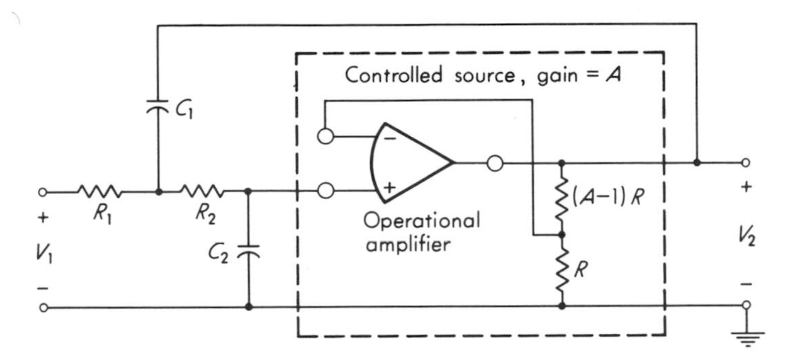

General transfer function The voltage transfer function in terms of the circuit elements and also in terms of the frequency-normalization constant ω_0 and the constant a is

$$\frac{V_2}{V_1} = \frac{A/R_1R_2}{p^2C_1C_2 + p[(C_2/R_1) + (C_2/R_2) + (C_1/R_2)(1 - A)] + 1/R_1R_2} = \frac{H\omega_0^2}{p^2 + a\omega_0 p + \omega_0^2}$$

General circuit characteristics An idealized Bode plot illustrating the relative gain characteristic of the transfer function and of the (open-loop) operational amplifier is shown below:

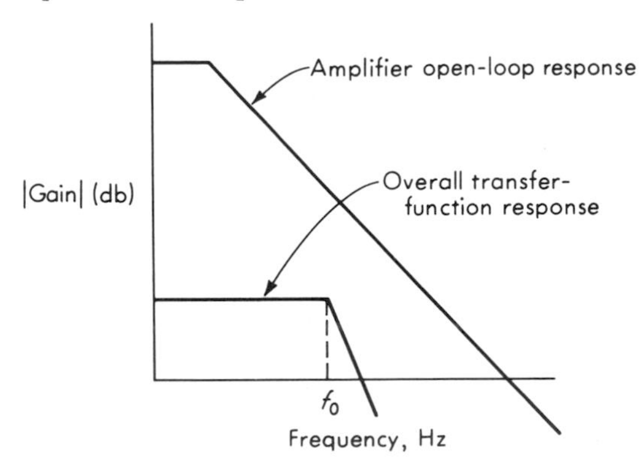

Design procedure Given H, ω_0, a:

1. Set $A = H$ (Note: $H > 0$)
2. Define the element spread constant $m = (a^2/4) + (A - 1)$

3. Choose a convenient value of C_1 (farads)
4. Define $b = C_1\omega_0$
5. Calculate (ohms and farads)

$$C_2 = mC_1 \qquad R_1 = \frac{2}{ab} \qquad R_2 = \frac{a}{2mb}$$

[Note: Choose R and $(A - 1)R$ such that $R + (A - 1)R = 100$ kilohms or use a 100-kilohm potentiometer.]

Example of Circuit 1 The realization of a typical low-pass maximally-flat-magnitude (Butterworth) transfer function follows:

Given $f_0 = \dfrac{\omega_0}{2\pi} = 30$ Hz, $a = \sqrt{2}$, $H = 10$

$$\begin{aligned} A &= 10 & C_2 &= 0.95\ \mu\text{F} \\ m &= 9.5 & R_1 &= 75 \text{ kilohms} \\ C_1 &= 0.1\ \mu\text{F} & R_2 &= 3.94 \text{ kilohms} \\ b &= 1.89 \times 10^{-5} & & \end{aligned}$$

Transfer function for example problem

$$\frac{V_2}{V_1} = \frac{3.55 \times 10^5}{p^2 + 2.67 \times 10^2 p + 3.55 \times 10^4}$$

*Circuit schematic for example problem**

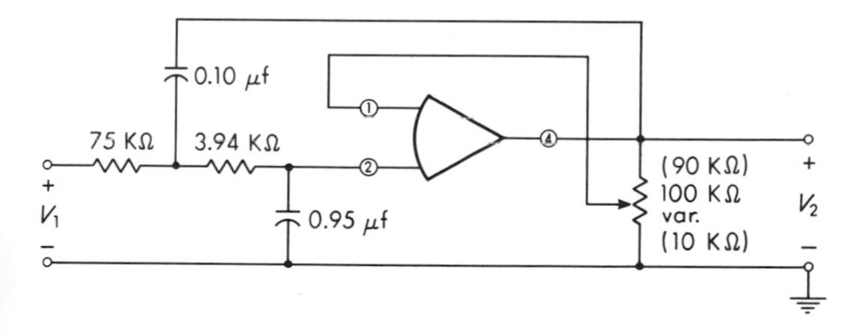

Circuit characteristic for example problem

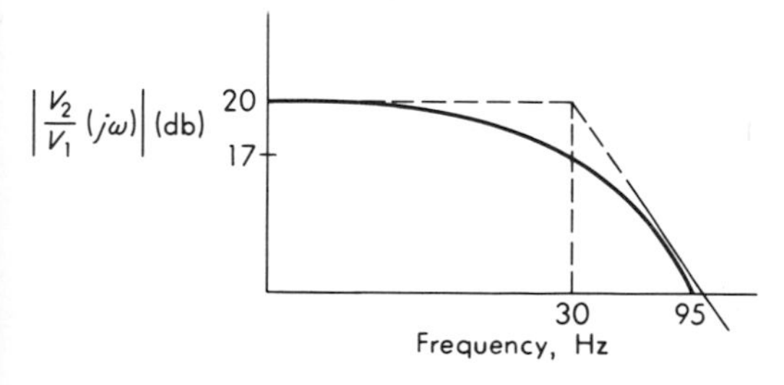

* The operational amplifier used in constructing this realization was a Burr-Brown Model 3003/15.

Circuit 2 Design procedure for the realization of a second-degree high-pass voltage transfer function using an operational amplifier realization for a voltage-controlled voltage source.

General circuit schematic

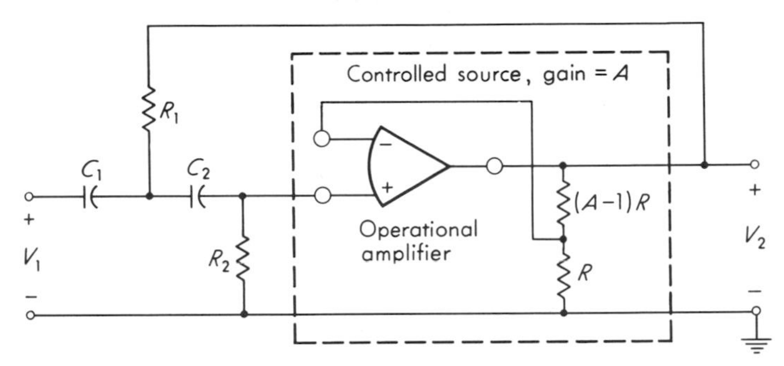

General transfer function The voltage transfer function in terms of the circuit elements and also in terms of the frequency-normalization constant ω_0 and the constant a is

$$\frac{V_2}{V_1} = \frac{p^2(A/C_1C_2)}{p^2C_1C_2 + p[(C_2/R_2) + (C_1/R_2) + (C_2/R_1)(1 - A)] + 1/R_1R_2}$$

$$= \frac{Hp^2}{p^2 + a\omega_0 p + \omega_0{}^2}$$

General circuit characteristics An idealized Bode plot illustrating the relative gain characteristics of the transfer function and of the (open-loop) operational amplifier is shown below:

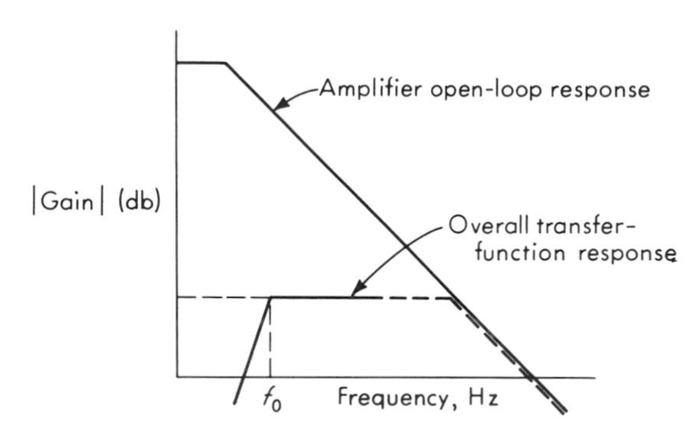

Design procedure Given H, ω_0, a:

1. Set $A = H$ (Note: $H > 0$)
2. Choose a convenient value of C_1 (farads)

3. Set $C_2 = C_1$
4. Define the constant $b = C_1\omega_0$
5. Calculate (ohms)

$$R_1 = \frac{a + \sqrt{a^2 + 8(A - 1)}}{4b} \qquad R_2 = \frac{1}{R_1 b^2}$$

[Note: Choose R and $(A - 1)R$ such that $R + (A - 1)R = 100$ kilohms or use a 100-kilohm potentiometer.]

Example of Circuit 2 The realization of a typical high-pass maximally-flat-magnitude (Butterworth) transfer function follows:

Given $f_0 = \frac{\omega_0}{2\pi} = 300$ Hz, $a = \sqrt{2}$, $H = 100$, $C_1 = C_2 = 0.1\ \mu$F

$$b = 1.884 \times 10^{-4} \qquad R_1 = 39.3 \text{ kilohms}$$
$$A = 100 \qquad R_2 = 717 \text{ ohms}$$

Transfer function for example problem

$$\frac{V_2}{V_1} = \frac{100p^2}{p^2 + 2.67 \times 10^3 p + 3.55 \times 10^6}$$

*Circuit schematic for example problem**

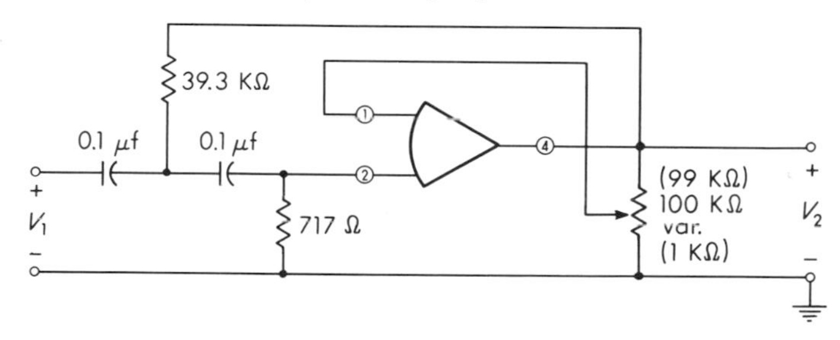

Circuit characteristic for example problem

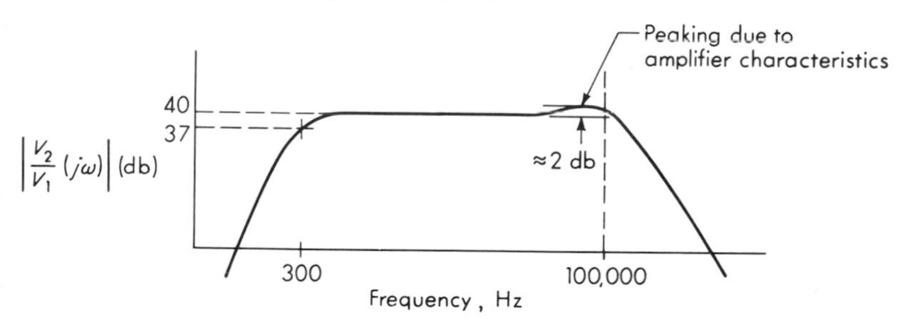

* The operational amplifier used in constructing this realization was a Burr-Brown Model 1552/15.

Circuit 3 Design procedure for the realization of a second-degree band-pass voltage transfer function using an operational amplifier realization for a voltage-controlled voltage source.

General circuit schematic

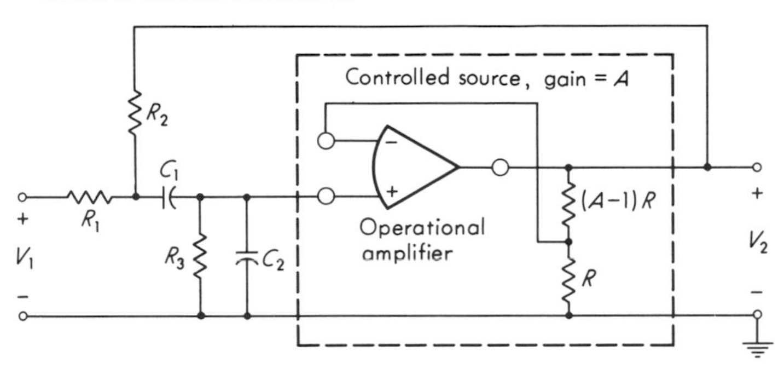

General transfer function The voltage transfer function in terms of the circuit elements and also in terms of the frequency-normalization constant ω_0 and the constant a is

$$\frac{V_2}{V_1} = \frac{(AC_1/R_1)p}{p^2C_1C_2 + p[(C_1/R_3) + (C_1 + C_2)/R_1 + (C_2/R_2) + (C_1/R_2)(1 - A)] + 1/R_3[(R_1 + R_2)/R_1R_2]} = \frac{H\omega_0 p}{p^2 + a\omega_0 p + \omega_0^2}$$

General circuit characteristics An idealized Bode plot illustrating the relative gain characteristic of the transfer function and of the (open-loop) operational amplifier is shown below:

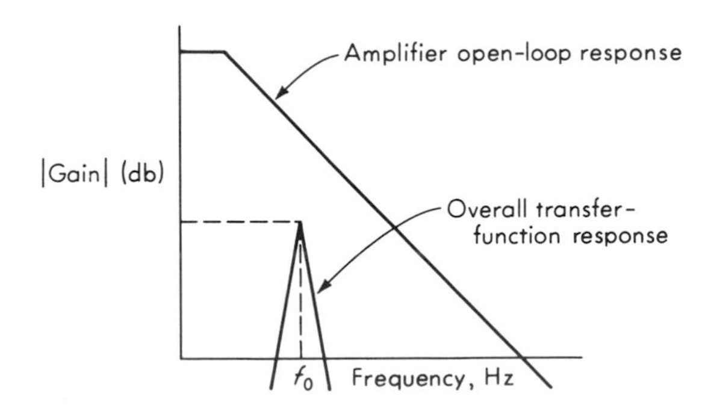

Design procedure Given ω_0, a (Note: $Q = 1/a$):

1. Choose a convenient value of C_1 (farads)
2. Choose $C_2 = \frac{1}{2}C_1$

3. Define the constant $b = C_1\omega_0$
4. Calculate (ohms)

$$R_1 = \frac{2}{b} \qquad R_2 = \frac{R_1}{3} \qquad R_3 = 2R_1$$

5. Calculate

$$A = \tfrac{1}{3}(6.5 - a)$$

[Note: Choose R and $(A - 1)R$ such that $R + (A - 1)R = 100$ kilohms or use a 100-kilohm potentiometer.]

Example of Circuit 3 The realization of a typical bandpass transfer function with a Q of 10 follows:

Given $f_0 = \omega_0/2\pi = 300$ Hz, $Q = 10$

$$C_1 = 0.02\ \mu\text{F} \qquad R_1 = 53 \text{ kilohms}$$
$$b = 37.8 \times 10^{-6} \qquad R_2 = 17.7 \text{ kilohms}$$
$$C_2 = 0.01\ \mu\text{F} \qquad R_3 = 106 \text{ kilohms}$$
$$A = 2.133$$

Transfer function for example problem

$$\frac{V_2}{V_1} = \frac{4.03 \times 10^3 p}{p^2 + 1.884 \times 10^2 p + 3.55 \times 10^6}$$

*Circuit schematic for example problem**

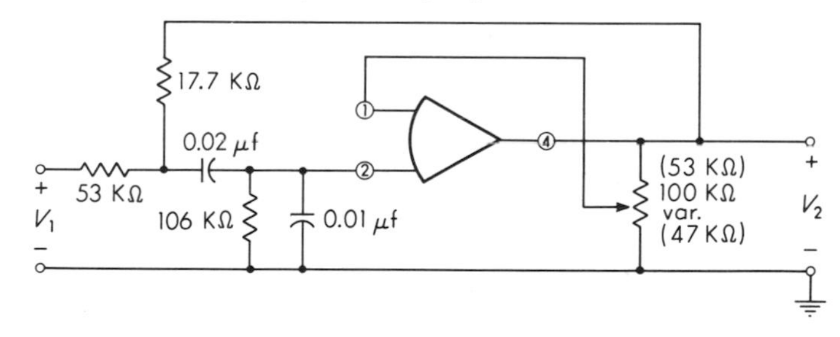

Circuit characteristic for example problem

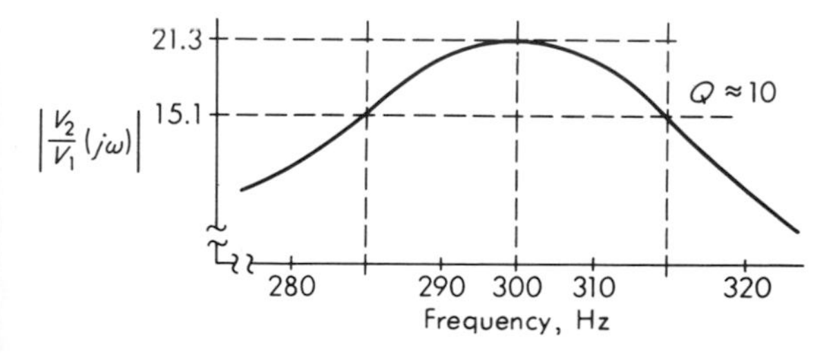

* The operational amplifier used in constructing this realization was a Burr-Brown Model 1552/15.

3.9 Conclusion

In this chapter, the use of one type of active element, namely the controlled source, in the realization of network functions has been discussed. It has been shown that the resulting functions are bilinear with respect to the gain of the controlled source. Thus it was possible to apply the polynomial decomposition techniques discussed in the preceding chapter.

As a class, controlled-source realizations have several advantages. First, the gain of the source appears as a parameter of the network function in such a way that various characteristics of the function may be easily adjusted by varying the gain. For example, a high-Q bandpass realization with a voltage transfer function of the type given in (35) may have its Q readily varied by changing the gain K. Similarly, for the low-pass function of the type given in (52), the passband gain may be changed by varying K without altering the frequency characteristics of the network. Other examples are easily found. Another advantage of this class of active RC circuits is found in the type of realizations discussed in detail in this chapter, i.e., realizations using VCVSs, in that such realizations may be cascaded without interaction occurring between the networks. Thus, complicated network functions of a relatively high degree may be realized by a cascade connection of the relatively simple structures described in this chapter.

Realization procedures may be found in the literature describing the use of other types of controlled sources in realizing various network functions. In general, these procedures are of varying degrees of practicality. For example, some of them may be built with a single transistor, obviously an advantage. On the other hand, the synthesis procedures for determining the passive networks for such realizations are considerably more complicated than the ones described in this chapter. The large quantity of such realization techniques which have appeared in the literature precludes any detailed coverage of them in an introductory book of this type. A representative bibliography of references to such realization procedures, however, has been provided in Appendix D for the reader who wishes to pursue the subject further. Analysis of the circuits given in these references may be easily accomplished by procedures similar to those outlined in this chapter and the preceding chapter, using the fundamental concept of polynomial decomposition. Similarly, sensitivity studies may be made of such realizations to establish a basis for comparison between the different techniques.

PROBLEMS

3.1 Derive the relation given in (1) for the network shown in Fig. 3.2.

3.2 (*a*) Find an active RC realization for a low-pass second-degree voltage transfer function using an ICVS as the active element. Identify the case number of the realization from Table 2.1 of Chap. 2. (*b*) Repeat (*a*) for a high-pass function. (*c*) Repeat (*a*) for a bandpass function.

3.3 Repeat the three parts of Prob. 3.2 using a VCIS to realize a second-degree short-circuit current transfer function.

3.4 Repeat the three parts of Prob. 3.2 using an ICIS to realize a second-degree short-circuit current transfer function.

3.5 Find active *RC* realizations using a VCVS which will be of the type shown as case 6 and case 12 of Table 2.1 for a low-pass voltage transfer function.

3.6 The actual voltage transfer function for the inverting VCVS shown in Fig. 3.25 is

$$\frac{V_{\text{out}}}{V_{\text{in}}} = \frac{-K_0 R_b}{R_b + (1 + K_0)R_a}$$

where K_0 is the open-loop gain of the operational amplifier. Using the magnitude of this expression in place of the term $|K|$ in (30) (for the circuit shown in Fig. 3.11), calculate the sensitivity of the coefficients b_1 and b_2 of the example realization to the parameters K_0, R_a, and R_b for the case where $K_0 = 10^3$. Repeat for $K_0 = 10^4$.

3.7 The actual voltage transfer function for the noninverting VCVS shown in Fig. 3.21 is

$$\frac{V_{\text{out}}}{V_{\text{in}}} = \frac{K_0}{1 + K_0 R_a/(R_a + R_b)}$$

where K_0 is the gain of the operational amplifier. Using this expression for the gain K given in (35) for the circuit shown in Fig. 3.13, calculate the sensitivity of the coefficients b_1 and b_2 of the example realization to the parameters K_0, R_a, and R_b for the case where $K_0 = 10^3$. Repeat for $K_0 = 10^4$.

3.8 Find a realization for the bandpass function

$$\frac{V_2}{V_1} = \frac{-p}{p^2 + b_1 p + b_2}$$

for the values $b_1 = 0.01$, $b_2 = 1.0$. Use the network configuration shown in Fig. 3.11. Find the sensitivity matrix for the realization.

3.9 Find a realization for the bandpass function given in Prob. 3.8. Use the network configuration shown in Fig. 3.13 for a positive sign in the numerator. Find the sensitivity matrix for the realization.

3.10 Find a realization for the bandpass function given in Prob. 3.8. Use the network configuration shown in Fig. 3.15 for a positive sign in the numerator. Find the sensitivity matrix for the realization.

3.11 Find two different realizations for the network function

$$\frac{V_2}{V_1} = \frac{H(p^2 + 0.5)}{p^2 + 0.1p + 1}$$

Use the method given in Sec. 3.5

3.12 Prove that the expressions for the element values given in (42) produce the network functions given in (43) for the ladder network of Fig. 3.16. Find expressions for h_0 and b_0 of (43) in terms of b.

3.13 Find a realization for the bandpass function given in Prob. 3.8. Use the network configuration shown in Fig. 3.18. Find the sensitivity matrix for the realization.

3.14 Find the g parameters of the transistor circuit shown in Fig. P3.14 (the biasing elements have been deleted for simplicity of representation). Determine whether, in the limit as the α's of the transistors approach unity, the circuit acts as an ideal VCVS.

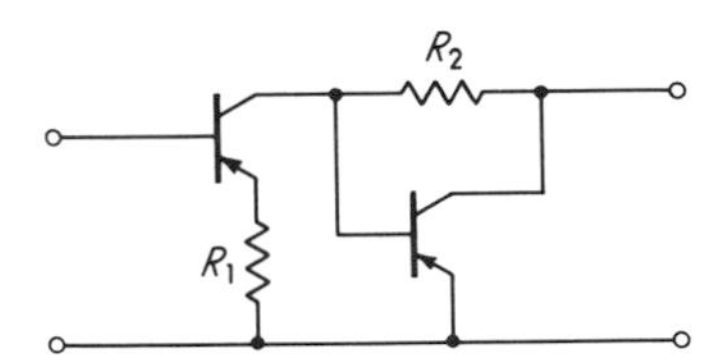

Figure P3.14

3.15 Repeat Prob. 3.14 for the circuit shown in Fig. P3.15.

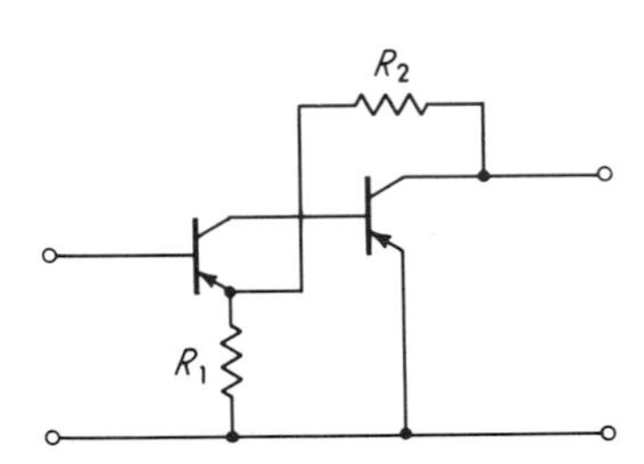

Figure P3.15

3.16 Find the h parameters of the transistor circuit shown in Fig. P3.16 (the biasing elements have been deleted for simplicity of representation). Determine whether, in the limit as the α's of the transistors approach unity, the circuit acts as an ideal ICIS.

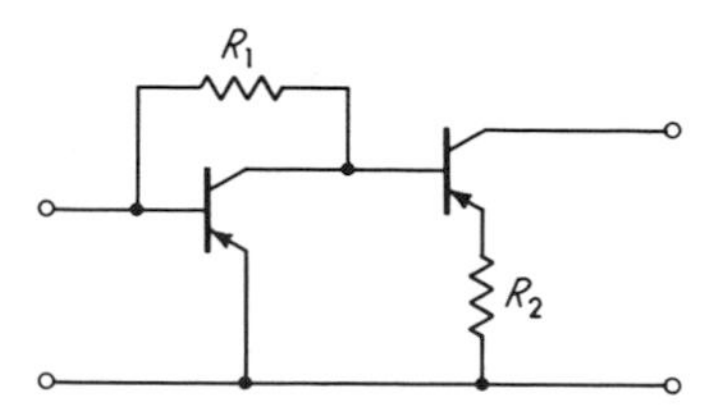

Figure P3.16

3.17 Repeat Prob. 3.16 for the circuit shown in Fig. P3.17.

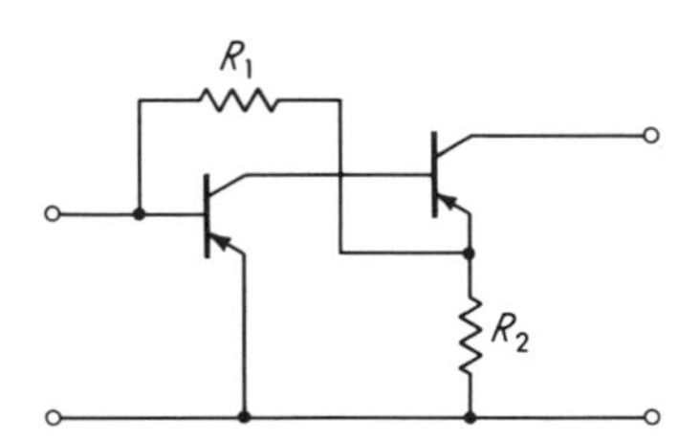

Figure P3.17

3.18 Prove that the circuit using a VCVS shown in Fig. P3.18 may be used to realize a short-circuit current transfer function in which the denominator is realized by an optimum decomposition.

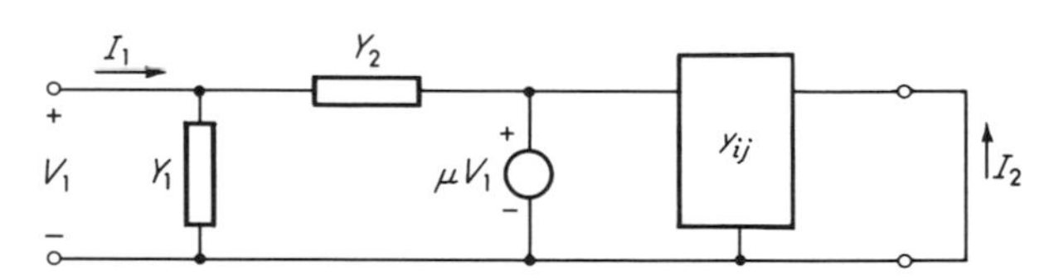

Figure P3.18

3.19 Find the output impedance of the VCVS circuit shown in Fig. 3.26.

Chapter 4 *Negative-immittance converter realizations*

In the last chapter, the use of a controlled source as the active element in active RC realizations of network transfer functions was discussed. In this chapter we shall consider the use of a quite different active device, the NIC (negative-immittance converter). We have already made references to such a device. For example, when we discussed the "difference" case of polynomial decomposition in Sec. 2.6, a simple realization using an NIC was given as an example of the application of such a decomposition (see Fig. 2.15). As another example, when the detailed treatment of the different polynomial decomposition cases which are possible for the second-degree case was described in Sec. 2.8, a pair of examples was cited to illustrate the difference in sensitivity between cascaded second-degree NIC realizations and a single fourth-degree NIC realization (see Figs. 2.19 and 2.20). In this chapter we shall study NICs and their application to active RC circuit realizations in detail. Thus, in Sec. 4.1 we shall define the various types of NICs and illustrate their properties. In Secs. 4.2 and 4.3 we shall present some approaches to the general theory of active RC circuit realizations using NICs. It will be shown that a single NIC is sufficient for the realization of an arbitrary rational voltage transfer function. In Sec. 4.4 we shall develop specific realizations for the case of low-pass, high-pass, and bandpass voltage transfer functions, and indicate how these realizations may be made optimally insensitive to changes in the gain of the NICs. In Sec. 4.5, some methods of realizing NICs will be presented. Finally, in Sec. 4.6, detailed realization techniques complete with design formulas and numerical examples for the realization of the network functions presented in Sec. 4.4 will be given.

4.1 *Properties of the negative-immittance converter*

An NIC is a two-port device characterized by the property that the input impedance seen at either port is the negative (times some constant) of the impedance connected to the other port. Necessary and sufficient conditions for such behavior may be defined in terms of the $ABCD$ (transmission) parameters for the two-port as follows:*

$$B = C = 0 \qquad \frac{A}{D} < 0 \tag{1}$$

where A and D are real but may be positive or negative. Thus, such devices have their behavior characterized by operation in the second and fourth quadrants of the AD plane, i.e., a plane defined by plotting the real values of the A transmission parameter along the abscissa and the D parameter along the ordinate, as shown in Fig. 4.1. In terms of their

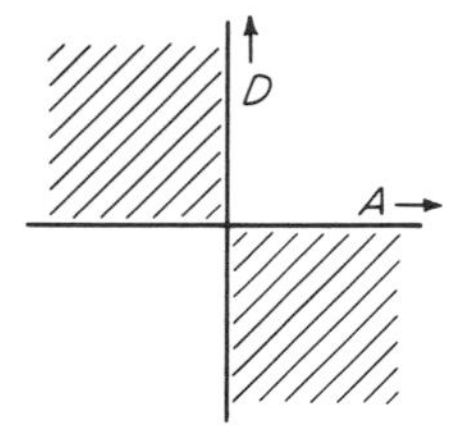

***Figure 4.1** Regions of NIC action in the AD plane.*

observed behavior, practical NICs fall into two classes. The first of these is the class in which the NIC reverses the current flow at one of the ports with respect to the direction of current flow that would normally be encountered in a purely passive device. The process by which the current is inverted may usually be adjusted by varying the elements of the realization. Such a device is referred to as a *current-inversion* NIC. It normally preserves a one-to-one correspondence between the input and output voltages. We may thus define an *ideal current-inversion* NIC (INIC) by the equations

$$\begin{aligned} V_2 &= V_1 \\ I_2 &= KI_1 \end{aligned} \tag{2}$$

where K is a positive constant usually referred to as the *gain* of the INIC. Thus, the transmission parameters of the INIC are

$$\begin{bmatrix} 1 & 0 \\ 0 & \dfrac{-1}{K} \end{bmatrix} \tag{3}$$

A second class of NICs operates by inverting the voltage while leaving the normal direction of current unchanged. It is called a *voltage-inversion*

* These conditions were originally derived in terms of the g parameters for a two-port network by A. I. Larky, Negative Impedance Converters, *IRE Trans. Circuit Theory*, vol. CT-4, no. 3, pp. 124–131, Sept., 1957.

NIC. We may define an *ideal voltage-inversion* NIC (VNIC) by the equations

$$\begin{aligned} V_2 &= -KV_1 \\ I_2 &= -I_1 \end{aligned} \tag{4}$$

where K is a positive constant referred to as the *gain* of the VNIC. The transmission parameters for the VNIC are

$$\begin{bmatrix} \dfrac{-1}{K} & 0 \\ 0 & 1 \end{bmatrix} \tag{5}$$

From the values of A and D given for the INIC and VNIC in (3) and (5), respectively, we see that such devices have the loci of operating points represented by the straight lines shown in Fig. 4.2.*

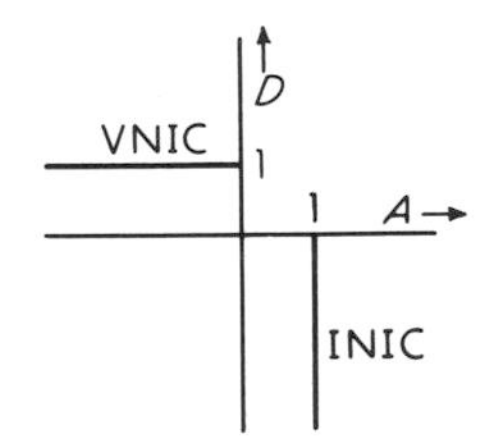

Figure 4.2 Loci of operating points for the INIC and VNIC.

As an aid in understanding the properties of NICs, let us consider some general characteristics of the class of two-port networks which have transmission parameters such that $B = C = 0$.† This class of networks has the property that if an impedance transformation is realized from port 1 to port 2, the reciprocal impedance transformation will be realized from port 2 to port 1. This property is illustrated in Fig. 4.3, where a

* It should be noted that interchanging the port designations for the INIC or the VNIC leaves the loci as shown in Fig. 4.2 for these devices invariant. Such an interchange, however, does reverse the direction of increasing K on these loci.

† L. P. Huelsman, A Fundamental Classification of Negative-immittance Converters, *IEEE Intern. Conv. Record*, vol. 13, pt. 7, pp. 113–118, March, 1965.

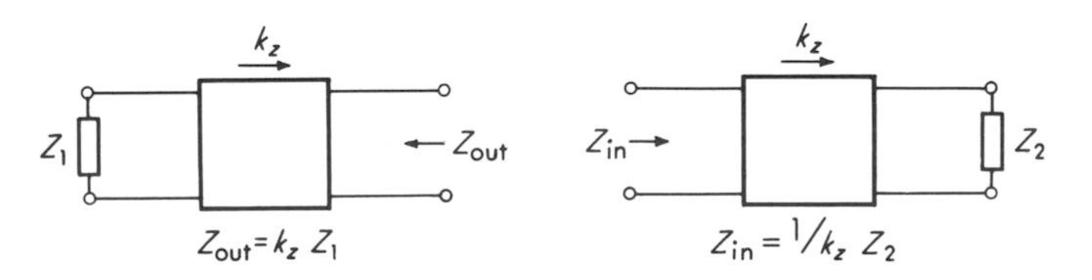

Figure 4.3 The impedance transformation constant k_z.

dimensionless impedance transformation constant k_z is defined. This constant may be positive or negative. For this class of networks $k_z = D/A$. Thus, we may construct loci of constant k_z on the AD plane as shown in Fig. 4.4. From Figs. 4.2 and 4.4 we see that k_z is always negative for an

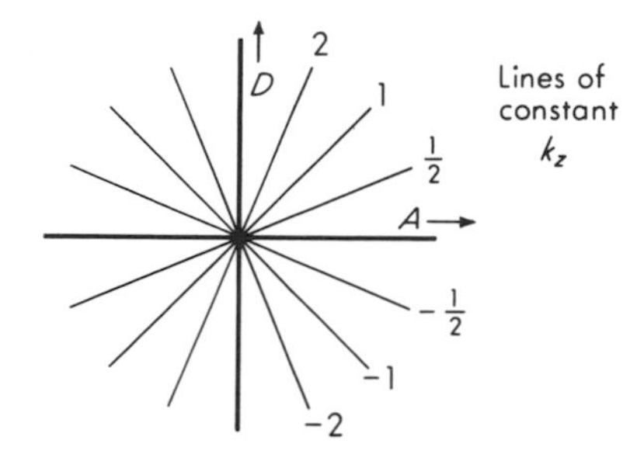

***Figure 4.4** The loci of constant impedance transformation.*

NIC. Thus, an NIC's negative-immittance action operates in either direction, but the effect may not be the same in the two directions. For an INIC, $k_z = -1/K$; i.e., it is equal to the negative of the reciprocal of the INIC gain. For a VNIC, $k_z = -K$; i.e., it is equal to the negative of the VNIC gain. Similarly, for this class of networks, i.e., those in which $B = C = 0$, we may define a power transformation constant k_p relating the input power and the output power as shown in Fig. 4.5. It is easily

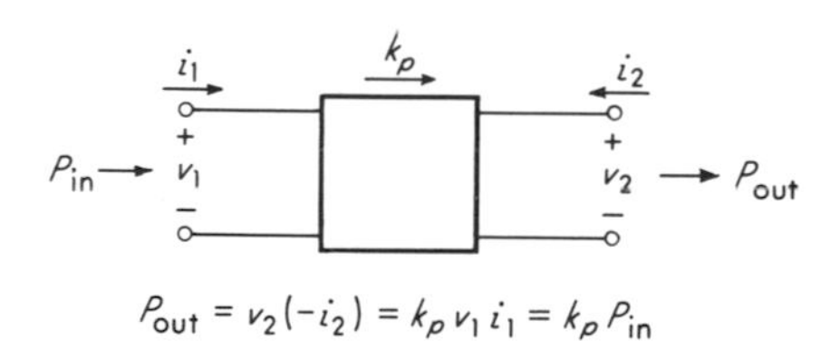

***Figure 4.5** The power transformation constant k_p.*

shown that $k_p = 1/AD$. Thus, we may construct hyperbolas which are the loci of constant values of k_p as shown in Fig. 4.6. For an INIC or a VNIC, $k_p = -K$. Thus, we see that k_p is always negative for an NIC. As a result, an NIC is capable of having power simultaneously flow out of both of its ports, a clear indication of the active behavior of the device.

In Fig. 4.7, the loci of constant k_z, constant k_p, and the loci of operating points for the INIC and VNIC have been superimposed. It is readily apparent how, as the gain of an NIC is varied, the impedance transformation and power transformation properties of the two-port device change as indicated by the various loci. It should be noted that for the case in which the gain of the NIC is unity, k_z and k_p have unity magnitude. Thus, NICs with unity gain are sometimes referred to as having a *unity conver-*

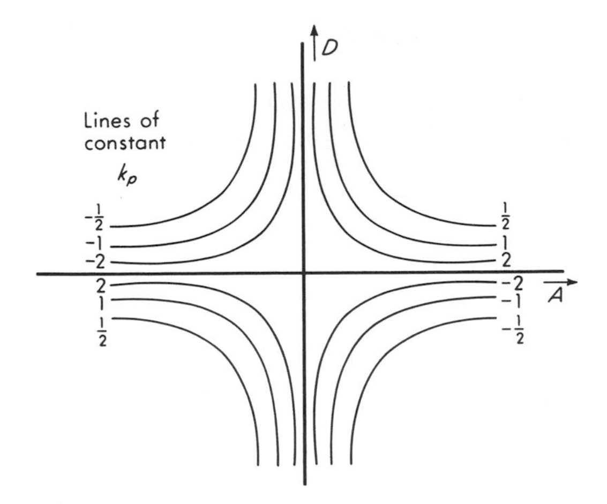

Figure 4.6 The loci of constant power transformation.

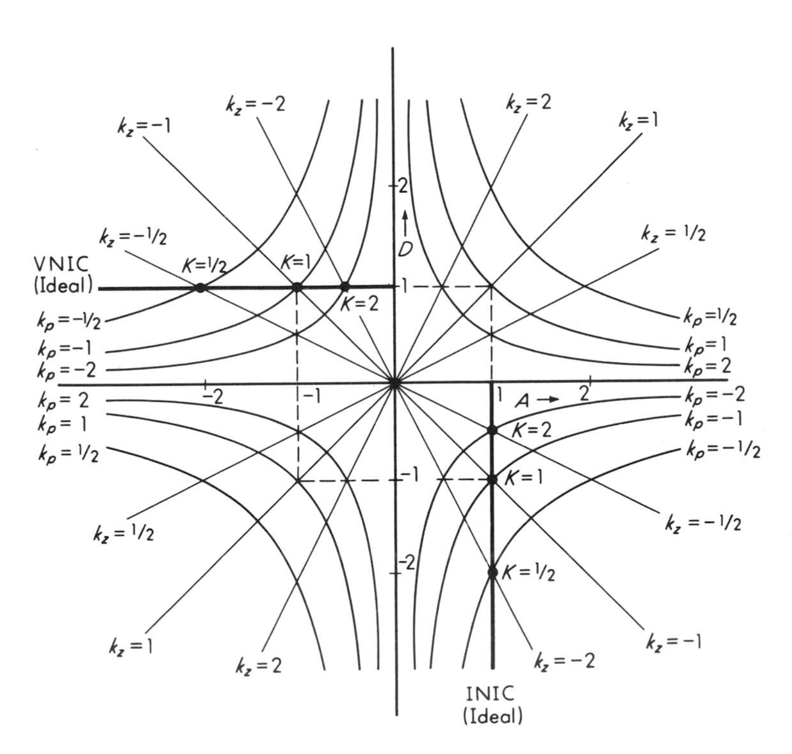

Figure 4.7 The AD plane.

sion ratio in the sense that the impedance and power transformation ratios are unity and are the same in both directions.

As a final property of the NIC, we may note that the condition for reciprocity for the class of networks in which $B = C = 0$ is $AD = 1$. From (1) we see that the product AD is always negative. Therefore, *the NIC is a nonreciprocal device.*

The conditions for NIC behavior given in (1) may also be expressed in terms of the g parameters for a two-port network. In terms of these parameters, an NIC is defined by the conditions

$$g_{11} = g_{22} = 0 \qquad g_{12}g_{21} > 0 \tag{6}$$

For an INIC, it is easily shown that the g parameters have the form

$$\begin{bmatrix} 0 & \dfrac{1}{K} \\ 1 & 0 \end{bmatrix} \tag{7}$$

Now let us consider the case where the INIC is nonideal in the sense that $g_{11} \neq 0$. We may treat this case by considering an ideal INIC with a shunt admittance $Y_1 = g_{11}$ connected across its input port as shown in Fig. 4.8.

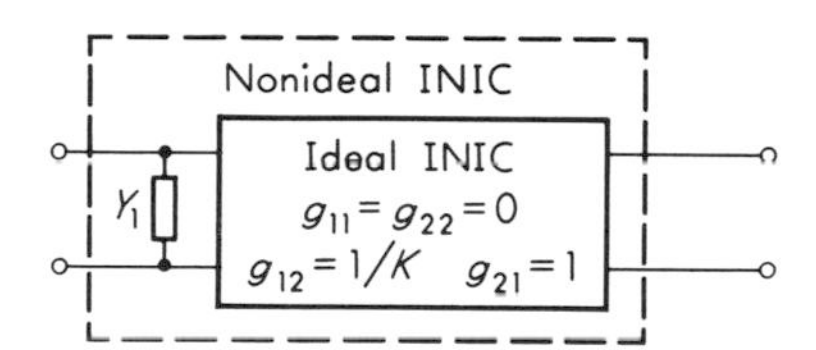

***Figure 4.8** A nonideal INIC with* $g_{11} \neq 0$.

The output admittance of the two-port device is now equal to $-KY_1$. Thus, we may compensate for this nonidealness by connecting a shunt admittance of value KY_1 across the output port as indicated in Fig. 4.9.

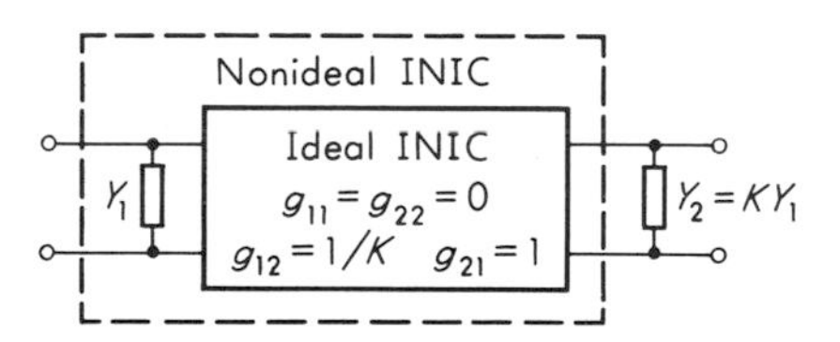

***Figure 4.9** Compensating the INIC when* $g_{11} \neq 0$.

Similarly, if $g_{22} \neq 0$, the two-port may be considered as an ideal INIC with an impedance $Z_2 = g_{22}$ in series with its output port as shown in Fig. 4.10. Compensation for this nonidealness is obtained by connecting

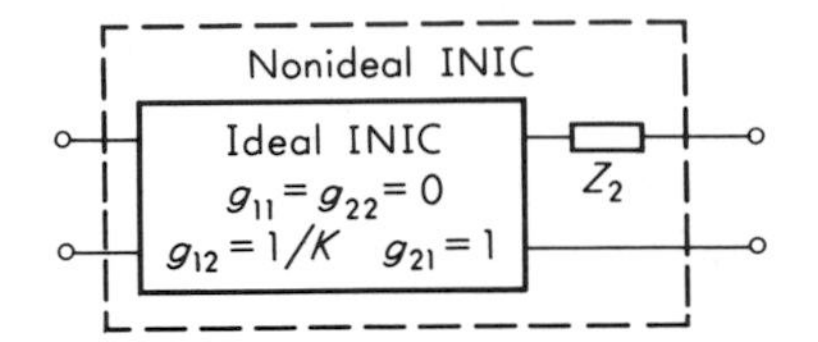

Figure 4.10 *A nonideal INIC with* $g_{22} \neq 0$.

an impedance of value KZ_2 in series with the input port as shown in Fig. 4.11. Obviously, compensation may be made for the case in which the g_{11} or g_{22} terms are complex as well as for the case in which they are real.*

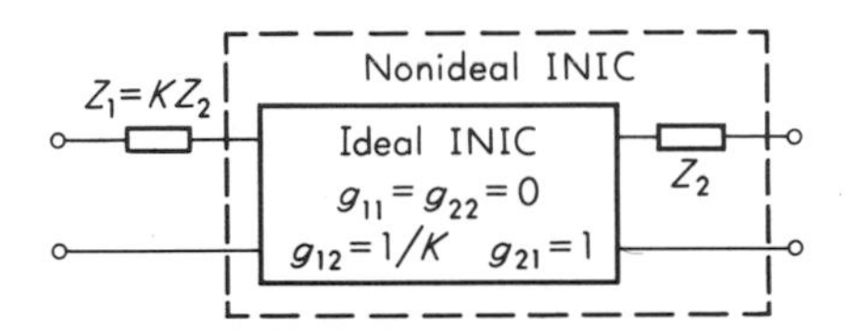

Figure 4.11 *Compensating the INIC when* $g_{22} \neq 0$.

A VNIC which is nonideal in the sense that its g_{11} or g_{22} parameter is nonzero may be similarly compensated to make it an ideal device. In this case, a shunt admittance of value g_{11}/K is required at the output port, or an impedance of value g_{22}/K must be placed in series with the input port. The simplicity with which an NIC can be used to compensate for its own possible nonidealness adds considerable attractiveness to the use of this device for circuit realizations. We shall consider such applications in the following sections of this chapter.

4.2 *The general theory of NIC realizations*

In the last section it was shown that there are two basic types of ideal NICs, the voltage-inversion type or VNIC and the current-inversion type or INIC. In this section we shall investigate the effects of combining these two-port ideal devices with various passive networks. It will be our goal to show that realizations which involve NICs are bilinear with respect to the gain of the NIC and also that such realizations may be considered under the general polynomial decomposition approach which was introduced in Chap. 2.

* The methods of compensation described above are only applicable in the case in which *either* g_{11} *or* g_{22} is nonzero. For a treatment of the case in which *both* g_{11} *and* g_{22} are nonzero, see L. P. Huelsman, The Compensation of Negative-immittance Converters, *Proc. IEEE*, vol. 54, no. 7, pp. 1015–1016, July, 1966.

As a first step in investigating active RC realizations using NICs, let us examine the effect of connecting an NIC in cascade with an arbitrary two-port network. There are four possible combinations, depending on whether the NIC appears at the input or the output terminals of the resulting two-port and on whether an INIC or a VNIC is used. The combinations are shown in Fig. 4.12, and the resulting two-port networks have been labeled as networks A, B, C, and D as indicated in the figure. The effect that the NICs have in determining the properties of the overall two-port network can be seen by examining Table 4.1. The relations of this table are based on the definitions of the INIC and VNIC given in (2) and (4), respectively. This table lists the y, z, g, and h parameters of the various network combinations shown in Fig. 4.12. A significant fact that is easily observed from these parameters is that the effect of the NIC is to multiply both a driving-point function and a transfer function by $-K$ (or $-1/K$) for each of the network configurations shown in Fig. 4.12 and for each set of

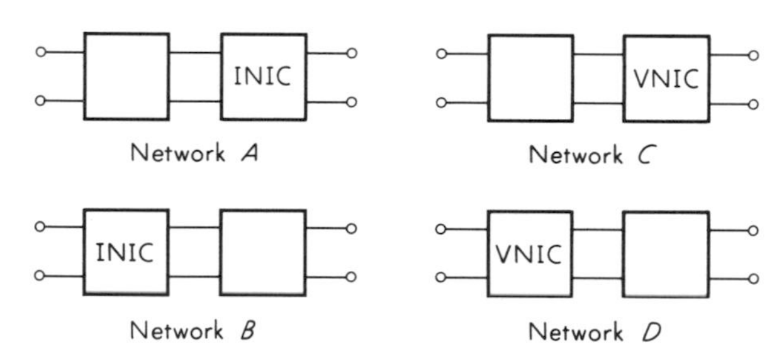

Figure 4.12 Various combinations of networks cascaded with NICs.

parameters of these networks. K, of course, is a positive constant giving the gain of the NIC that is used in the particular network. From a study of Table 4.1 we see that by the use of an NIC of appropriate type, we can change the sign of any two parameters of a given two-port network. This fact may be applied to establish a general synthesis approach.

First of all, let us consider the realization of an open-circuit voltage transfer function. This may be expressed in terms of the y parameters of a given two-port network as

$$\frac{V_2}{V_1} = \frac{-y_{21}}{y_{22}} \tag{8}$$

To establish in the numerator and denominator of such a function a sum polynomial decomposition of the type described in Sec. 2.7, it is only

Table 4.1 Parameters for the networks of Fig. 4.12

Network	y Parameters	z Parameters	g Parameters	h Parameters
A	$\begin{matrix} y_{11} & y_{12} \\ -Ky_{21} & -Ky_{22} \end{matrix}$	$\begin{matrix} z_{11} & \frac{-z_{12}}{K} \\ z_{21} & \frac{-z_{22}}{K} \end{matrix}$	$\begin{matrix} g_{11} & \frac{-g_{12}}{K} \\ g_{21} & \frac{-g_{22}}{K} \end{matrix}$	$\begin{matrix} h_{11} & h_{12} \\ -Kh_{21} & -Kh_{22} \end{matrix}$
B	$\begin{matrix} \frac{-y_{11}}{K} & \frac{-y_{12}}{K} \\ y_{21} & y_{22} \end{matrix}$	$\begin{matrix} -Kz_{11} & z_{12} \\ -Kz_{21} & z_{22} \end{matrix}$	$\begin{matrix} \frac{-g_{11}}{K} & \frac{-g_{12}}{K} \\ g_{21} & g_{22} \end{matrix}$	$\begin{matrix} -Kh_{11} & h_{12} \\ -Kh_{21} & h_{22} \end{matrix}$
C	$\begin{matrix} y_{11} & \frac{-y_{12}}{K} \\ y_{21} & \frac{-y_{22}}{K} \end{matrix}$	$\begin{matrix} z_{11} & z_{12} \\ -Kz_{21} & -Kz_{22} \end{matrix}$	$\begin{matrix} g_{11} & g_{12} \\ -Kg_{21} & -Kg_{22} \end{matrix}$	$\begin{matrix} h_{11} & \frac{-h_{12}}{K} \\ h_{21} & \frac{-h_{22}}{K} \end{matrix}$
D	$\begin{matrix} -Ky_{11} & y_{12} \\ -Ky_{21} & y_{22} \end{matrix}$	$\begin{matrix} \frac{-z_{11}}{K} & \frac{-z_{12}}{K} \\ z_{21} & z_{22} \end{matrix}$	$\begin{matrix} -Kg_{11} & g_{12} \\ -Kg_{21} & g_{22} \end{matrix}$	$\begin{matrix} \frac{-h_{11}}{K} & \frac{-h_{12}}{K} \\ h_{21} & h_{22} \end{matrix}$

necessary to connect a second network in parallel with the first. The y parameters will then add, and the resulting voltage transfer function is*

$$\frac{V_2}{V_1} = \frac{-y_{21} - y'_{21}}{y_{22} + y'_{22}} \tag{9}$$

where the y'_{ij} parameters are those of the paralleled network. Obviously, if the y_{ij} and y'_{ij} parameters of (9) all have the same denominator, the numerators of these functions provide the component polynomials in the decomposition process.

We have already seen some uses of the sum decomposition in connection with the controlled-source realizations of the last chapter. We shall find other uses in connection with the gyrator realizations to be discussed in Chap. 5. Actually, however, the difference decomposition of Sec. 2.6 is considerably more flexible and usually of greater interest. To achieve such

* In certain network configurations, precautions must be taken to ensure that the different types of parameters will add correctly when the input and output ports are appropriately connected in series or parallel. For the case of y parameters, this condition is satisfied by the use of three-terminal networks, i.e., networks with a common ground. A discussion of this problem may be found in E. A. Guillemin, "Synthesis of Passive Networks," chap. 6, John Wiley & Sons, Inc., New York, 1957.

a decomposition in the numerator and denominator of the voltage transfer function, we require a network in which the y'_{21} and y'_{22} parameters have had their signs changed. From Table 4.1, we see that network A of Fig. 4.12 provides just such a change. Therefore, if we parallel this network

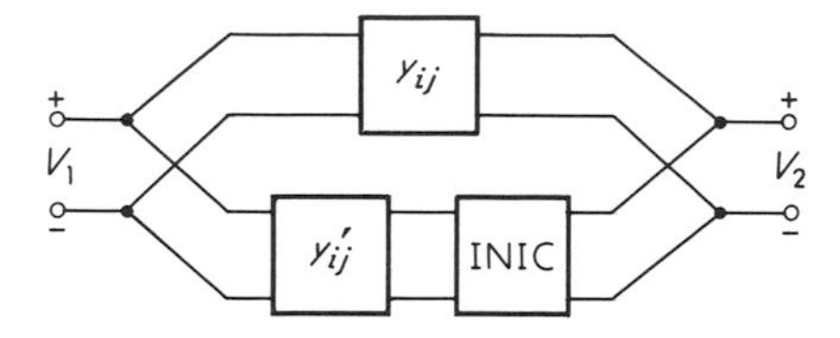

Figure 4.13 A realization for V_2/V_1.

with another two-port network as shown in Fig. 4.13, we obtain the voltage transfer function

$$\frac{V_2}{V_1} = \frac{-y_{21} + Ky'_{21}}{y_{22} - Ky'_{22}} \tag{10}$$

where the primed and unprimed parameters are identified in the figure, and K is a positive constant specifying the gain of the INIC. Obviously, if the y parameters of both networks have the same denominators, the numerators of these parameters yield the desired difference decomposition. If a difference decomposition is desired in only the numerator or only the denominator of (8), the appropriate network from Fig. 4.12 may be chosen to provide this. For example, the configuration shown in Fig. 4.13 uses network A of Fig. 4.12. If we substitute network C, the resulting voltage transfer function will have a sum decomposition in the numerator and a difference decomposition in the denominator. Similarly, the use of network D will yield a sum decomposition in the denominator and a difference decomposition in the numerator.

In a similar manner we may provide a difference decomposition in terms of the z parameters. In terms of these parameters, the voltage transfer function is

$$\frac{V_2}{V_1} = \frac{z_{21}}{z_{11}} \tag{11}$$

For the z parameters to add, the component networks are connected in series. Thus, we require a network in which the z_{21} and z_{11} parameters have had their signs reversed to connect in series with an unaltered network. From Table 4.1 we see that network B of Fig. 4.12 has the desired characteristics. Thus, with the network configuration shown in Fig. 4.14, we obtain the voltage transfer function

$$\frac{V_2}{V_1} = \frac{z_{21} - Kz'_{21}}{z_{11} - Kz'_{11}} \tag{12}$$

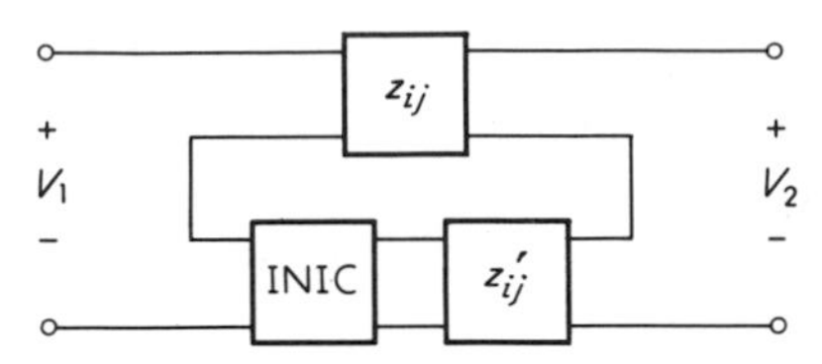

Figure 4.14 A realization for V_2/V_1.

The difference decomposition is readily apparent, and, as in the case of the y parameters, other networks from Fig. 4.12 may be used if a difference decomposition is desired in only one of the numerator and denominator polynomials.

Similar procedures may be used for the realization of short-circuit current transfer functions. In terms of the y parameters, we may write

$$\frac{I_2}{I_1} = \frac{y_{21}}{y_{11}} \tag{13}$$

For example, a realization using paralleled networks to produce a difference decomposition is possible with network D of Fig. 4.12. The resulting

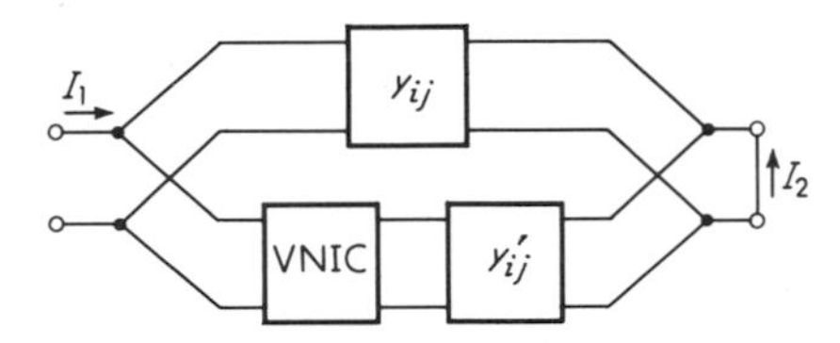

Figure 4.15 A realization for I_2/I_1.

overall network is shown in Fig. 4.15. For this figure, the short-circuit current transfer function is

$$\frac{I_2}{I_1} = \frac{y_{21} - Ky'_{21}}{y_{11} - Ky'_{11}} \tag{14}$$

A realization using networks connected in series is possible with network C of Fig. 4.12. The overall network configuration is shown in Fig. 4.16. For this figure we obtain

$$\frac{I_2}{I_1} = \frac{-z_{21} + Kz'_{21}}{z_{22} - Kz'_{22}} \tag{15}$$

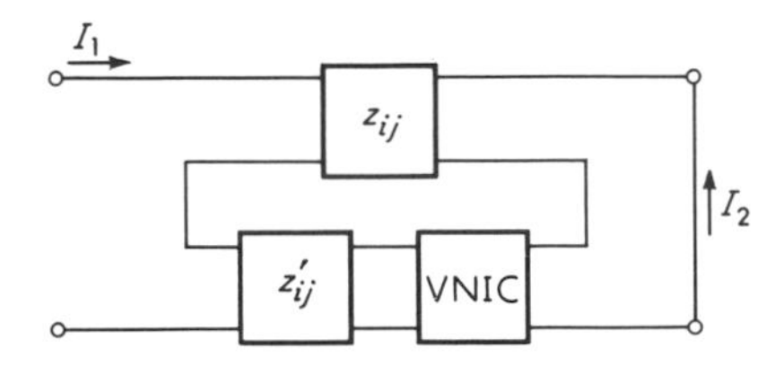

Figure 4.16 A realization for I_2/I_1.

In a similar manner, we may obtain difference decompositions in the numerator and denominator of open-circuit transfer impedances and short-circuit transfer admittances. These may be accomplished by using network interconnections such that their g parameters add (the input ports are connected in parallel, and the output ports are connected in series) or such that their h parameters add (the input ports are connected in

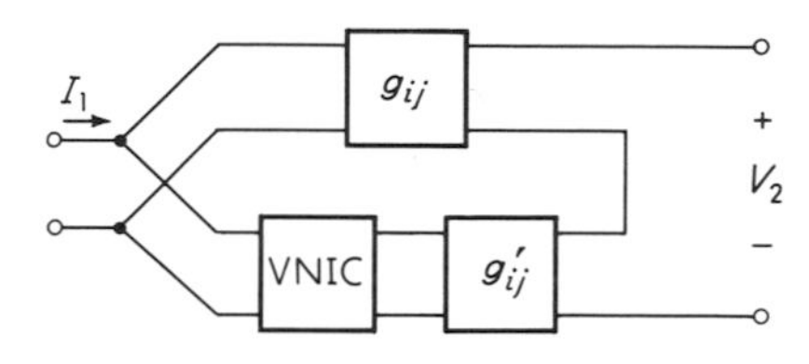

Figure 4.17 A realization for Z_{21}.

series, and the output ports are connected in parallel). For example, for the network configuration shown in Fig. 4.17, we obtain

$$\frac{V_2}{I_1} = \frac{g_{21} - Kg'_{21}}{g_{11} - Kg'_{11}} \tag{16}$$

Similarly, for Fig. 4.18,

$$\frac{V_2}{I_1} = \frac{-h_{21} + Kh'_{21}}{h_{22} - Kh'_{22}} \tag{17}$$

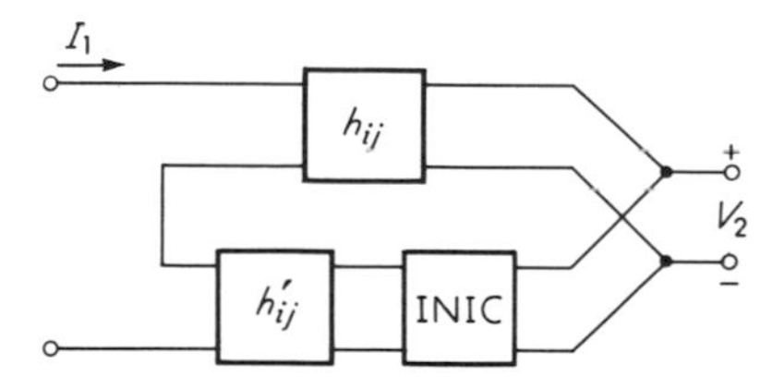

Figure 4.18 A realization for Z_{21}.

The network configuration shown in Fig 4.19 realizes the short-circuit transfer admittance

$$\frac{I_2}{V_1} = \frac{-g_{21} + Kg'_{21}}{g_{22} - Kg'_{22}} \tag{18}$$

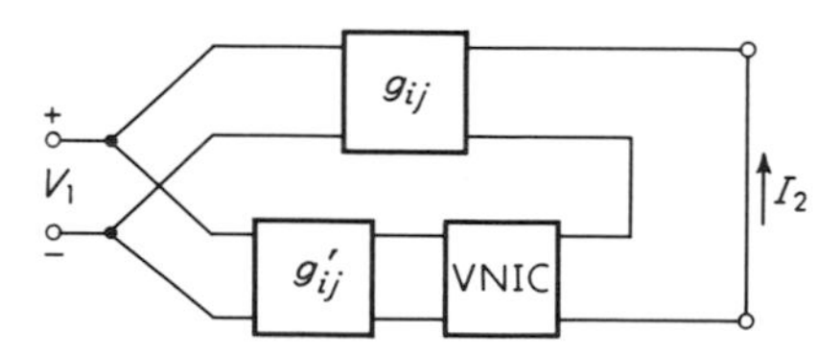

Figure 4.19 A realization for Y_{21}.

Similarly, for Fig. 4.20

$$\frac{I_2}{V_1} = \frac{h_{21} - Kh'_{21}}{h_{11} - Kh'_{11}} \tag{19}$$

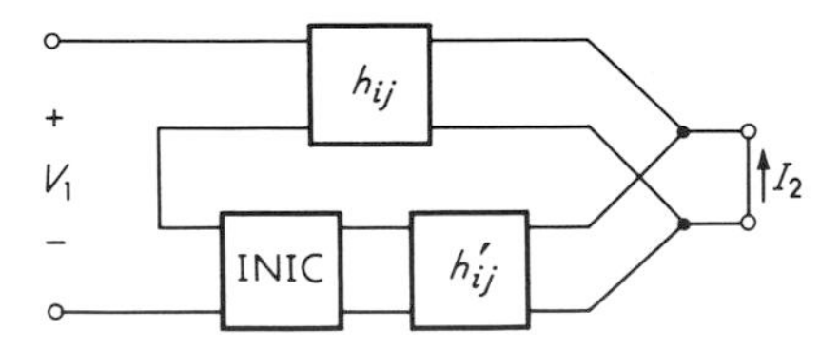

Figure 4.20 A realization for Y_{21}.

In this section we have shown that NICs may be used in combination with passive two-port networks to produce network functions which may have a sum or a difference polynomial decomposition in the numerator and the denominator. The functions are, of course, bilinear with respect to the gain of the NICs. In the next section, we shall select some specific network configurations and develop detailed realization procedures for them.

4.3 *Some realization procedures using NICs*

In this section we shall investigate some detailed realization procedures requiring the use of NICs. As the first example of such a procedure, let us consider the use of an INIC to realize a voltage transfer function. We shall select the paralleled network configuration shown in Fig. 4.13, in which the INIC is connected in cascade with the network with the y'_{ij} parameters. For this network, the voltage transfer function is given in (10). If the two passive networks are restricted to an L configuration as shown in

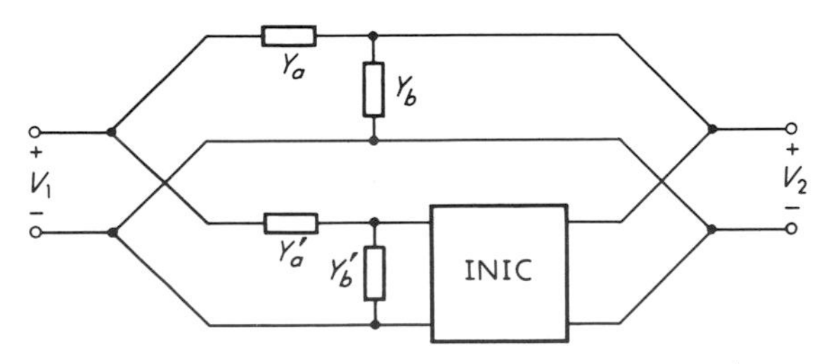

Figure 4.21 The use of L configurations for RC-NIC synthesis.

Fig. 4.21, the voltage transfer function becomes*

$$\frac{V_2}{V_1} = \frac{Y_a - KY'_a}{Y_a + Y_b - K(Y'_a + Y'_b)} \tag{20}$$

Let $N(p)$ be the numerator of the desired voltage transfer function, and let $D(p)$ be the denominator. If we divide both numerator and denominator by a polynomial $Q(p)$, we obtain

$$\frac{V_2}{V_1} = \frac{N(p)/Q(p)}{D(p)/Q(p)} \tag{21}$$

Comparing (20) and (21), we see that

$$\frac{N(p)}{Q(p)} = Y_a - KY'_a \qquad \frac{D(p) - N(p)}{Q(p)} = Y_b - KY'_b \tag{22}$$

If $Q(p)$ is chosen so that its zeros lie on the negative-real axis (not including the origin) and so that its degree is 1 less than the degree of either $N(p)$ or $D(p) - N(p)$ (whichever is higher), each of the expressions in (22) may be expanded in the form

$$\begin{aligned} \frac{N(p)}{Q(p)} &= k_a{}^{(\infty)}p + k_a{}^{(0)} + \sum_i \frac{p}{p + \sigma_i} k_a{}^{(i)} = Y_a - KY'_a \\ \frac{D(p) - N(p)}{Q(p)} &= k_b{}^{(\infty)}p + k_b{}^{(0)} + \sum_i \frac{p}{p + \sigma_i} k_b{}^{(i)} = Y_b - KY'_b \end{aligned} \tag{23}$$

The various residues k in (23) may be positive or negative. The gain constant K of the INIC is positive; therefore, the positive residue terms may be associated with the unprimed admittances, and the negative residue terms with $-K$ times the primed admittances. The realization for the component admittances of Fig. 4.21 follows directly, and the passive RC nature of these admittances is guaranteed.

As an example of the technique, consider the realization of the bandpass voltage transfer function

$$\frac{V_2}{V_1} = \frac{ap}{p^2 + ap + 1}$$

If we choose $Q(p) = p + 1$, from (22) we see that

$$Y_a = \frac{ap}{p+1} \qquad Y'_a = 0$$

$$Y_b = p + 1 \qquad KY'_b = \frac{2p}{p+1}$$

The network realization is shown in Fig. 4.22.

* T. Yanagisawa, *RC* Active Networks Using Current Inversion Type Negative Impedance Converters, *IRE Trans. Circuit Theory*, vol. CT-4, no. 3, pp. 140–144, Sept., 1957.

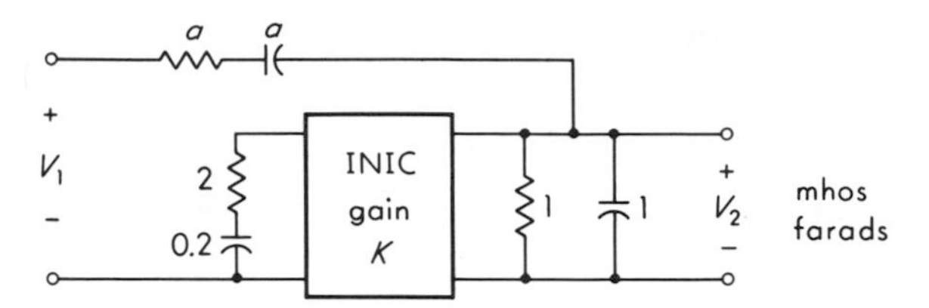

***Figure 4.22** A realization for a voltage transfer function.*

An extension of this method may be used to provide a summing function, i.e., a means by which the output may be made equal to the sum of a set of different input voltages, each input voltage multiplied by some appropriate network function. Thus for an n-port network we would obtain an expression of the type

$$V_n = \frac{1}{D(p)} \sum_{i=1}^{n-1} N_i(p) V_i \tag{24}$$

where V_n is considered as the output voltage, the V_i ($i = 1, \ldots, n-1$) are the various input voltages, the $N_i(p)$ are the arbitrary polynomials, and $D(p)$ is the polynomial specifying the natural frequencies of the overall network. Equation (24) may be realized by passive RC networks and a single INIC.* To see this, consider the network configuration shown in Fig. 4.23 (the similarity between this figure and Fig. 4.21 should be noted). If we divide the numerator and denominator of (24) by a polynomial $Q(p)$ consisting only of negative-real zeros and of degree 1 less than the

* J. Barranger, Voltage Transfer Function Matrix Realization Using Current Negative Immittance Converters, *IEEE Trans. Circuit Theory*, vol. CT-13, no. 1, pp. 97–98, March, 1966.

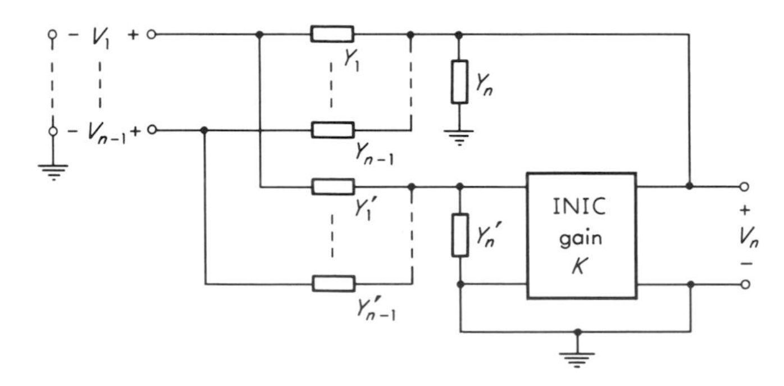

***Figure 4.23** Use of an INIC for a summing function.*

degree of the $N_i(p)$ or of the function $D(p) - \sum_i N_i(p)$ (whichever is higher), we obtain

$$V_n = \sum_{i=1}^{n-1} \frac{N_i(p)/Q(p)}{D(p)/Q(p)} V_i$$

An analysis similar to that made above shows that the following equations hold:

$$\frac{N_i(p)}{Q(p)} = Y_i - KY_i' \qquad i = 1, \ldots, n-1$$
$$\frac{D(p) - \sum_{i=1}^{n-1} N_i(p)}{Q(p)} = Y_n - KY_n' \tag{25}$$

Thus, we may make expansions of the left-hand members of (25) in a manner similar to that done in (23). Equating positive and negative terms on both sides of the equations determines the values of the various Y_i.

The basic procedure for a single input given above is completely general. However, the freedom that is available in the choice of the locations of the zeros of $Q(p)$ may frequently be used to optimize the sensitivity of the denominator or numerator polynomial of the voltage transfer function with respect to changes in the gain of the INIC. For example, we may write the denominator of the voltage transfer function in the form given in (71) of Chap. 2. Thus, we obtain*

$$\frac{V_2}{V_1} = \frac{N(p)}{D(p)} = \frac{N(p)}{a^2(p) - Kpb^2(p)} \tag{26}$$

If the numerator polynomial is decomposed into the form

$$N(p) = N_1(p)b(p) - KN_2(p)a(p)$$

where $a(p)$ and $b(p)$ are chosen to satisfy the optimum decomposition of the denominator, and $N_1(p)$ and $N_2(p)$ are chosen to satisfy the numerator decomposition (which is not necessarily optimum), then, dividing the numerator and denominator of (26) by $a(p)b(p)$, we obtain

$$\frac{V_2}{V_1} = \frac{N_1(p)/a(p) - KN_2(p)/b(p)}{a(p)/b(p) - Kpb(p)/a(p)}$$

* In this expression it has been assumed that the nominal value of K is unity. The case in which a nonunity K is desired is easily considered by making an adjustment of the coefficients of the polynomial $b^2(p)$ so that the product of K and these coefficients retains the values satisfying the decomposition.

If we compare this expression with (10), we see that we may make the following associations with respect to the network shown in Fig. 4.13:

$$\begin{aligned} y_{22} &= \frac{a(p)}{b(p)} & y_{21} &= K\frac{N_2(p)}{b(p)} \\ y'_{22} &= \frac{pb(p)}{a(p)} & y'_{21} &= \frac{1}{K}\frac{N_1(p)}{a(p)} \end{aligned} \tag{27}$$

It was shown in Sec. 2.6 that the driving-point admittances of (27) are realizable by passive *RC* networks. It may be necessary, however, to use a different configuration for the passive networks than the simple L configuration shown in Fig. 4.21 to efficiently realize the transfer admittances of (27). For such a case, any of the standard passive *RC* synthesis techniques that simultaneously realize a y_{22} and y_{21} parameter may be applied.* If the zeros of $Q(p)$ in (21) are not chosen so as to minimize the sensitivity, it is frequently possible to choose them in such a manner as to minimize the number of elements required in the realization. Examples of these cases will be made for the realizations which are given in the following section.

As another example of a specific realization technique, consider the realization of a short-circuit current transfer function by the network configuration shown in Fig. 4.15. The function is given in terms of the parameters of the component networks in (14). Since the decomposition is in terms of the y_{11} and y_{21} parameters of the passive component net-

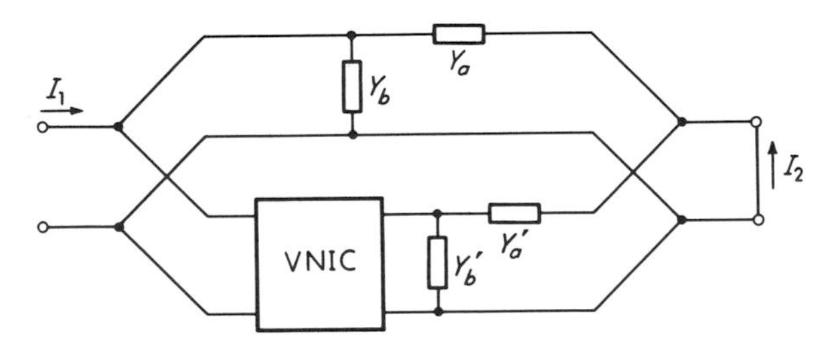

***Figure 4.24** A general realization for the current transfer function I_2/I_1.*

works, let us choose the L configuration for these networks shown in Fig. 4.24. The transfer function of (14) then becomes

$$\frac{I_2}{I_1} = \frac{-Y_a + KY'_a}{Y_a + Y_b - K(Y'_a + Y'_b)} \tag{28}$$

* A good coverage of passive *RC* synthesis techniques may be found in N. Balabanian, "Network Synthesis," chap. 7, Prentice-Hall, Inc., Englewood Cliffs, N.J., 1958.

Obviously, all the details of the realization procedure made with respect to the voltage transfer function of (20) also apply to this situation.

The details of applying the other general realization configurations shown in Figs. 4.13 to 4.20 are similar to the techniques described above, although care must be taken in choosing the component networks so that the port conditions are not violated by the interconnection. It should be pointed out that these configurations do not include every possible realization technique. For example, they do not include the configuration shown in Fig. 4.25. This has the transfer impedance*

$$\frac{V_2}{I_1} = Z_{21} = \frac{-Kz'_{21}z_{21}}{z_{11} - Kz'_{22}} \tag{29}$$

Thus, it provides for a polynomial decomposition in the denominator although no decomposition can be made of the numerator.

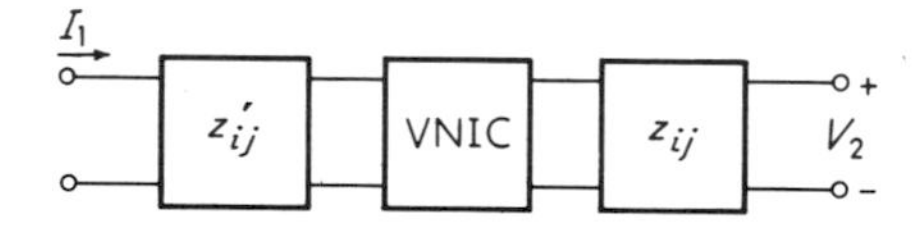

***Figure 4.25** A realization for a transfer impedance V_2/I_1.*

One of the disadvantages of NIC realizations in general is the fact that their output impedance is not zero. Thus, it is not possible to cascade such realizations without using isolating amplifiers. Although, in general, this requires additional circuitry, in some specific cases, it is possible to simultaneously realize the NIC and the isolating amplifier by a single VCVS. The basic principle of such a technique may be seen from Fig. 4.26.† The circuits shown in parts (*a*) and (*b*) of this figure, each involving an admittance and an ideal VCVS of gain A, have exactly the same two-port parameters. Both, of course, have zero output impedance because of the

* J. G. Linvill, *RC* Active Filters, *Proc. IRE,* vol. 42, no. 3, pp. 555–564, March, 1954.

† A. Antoniou, New Active *RC* Synthesis Procedure Using Negative-impedance Convertors, *Electron. Letters,* vol. 1, no. 7, pp. 203–204, Sept., 1965. See also J. Gorski-Popiel, *RC* Active Networks, *Electron. Letters,* vol. 1, no. 10, pp. 288–289, Dec., 1965.

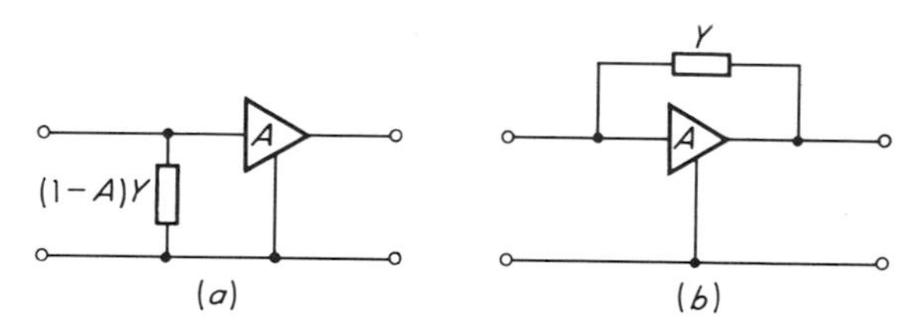

***Figure 4.26** Two two-port networks which have the same parameters.*

VCVS. To see how these circuits are used, assume that a VCVS with a gain A greater than unity is connected as an isolating amplifier at the output of the network configuration shown in Fig. 4.21. The circuit, including the isolating amplifier, has been redrawn in Fig. 4.27. In this

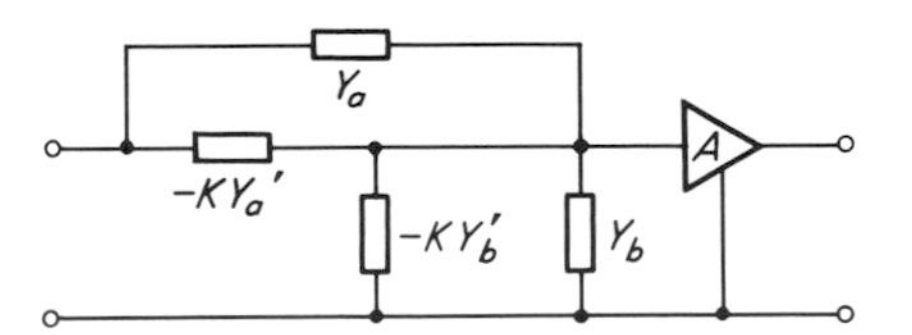

Figure 4.27 An INIC realization with an isolating amplifier.

figure, the INIC has not been shown explicitly, but its effect on the primed network has been given by multiplying the admittances Y_a' and Y_b' by $-K$, where K is the INIC gain.* If we have a realization in which Y_a' is zero, the network configuration shown in Fig. 4.28*a* may be used to

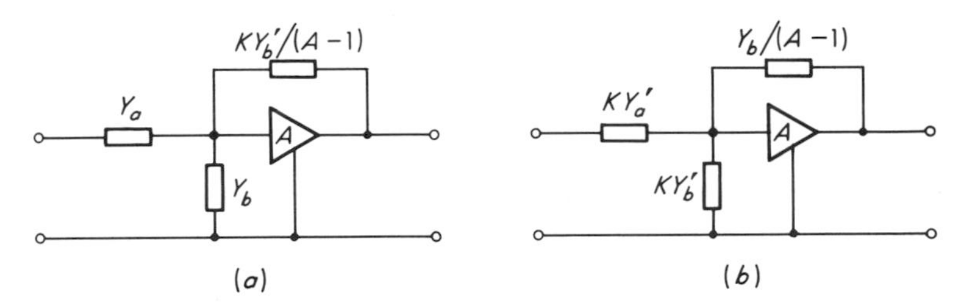

Figure 4.28 (a) Eliminating the INIC for the case where $Y_a' = 0$. (b) Eliminating the INIC for the case where $Y_b' = 0$.

provide the desired voltage transfer function. The realization uses only passive two-terminal admittances and a VCVS. Thus, it has zero output impedance. Similarly, if we have a realization in which Y_a is zero, the network configuration shown in Fig. 4.28*b* will realize the desired voltage transfer function. The technique cannot be used if both Y_a and Y_a' are nonzero.

4.4 *Realization of the second-degree voltage transfer function*

As a more detailed example of the actual realization of some of the more common network functions through the use of NICs, in this section

* This form of representation is valid where only the y_{21}' and y_{22}' parameters are considered. Thus, it is valid for the case in which the overall voltage transfer function is being considered.

we shall consider the use of the network configuration shown in Fig. 4.21, with the voltage transfer function given in (20) to realize biquadratic voltage transfer functions. The general form of such a function is

$$\frac{V_2}{V_1} = \frac{H(p^2 + a_1 p + a_2)}{p^2 + b_1 p + b_2} \tag{30}$$

where a_1, a_2, b_1, b_2, and H are real constants. We shall restrict our attention to the case in which b_1 and b_2 are also positive-valued. The numerator and denominator polynomials of the biquadratic function of (30) may be related to the y parameters of (10) by dividing the polynomials by the factor $p + d$, where d is real and positive. Thus, we obtain

$$\begin{aligned} -y_{21} + Ky'_{21} &= \frac{H(p^2 + a_1 p + a_2)}{p + d} \\ y_{22} - Ky'_{22} &= \frac{p^2 + b_1 p + b_2}{p + d} \end{aligned} \tag{31}$$

A realization for the y parameters of the component networks may be made in the form shown in Fig. 4.29. The values of the series elements may

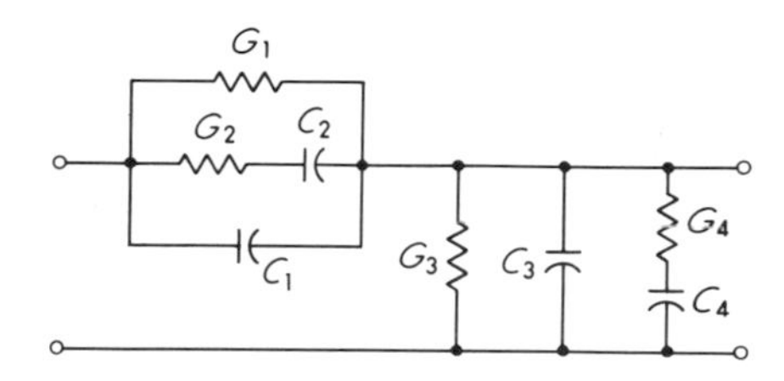

Figure 4.29 A general realization for the biquadratic voltage transfer function.

be found by making a partial-fraction expansion of $H(p^2 + a_1 p + a_2)/(p + d)$. Thus, we obtain

$$-y_{21} + Ky'_{21} = C_1 p + G_1 + \frac{pG_2}{p + G_2/C_2} \tag{32}$$

where $G_2/C_2 = d$. A similar expansion for

$$[p^2(1 - H) + p(b_1 - Ha_1) + (b_2 - Ha_2)]/(p + d)$$

gives the values of the shunt elements of the network. The expression is

$$(y_{22} - Ky'_{22}) - (-y_{21} + Ky'_{21}) = C_3 p + G_3 + \frac{pG_4}{p + G_4/C_4} \tag{33}$$

where $G_4/C_4 = d$. The elements of the network shown in Fig. 4.29, as specified by (32) and (33), may be positive- or negative-valued (or zero).

The positive-valued elements constitute the network with the unprimed y parameters and thus form Y_a and Y_b of Fig. 4.21. The negative-valued elements form the network with the primed y parameters and thus form Y'_a and Y'_b of Fig. 4.21. The latter elements are, of course, actually realized with positive-valued components, the negative signs and a multiplicative constant being provided by the INIC in cascade with the network. Thus, we see that the network shown in Fig. 4.29 provides a general realization for the biquadratic open-circuit voltage transfer function of (30). In the specific cases of low-pass, high-pass, and bandpass transfer functions, a simpler network results since some of the elements may usually be set to zero. These cases are covered in detail in the following paragraphs.

In applying the realization procedure discussed above to specific classes of network functions, additional constraints may be specified to make the realizations optimal in some sense. For example, it may be desirable to minimize the number of elements used in the network so that not all of the eight elements shown in Fig. 4.29 are required. Another example of optimization is the design of the network so that the poles of the voltage transfer function are optimally insensitive to changes in the gain of the INIC. To simplify the application of this class of networks to the common filtering situations, tables have been prepared for the low-pass, high-pass, and bandpass functions. For each of these functions, realizations have been specified for the general case, as well as for the cases which are optimal in each of the above senses, i.e., minimization of the number of elements and minimization of sensitivity to the gain of the INIC. In giving the expressions for the element values, the gain of the INIC has been assumed to be unity. The case for nonunity gains is easily considered by making an appropriate admittance normalization on the specified element values of the network with the y'_{ij} parameters.

We may first consider the low-pass open-circuit voltage transfer function. The general biquadratic form of (30) becomes, for this case,

$$\frac{V_1}{V_2} = \frac{H}{p^2 + b_1 p + b_2} \tag{34}$$

where it has been assumed that the coefficient a_2 in the numerator of (30) equals unity. Table 4.2 gives the realization information for this case. The general formulas are given as case 1, and the additional restrictions and the necessary formulas for making the realization optimally insensitive to changes in the INIC gain are given in case 2. The conditions under which a realization with the minimum number of elements may be obtained are given in case 3. These cases will be considered in more detail below.

Let us examine the optimally insensitive realization specified as case 2. First of all let us consider the general frequency-normalized low-pass

Table 4.2 Realizations for the low-pass transfer function

$$\frac{V_2}{V_1} = \frac{H}{p^2 + ap + b} = \frac{H/(p+d)}{(p^2 + ap + b)/(p+d)} \qquad a > 0,\ b > 0,\ d > 0$$

Case	1	2	3
Restrictions	*None*	$H = 2b - ab$ $\sqrt{b} < a < 2\sqrt{b}$	$H = b$
Value of d	*Any*	$\sqrt{b}$	a
R_1	d/H	$1/(2\sqrt{b} - a)$	a/H
C_1	0	0	0
R_2	$-d/H$	$-1/(2\sqrt{b} - a)$	$-a/H$
C_2	$1/dR_2$	$1/R_2\sqrt{b}$	$1/aR_2$
R_3	$d/(b - H)$	$1/(a - \sqrt{b})$	0
C_3	1.0	1.0	1.0
R_4	See below	0	0
C_4	$1/dR_4$	0	0

Notes. Case 1: $R_4 = (-d)/(d^2 - da + b - H)$. Case 2: Realization has optimum insensitivity to changes in INIC gain.

open-circuit voltage transfer function of the form

$$\frac{V_2}{V_1} = \frac{H}{p^2 + ap + 1} \tag{35}$$

In order to achieve an optimally insensitive realization, the denominator polynomial of (35) must be decomposed in the manner determined in Sec. 2.6. Thus, we obtain

$$p^2 + ap + 1 = (p+1)^2 - (2-a)p$$

This decomposition is of the general type shown as case 13 in Table 2.1. If this decomposition is used for the denominator of (35) and if we divide both numerator and denominator by the factor $p + 1$ and compare the result with (10), we may make the associations

$$\begin{aligned} -y_{21} + Ky'_{21} &= \frac{H}{p+1} = H - \frac{Hp}{p+1} \\ y_{22} - Ky'_{22} &= p + 1 - \frac{(2-a)p}{p+1} \end{aligned} \tag{36}$$

To simplify the number of elements required in the component networks, it is convenient to choose H equal to $2 - a$. Thus $-Ky'_{22}$ and Ky'_{21} are equal, and the "primed" network can be realized by a simple circuit consisting of a resistor and a capacitor in series. The "unprimed" network parameters are also readily synthesized. An overall network realization

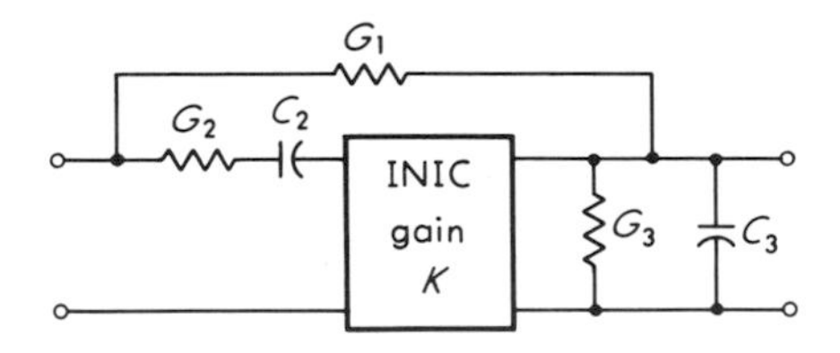

Figure 4.30 ***An optimally insensitive low-pass network realization.***

satisfying (36) is given in Fig. 4.30. For the circuit shown in this figure, the voltage transfer function is

$$\frac{V_2}{V_1} = \frac{pS_3(G_1 - KG_2) + G_1G_2S_2S_3}{p^2 + p(G_1S_3 + G_3S_3 + G_2S_2 - KG_2S_3) + G_2(G_1 + G_3)S_2S_3} \tag{37}$$

where the S_i are values of reciprocal capacitance. It should be noted that the choice of element values must be such that $G_1 = KG_2$ to ensure that the coefficient of the first-degree term in the numerator of (37) is zero.

The following properties may be noted with respect to this transfer function:

1. It is bilinear with respect to the gain K and with respect to the passive elements.
2. The decomposition of the denominator with respect to K is of the optimally insensitive type described in Sec. 2.6.
3. The denominator decomposition is of the type shown in case 13 of Table 2.1. Thus, changes in K can make the realization unstable.
4. The low-frequency (passband) gain is $G_1/(G_1 + G_3)$. Thus, the constant H of (34) is positive.

The following comments apply to the elements of the sensitivity matrix that will result for this realization:

1. The sensitivity for the b_1 coefficient of (34) with respect to K will be equal to $-2Q + 1$, where $Q = \sqrt{b_2}/b_1$ (see Sec. 2.6).
2. The sensitivities for the b_2 coefficient of (34) with respect to the elements G_2, S_2, and S_3, will be unity; with respect to the elements G_1 and G_3 they will be positive and less than unity (see properties 3 and 4, Sec. 2.5).

The above conclusions are easily verified by an example.

Example 4.1 As an example of the use of the network configuration shown in Fig. 4.30 to realize a low-pass network function, consider the frequency-normalized, maximally-flat-magnitude transfer function.

$$\frac{V_2}{V_1} = \frac{2 - \sqrt{2}}{p^2 + \sqrt{2}\,p + 1}$$

To realize this function, from Table 4.2, case 2, we obtain the following element values:

$$\begin{aligned} G_1 &= 0.586 \text{ mho} & S_2 &= 1.0 \text{ daraf} \\ G_2 &= 1.0 \text{ mho} & S_3 &= 1.0 \text{ daraf} \\ G_3 &= 0.414 \text{ mho} & K &= 0.586 \end{aligned}$$

where we have chosen a nonunity K so as to permit having both capacitors equal in value. If we compute the sensitivity matrix by the method of Sec. 2.5, we obtain

$$\begin{bmatrix} \Delta b_1^{(n)} \\ \Delta b_2^{(n)} \end{bmatrix} = \begin{bmatrix} 0.414 & 0.292 & 0.292 & 0.707 & 0.292 & -0.414 \\ 0.586 & 1.0 & 0.414 & 1.0 & 1.0 & 0 \end{bmatrix} \begin{bmatrix} \Delta G_1^{(n)} \\ \Delta G_2^{(n)} \\ \Delta G_3^{(n)} \\ \Delta S_2^{(n)} \\ \Delta S_3^{(n)} \\ \Delta K^{(n)} \end{bmatrix}$$

Practical experience has indicated that the optimally insensitive realization described above is well suited to actual implementation. Detailed design information for this circuit is given in Sec. 4.6 as circuit 4. For purposes of actual realization, an operational amplifier is used to construct the INIC. The details of such a construction are given in the next section.

Now let us consider the low-pass minimal element realization shown as case 3 in Table 4.2. A schematic realization for this case is shown in Fig.

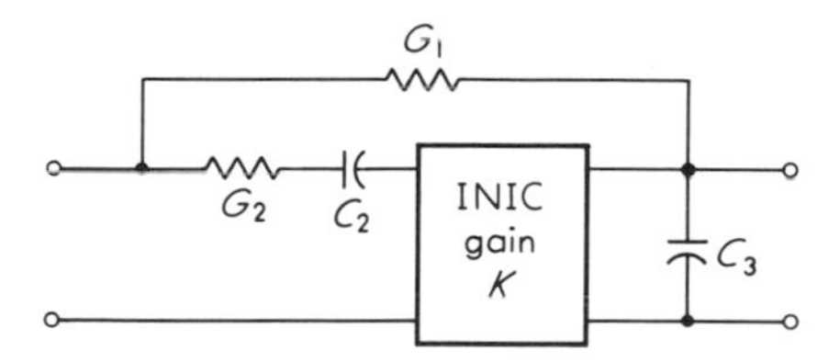

Figure 4.31 A low-pass network realization.

4.31. For this figure, the y parameters of the component networks have the form

$$-y'_{21} = y'_{22} = \frac{ph_1}{p + \sigma_1}$$

$$-y_{21} = h_2 \qquad y_{22} = h_3(p + \sigma_2)$$

Substituting these expressions in (10), we obtain

$$\frac{V_2}{V_1} = \frac{h_2(p + \sigma_1) - Kph_1}{h_3(p + \sigma_2)(p + \sigma_1) - Kph_1}$$

Thus, the denominator decomposition corresponds to case 13 of Table 2.1. The voltage transfer function may be shown to be

$$\frac{V_2}{V_1} = \frac{p(G_1S_3 - KG_2S_3) + G_1G_2S_2S_3}{p^2 + p(G_2S_2 + G_1S_3 - KG_2S_3) + G_1G_2S_2S_3} \tag{38}$$

The following properties may be noted with respect to this transfer function:

1. It is bilinear with respect to K and with respect to the passive elements.
2. The decomposition of the denominator with respect to K is a difference decomposition. However, the optimum decomposition described in Sec. 2.6 cannot be applied.
3. The denominator decomposition is of the type shown in case 13 of Table 2.1. Thus, changes in K can make the realization unstable.
4. The low-frequency (passband) gain is unity. Thus, the constant H of (34) is positive.

The following comments apply to the elements of the sensitivity matrix that will result for this realization:

1. The sensitivity for the b_1 coefficient of (34) with respect to K will be negative and greater in magnitude than $2Q - 1$, where $Q = \sqrt{b_2}/b_1$ (see Sec. 2.6).
2. The sensitivity for the b_2 coefficient of (34) with respect to the elements G_1, G_2, S_2, and S_3 will be unity (see property 3, Sec. 2.5).

The above conclusions are easily verified by an example.

Example 4.2 As an example of the use of the network configuration shown in Fig. 4.31 to realize a low-pass network function, consider the frequency-normalized, maximally-flat-magnitude transfer function

$$\frac{V_2}{V_1} = \frac{1}{p^2 + \sqrt{2}\,p + 1}$$

From Table 4.2, case 3, we obtain the element values

$$G_1 = 0.707 \text{ mho} \qquad S_2 = 2.0 \text{ darafs}$$
$$G_2 = 0.707 \text{ mho} \qquad S_3 = 1.0 \text{ daraf}$$
$$K = 1$$

In terms of the coefficients of the denominator of (34), we find the following sensitivity matrix:

$$\begin{bmatrix} \Delta b_1^{(n)} \\ \Delta b_2^{(n)} \end{bmatrix} = \begin{bmatrix} 0.5 & 0.5 & 1.0 & 0 & -0.5 \\ 1.0 & 1.0 & 1.0 & 1.0 & 0 \end{bmatrix} \begin{bmatrix} \Delta G_1^{(n)} \\ \Delta G_2^{(n)} \\ \Delta S_2^{(n)} \\ \Delta S_3^{(n)} \\ \Delta K^{(n)} \end{bmatrix}$$

It is easily seen from the above example that the sensitivity for the coefficient b_1 with respect to K is only slightly larger in magnitude than the optimum value realized in Example 4.1. It should be noted that realization of (38) requires that G_1 be set equal to KG_2. For this condition, (38) may be written in the form

$$\frac{V_2}{V_1} = \frac{G_1G_2S_2S_3}{p^2 + pG_2S_2 + G_1G_2S_2S_3}$$

For the high-pass case, the general biquadratic form of (30) becomes

$$\frac{V_2}{V_1} = \frac{Hp^2}{p^2 + b_1p + b_2} \tag{39}$$

Table 4.3 gives the realization information for this function. The various cases have the same significance as for the low-pass function; i.e., case 1

Table 4.3 *Realizations for the high-pass transfer function*

$$\frac{V_2}{V_1} = \frac{Hp^2}{p^2 + ap + b} = \frac{Hp^2/(p+d)}{(p^2 + ap + b)/(p+d)} \qquad a > 0,\ b > 0,\ d > 0$$

Case	1	2	3
Restrictions	*None*	$H = 2 - a/\sqrt{b}$ $\sqrt{b} < a < 2\sqrt{b}$	$H = 1$
Value of d	*Any*	$\sqrt{b}$	b/a
R_1	0	0	0
C_1	H	$2 - a/\sqrt{b}$	1.0
R_2	$-1/Hd$	$-1/(2\sqrt{b} - a)$	$-a/b$
C_2	$-H$	$1/R_2\sqrt{b}$	-1.0
R_3	d/b	$1/\sqrt{b}$	$1/a$
C_3	$1 - H$	$(a/\sqrt{b}) - 1$	0
R_4	See below	0	0
C_4	$1/dR_4$	0	0

Notes. Case 1: $R_4 = (-d)/[d^2(1 - H) - da + b]$. Case 2: Realization has optimum insensitivity to changes in INIC gain.

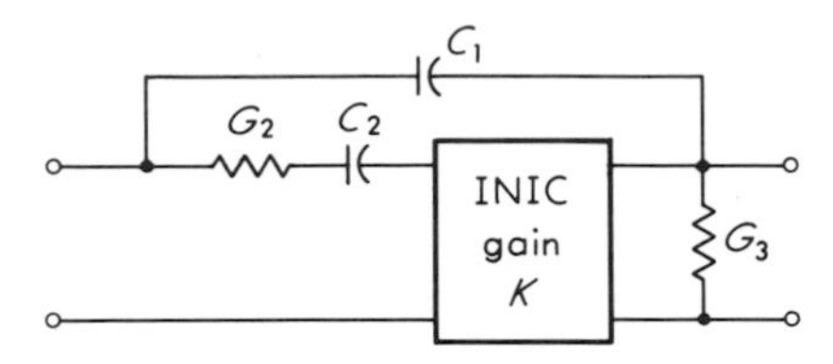

Figure 4.32 A high-pass network realization.

covers the general realization, case 2 specifies the conditions under which an optimally insensitive realization occurs, and case 3 provides a minimum number of elements. A schematic for the minimum number of elements case is given in Fig. 4.32. The voltage transfer function for this network is

$$\frac{V_2}{V_1} = \frac{p^2 + pG_2(S_2 - KS_1)}{p^2 + p(G_3S_1 + G_2S_2 - KG_2S_1) + G_2G_3S_1S_2} \tag{40}$$

It is easily shown that the decomposition is of the type given as case 13 in Table 2.1. Realization requires that $S_2 = KS_1$. The following properties may be noted with respect to this transfer function:

1. It is bilinear with respect to the gain K and with respect to the passive elements.
2. The decomposition of the denominator with respect to K is a difference decomposition. However, the optimum decomposition described in Sec. 2.6 cannot be applied.
3. The denominator decomposition is of the type shown in case 13 of Table 2.1. Thus, changes in K can make the realization unstable.
4. The high-frequency (passband) gain is unity. Thus, the constant H of (39) is unity.

The following comments apply to the elements of the sensitivity matrix that will result for this realization:

1. The sensitivity for the b_1 coefficient of (39) with respect to K will be negative and greater in magnitude than $2Q - 1$, where $Q = \sqrt{b_2}/b_1$ (see Sec. 2.6).
2. The sensitivities for the b_2 coefficient of (39) with respect to the elements G_2, G_3, S_1, and S_2 will be unity (see property 3, Sec. 2.5).

The above conclusions are easily verified by an example.

Example 4.3 As an example of the use of the network configuration shown in Fig. 4.32 to realize a high-pass network function, consider the frequency-normalized, maximally-flat-magnitude transfer function

$$\frac{V_2}{V_1} = \frac{p^2}{p^2 + \sqrt{2}\,p + 1}$$

The values of the elements may be directly determined from Table 4.3, case 3. Thus we obtain

$$G_2 = 0.707 \text{ mho} \qquad S_1 = 1.0 \text{ daraf}$$
$$G_3 = 1.414 \text{ mhos} \qquad S_2 = 1.0 \text{ daraf}$$
$$K = 1$$

The sensitivity matrix for this realization in terms of the coefficients of the denominator of (39) is given by the expression

$$\begin{bmatrix} \Delta b_1^{(n)} \\ \Delta b_2^{(n)} \end{bmatrix} = \begin{bmatrix} 0 & 1.0 & 0.5 & 0.5 & -0.5 \\ 1.0 & 1.0 & 1.0 & 1.0 & 0 \end{bmatrix} \begin{bmatrix} \Delta G_2^{(n)} \\ \Delta G_3^{(n)} \\ \Delta S_1^{(n)} \\ \Delta S_2^{(n)} \\ \Delta K^{(n)} \end{bmatrix}$$

The low sensitivities are characteristic of the "low-Q" nature of the poles. This realization has been found to be a useful one for practical applications. A detailed set of design information for it is given in Sec. 4.6 as circuit 5.

For the bandpass case, the biquadratic function of (30) becomes

$$\frac{V_2}{V_1} = \frac{Hp}{p^2 + b_1 p + b_2} \tag{41}$$

where it has been assumed that a_1 of (30) equals 1. Table 4.4 gives the realization information for this function. Only two cases are given in this table. Case 1 is the general case. Case 2 is a realization which has a minimum number of elements and in addition is optimally insensitive to gain changes in the INIC. To see this, let $b_2 = 1$ in (41), and apply the optimum decomposition to the denominator. If both numerator and denominator are then divided by the factor $p + 1$ and the result is compared with (10), we may make the associations

$$-y_{21} + Ky'_{21} = \frac{Hp}{p+1}$$
$$y_{22} - Ky'_{22} = p + 1 - \frac{(2 - b_1)p}{p+1}$$

For simplicity in the component networks, we may set H equal to $-(2 - b_1)$. For this value of H, the y parameters given above may be realized by the network configuration shown in Fig. 4.33, with the element

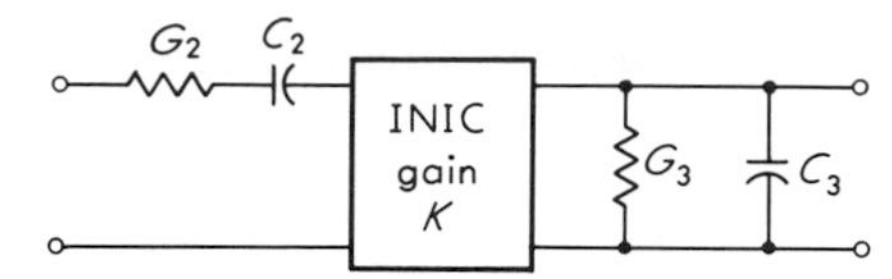

Figure 4.33 An optimally insensitive bandpass network realization.

values given in Table 4.4, case 2. For this realization, the voltage transfer function is

$$\frac{V_2}{V_1} = \frac{-KpG_2S_3}{p^2 + p(G_2S_2 + G_3S_3 - KG_2S_3) + G_2G_3S_2S_3} \tag{42}$$

The following properties may be noted with respect to this transfer function:

1. It is bilinear with respect to the gain K and with respect to the passive network elements.
2. The decomposition of the denominator with respect to K is of the optimally insensitive type described in Sec. 2.6.
3. The denominator decomposition is of the type shown in case 13 of Table 2.1. Thus, changes in K can make the realization unstable.
4. The passband gain at resonance is $-KG_2S_3/(G_2S_2 + G_3S_3 - KG_2S_3)$. Thus, the constant H of (41) is negative.

Table 4.4 Realizations for the bandpass transfer function

$$\frac{V_2}{V_1} = \frac{Hp}{p^2 + ap + b} = \frac{Hp/(p+d)}{(p^2 + ap + b)/(p+d)} \qquad a > 0, b > 0, d > 0$$

Case	1	2
Restrictions	*None*	$H = a - 2\sqrt{b}$ $a < 2\sqrt{b}$
Value of d	*Any*	$\sqrt{b}$
R_1	0	0
C_1	0	0
R_2	$1/H$	$-1/(2\sqrt{b} - a)$
C_2	H/d	$1/R_2\sqrt{b}$
R_3	d/b	$1/\sqrt{b}$
C_3	1.0	1.0
R_4	See below	0
C_4	$1/dR_4$	0

Notes. Case 1: $R_4 = (-d)/[d^2 + b - d(a - H)]$. Case 2: Realization has optimum insensitivity to changes in INIC gain.

5. Changing K changes the Q of the network function without changing the resonant frequency.
6. If the INIC gain is set equal to $2 - b_1$, the network may be realized with all unity-valued components.*

The following comments apply to the elements of the sensitivity matrix that will result for this realization:

1. The sensitivity for the b_1 coefficient of (41) with respect to K will be equal to $-2Q + 1$, where $Q = \sqrt{b_2}/b_1$ (see Sec. 2.6).
2. The sensitivities for the coefficient b_2 with respect to the elements G_2, G_3, S_2, and S_3 will be unity (see property 3, Sec. 2.5).

The above conclusions are easily verified by an example.

Example 4.4 As an example of the use of the network configuration shown in Fig. 4.33 to realize a bandpass network function, consider the frequency-normalized transfer function

$$\frac{V_2}{V_1} = \frac{Hp}{p^2 + 0.1p + 1}$$

Choosing a nonunity INIC gain and using Table 4.4, case 2, we obtain for the element values the following:

$$G_2 = 1.0 \text{ mho} \qquad S_2 = 1.0 \text{ daraf}$$
$$G_3 = 1.0 \text{ mho} \qquad S_3 = 1.0 \text{ daraf}$$
$$K = 1.9$$

The sensitivity matrix for the realization in terms of the coefficients of (41) is

$$\begin{bmatrix} \Delta b_1^{(n)} \\ \Delta b_2^{(n)} \end{bmatrix} = \begin{bmatrix} -9 & 10 & 10 & -9 & -19 \\ 1 & 1 & 1 & 1 & 0 \end{bmatrix} \begin{bmatrix} \Delta G_2^{(n)} \\ \Delta G_3^{(n)} \\ \Delta S_2^{(n)} \\ \Delta S_3^{(n)} \\ \Delta K^{(n)} \end{bmatrix}$$

For this example, the coefficient H of (41) equals -1.9.

This is an optimally insensitive realization. Thus the values of the sensitivities in the last column of the sensitivity matrix are minimal. A

* L. P. Huelsman, Optimum Sensitivity Active *RC* Bandpass Filter, *Electron. Letters*, vol. 1, no. 8, p. 226, Oct., 1965.

detailed design procedure for realizing the bandpass network is given as circuit 5 in Sec. 4.6.

In this section we have seen that general realization procedures may be set up for the realization of the biquadratic voltage transfer function by means of the *RC*-NIC class of networks. The decompositions are all of the type given as case 13 of Table 2.1, and they may be optimized with respect to the sensitivity of the gain of the INIC. Such optimization may, however, require a restriction on the gain constant H of the network function.

4.5 *Circuit realizations for NICs*

In this section, we shall present some methods for realizing the two types of ideal NICs, that is, the INIC and the VNIC. First let us consider the INIC, as defined by (2). A realization using an ICIS (current-controlled

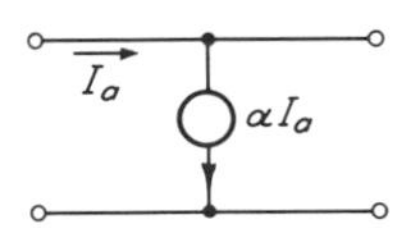

Figure 4.34 A simple INIC realization.

current source) is shown in Fig. 4.34. An analysis of this circuit shows that the transmission parameters are

$$\begin{bmatrix} 1 & 0 \\ 0 & \dfrac{1}{1-\alpha} \end{bmatrix} \tag{43}$$

Comparison of these parameters with those given in (3) shows that the gain K of the INIC equals $\alpha - 1$. Thus an ICIS with a gain of 2 produces a unity-conversion-ratio INIC. This circuit is of interest mostly for its theoretical value in showing the relationship between the *RC*-controlled source class of networks and the *RC*-NIC class of networks. Since a single controlled source can be used to realize an NIC, the two classes are obviously similar in their capabilities.

A more practical circuit for an INIC is shown in Fig. 4.35. This circuit uses a differential-input operational amplifier as an active element. In Sec. 3.7 it was pointed out that no current flows into the input terminals of such an amplifier and that the voltage difference between the input terminals is zero. From this it is easily seen that the overall two-port

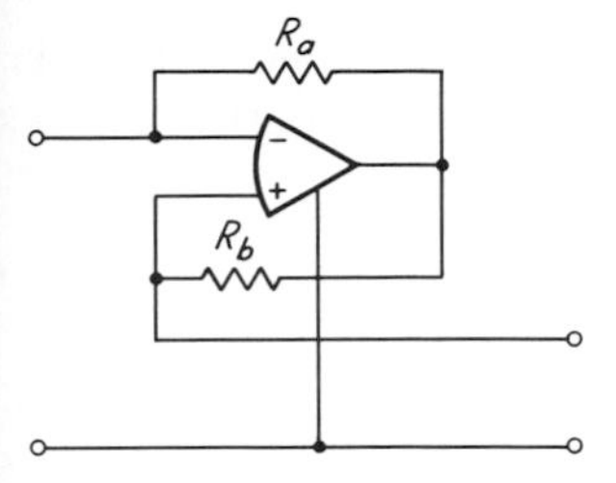

Figure 4.35 An operational amplifier INIC realization.

device will have the transmission parameters

$$\begin{bmatrix} 1 & 0 \\ 0 & \dfrac{-R_b}{R_a} \end{bmatrix} \tag{44}$$

Comparison of these parameters with those given in (3) shows that the device is an INIC with a gain K equal to R_a/R_b.

All NICs have stability characteristics such that one of their ports is an open-circuit-stable (OCS) port, while the other is a short-circuit-stable (SCS) port.* To determine the stability properties for the INIC shown in Fig. 4.35, we may consider the model of the operational amplifier shown in Fig. 4.36, where β is the gain of the amplifier and is a large number. If

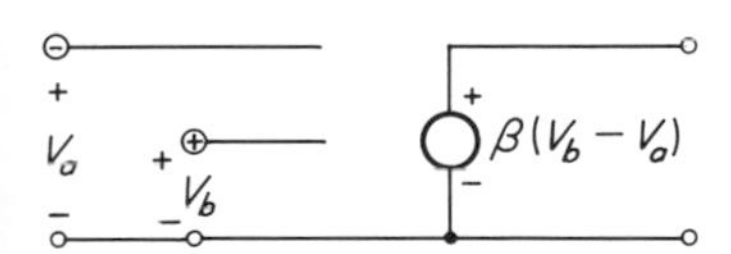

Figure 4.36 A simple model for an operational amplifier.

resistors R_1 and R_2 are placed across ports 1 and 2 of the INIC shown in Fig. 4.35, the circuit may be redrawn using the operational amplifier model with the result shown in Fig. 4.37. This circuit will only be stable if

* A more detailed treatment of open- and short-circuit stability in NICs may be found in J. D. Brownlie, On the Stability Properties of a Negative Impedance Converter, *IEEE Trans. Circuit Theory,* vol. CT-13, no. 1, pp. 98–99, March, 1966. See also R. F. Hoskins, Stability of Negative-impedance Convertors, *Electron. Letters,* vol. 2, no. 9, p. 341, Sept., 1966.

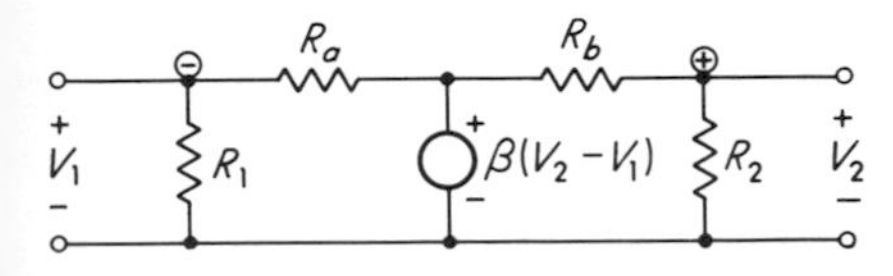

Figure 4.37 Stability considerations for the operational amplifier INIC.

the quantity $V_2 - V_1$ is nonpositive. Otherwise, positive feedback will occur, and the amplifier will be driven to saturation. Therefore, the condition for stability is*

$$V_1 \geq V_2 \tag{45}$$

In terms of the resistors shown in Fig. 4.37, this requires that

$$R_1 R_b \geq R_2 R_a \tag{46}$$

In other words, for a given conversion ratio (and thus for a fixed ratio of R_a and R_b) it is necessary that R_1 be sufficiently large with respect to R_2 to satisfy the inequality of (46). As a result we see that port 1 is the OCS port of the INIC shown in Fig. 4.35, and port 2 is the SCS port. A similar analysis may be used to establish the stability conditions on other NIC circuits. In some cases, it may be desirable to use a more realistic model for the device and also to take into account the nature of the actual networks in which the NIC is to be embedded to ensure stability over the desired frequency range of operation.

Another circuit realization for an INIC may be obtained by considering the basic circuit shown in Fig. 4.38. As indicated, this requires the use of

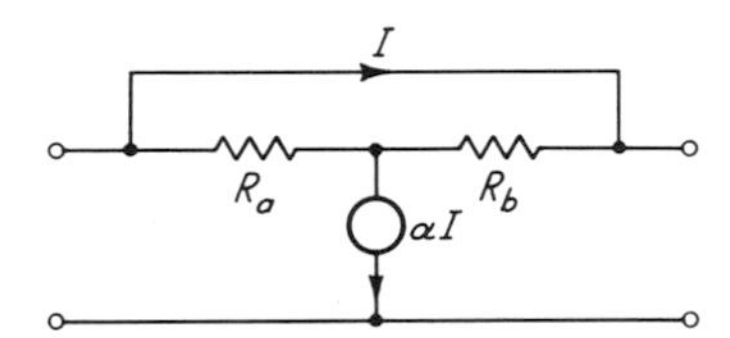

Figure 4.38 A simple circuit for an INIC.

an ICIS. In the limiting case as the gain of the ICIS approaches infinity, the transmission parameters of the two-port network become

$$\begin{bmatrix} 1 & 0 \\ 0 & \dfrac{-R_b}{R_a} \end{bmatrix} \tag{47}$$

Comparison of these parameters with those given in (3) shows that such a circuit realizes an INIC with a conversion gain K equal to R_a/R_b. A transistor realization of this circuit is easily constructed. Such a realization is shown in Fig. 4.39a. For convenience in showing the major components of

* The value of V_1 will, of course, be only slightly less than that of V_2.

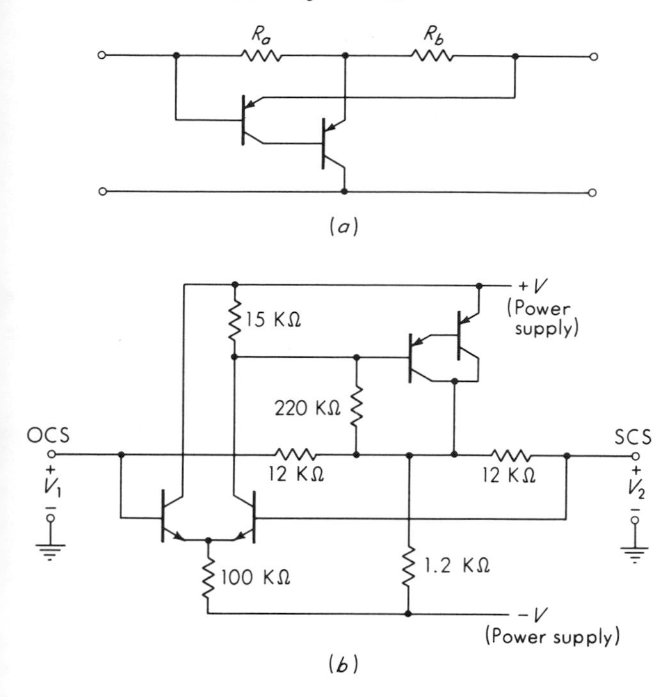

Figure 4.39 *(a) A practical INIC realization. (b) Complete schematic for the INIC shown in (a).*

the circuit, biasing elements have been deleted.* A schematic for a dc-coupled version of this circuit is shown in Fig. 4.39*b*.†

Now we shall consider some realizations for VNICs. A realization using a VCVS (voltage-controlled voltage source) is shown in Fig. 4.40. For the

* This circuit was originally presented by A. I. Larky, *op. cit.*, and is usually referred to as the *Larky circuit.* A complete schematic of the circuit, showing the biasing elements and power supplies, is given in B. K. Kinariwala, Synthesis of Active *RC* Networks, *Bell System Tech. J.*, vol. 38, pp. 1269–1316, Sept., 1959.

† D. P. Franklin, Direct-coupled Negative-impedance Convertor, *Electron. Letters*, vol. 1, no. 1, p. 1, March, 1965. Another direct-coupled circuit is given in A. J. Drew and J. Gorski-Popiel, Directly Coupled Negative Impedance Convertor, *Proc. IEE*, vol. 111, no. 7, pp. 1282–1283, July, 1964. Some variations of the original Larky circuit may be found in B. R. Myers, New Subclass of Negative-impedance Convertors with Improved Gain-product Sensitivities, *Electron. Letters*, vol. 1, no. 3, pp. 68–70, May, 1965.

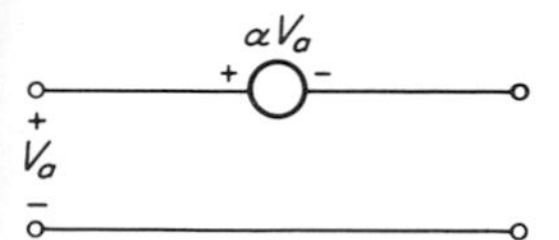

Figure 4.40 *A simple VNIC realization.*

two-port network shown in this figure, the transmission parameters are

$$\begin{bmatrix} \dfrac{-1}{\alpha - 1} & 0 \\ 0 & 1 \end{bmatrix} \tag{48}$$

Comparison of these parameters with those given in (5) shows that the device is a VNIC with a gain K equal to $\alpha - 1$. Thus, a VCVS with a gain α of 2 produces a unity-conversion-ratio VNIC.*

A more practical circuit realization for a VNIC may be developed based

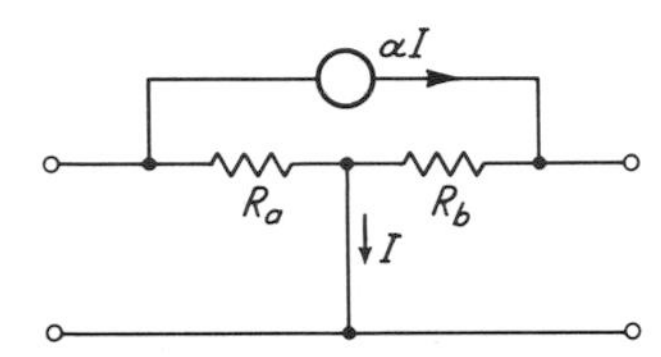

Figure 4.41 A simple circuit for a VNIC.

on a configuration similar to that shown in Fig. 4.38 but with the input and output of the ICIS interchanged as shown in Fig. 4.41. For large values of gain for the ICIS, the transmission parameters of this circuit approach the values

$$\begin{bmatrix} \dfrac{-R_a}{R_b} & 0 \\ 0 & 1 \end{bmatrix} \tag{49}$$

Comparison of these values with those given in (5) shows that the device acts as a VNIC with a gain K equal to R_b/R_a. A transistor realization of this circuit is easily constructed. Such a realization is shown in Fig. 4.42.

* An implementation of this circuit was given by W. J. Karplus, Synthesis of Non-PR Driving Point Impedance Functions Using Analog Computer Units, *IRE Trans. Circuit Theory*, vol. CT-4, no. 3, pp. 170–172, Sept., 1957. Although his realization may be used to produce negative immittances, it is impractical for VNIC use (as a two-port device) since in this application it would require operational amplifiers to be operated with a floating ground.

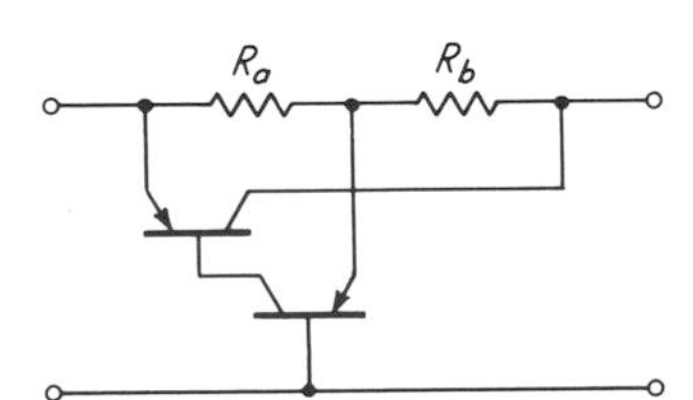

Figure 4.42 A practical VNIC realization.

The biasing components have been omitted for ease of representation of the circuit.*

Many other realizations for NICs have appeared in the literature. Thus, the ones described in this section should be considered as merely being representative of the developments that have been made in this area. A more complete coverage of this topic may be obtained by consulting the references listed in Appendix D.

4.6 *Realization procedures and design information*

In this chapter we have considered the use of negative-immittance converters as the active element for the realization of network functions. In the following pages, design information and actual numerical examples of circuit realizations for second-degree low-pass, high-pass, and bandpass network functions are given. These are titled, respectively, circuits 4, 5, and 6. The network function which is realized in each case is an open-circuit voltage transfer function. The negative-immittance converter which is used is a current-inversion type (INIC). In order to make the circuits realistic, an actual realization for the source using an operational amplifier is shown. Other realizations for NICs have been discussed earlier in this chapter. In each circuit, a general design procedure is described in terms of the elements shown in the schematic. In addition, a specific numerical example is given illustrating the application of the design procedure. It should be noted that in all these circuits the impedance normalization constant is free to be chosen. Thus, in all of the design procedures there will be one step in which some element is set to a convenient value. Once this value is chosen, the correct normalization is achieved for all the remaining elements. It should also be noted that the examples described in these circuit diagrams have actually been constructed and tested. Thus, the frequency-response curves indicated are those found by actual measurement.†

* The original configuration of the VNIC shown in Fig. 4.42 is similar to configurations shown in W. R. Lundry, Negative Impedance Circuits—Some Basic Relations and Limitations, *IRE Trans. Circuit Theory*, vol. CT-4, no. 3, pp. 132–139, Sept., 1957. The transistor realization of the circuit appeared in S. S. Hakim, Some New Negative-impedance Convertors, *Electron. Letters*, vol. 1, no. 1, pp. 9–10, March, 1965, and also in B. R. Myers, *op. cit.*

† The circuit diagrams and the design information given in these diagrams are reproduced through the permission of the copyright owner, Burr-Brown Research Corporation of Tucson, Arizona, from their publication, "Handbook of Operational Amplifier *RC* Networks."

Circuit 4 Design procedure for the realization of a second-degree low-pass voltage transfer function using an operational amplifier realization for a current-inversion negative-immittance converter (INIC).

General circuit schematic

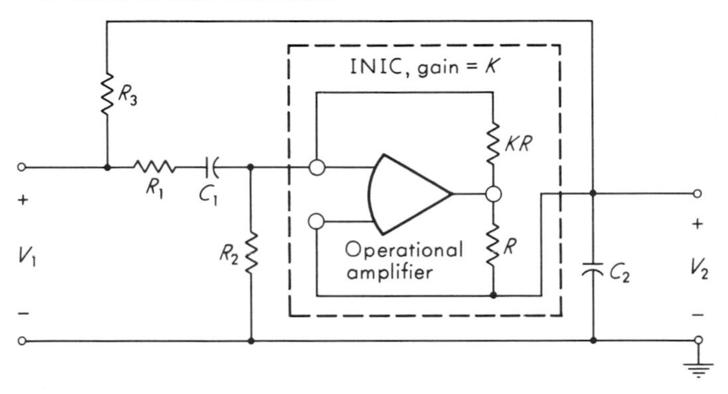

General transfer function The voltage transfer function in terms of the circuit elements and also in terms of the frequency-normalization constant ω_0 and the constant a is

$$\frac{V_2}{V_1} = \frac{pC_1\overbrace{[(1/R_3) - (K/R_1)]}^{=0} + 1/R_1R_3}{p^2C_1C_2 + p\{(C_1/R_2) + (C_2/R_1) + C_1\underbrace{[(1/R_3) - (K/R_1)]}_{=0}\} + (R_2 + R_3)/R_1R_2R_3}$$

$$= \frac{H\omega_0^2}{p^2 + a\omega_0 p + \omega_0^2}$$

General circuit characteristics An idealized Bode plot illustrating the relative gain characteristics of the transfer function and of the (open-loop) operational amplifier is shown below:

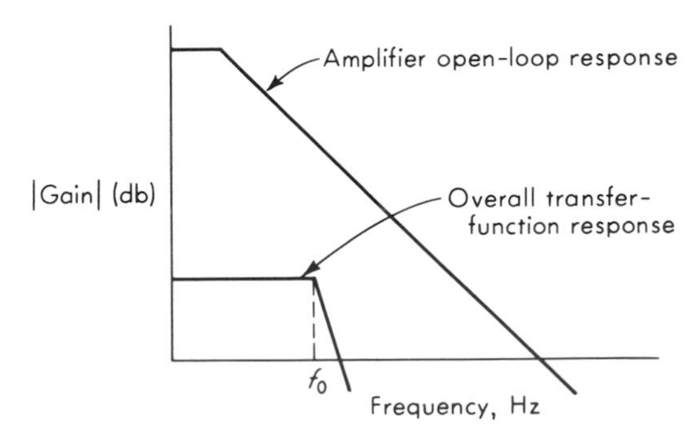

Design procedure Given ω_0, a:

1. Choose a convenient value of C_2 (farads)

2. Define the constant $b = C_2\omega_0$
3. Calculate (ohms and farads)

$$R_1 = \frac{1}{b} \qquad R_2 = \frac{1}{b(a-1)} \qquad R_3 = \frac{1}{b(2-a)} \qquad C_1 = C_2 \qquad K = 2 - a$$

[Note: R may be set to a convenient value. Ten kilohms works well in most applications.]

Example of Circuit 4 The realization of a typical low-pass maximally-flat-magnitude (Butterworth) voltage transfer function follows:

Given $f_0 = \dfrac{\omega_0}{2\pi} = 6.37$ Hz, $a = \sqrt{2}$

$$C_1 = C_2 = 10\ \mu\text{F}$$

$$b = 4 \times 10^{-4} \qquad R_1 = 2.5 \text{ kilohms}$$

$$K = 0.586 \qquad R_2 = 6.03 \text{ kilohms}$$

$$R_3 = 4.27 \text{ kilohms}$$

Transfer function for example problem

$$\frac{V_2}{V_1} = \frac{937}{p^2 + 56.56p + 1600}$$

*Circuit schematic for example problem**

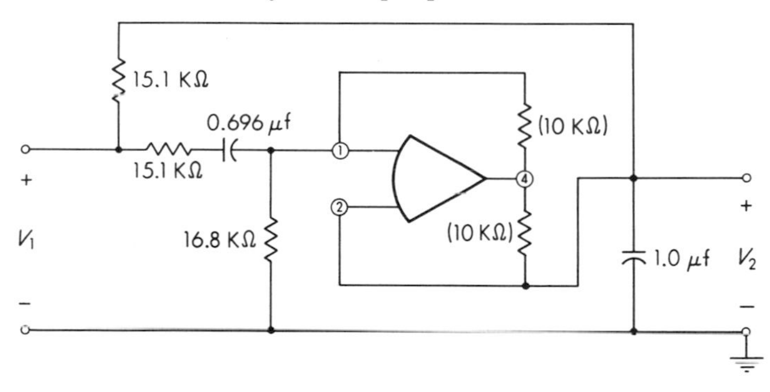

Circuit characteristic for example problem

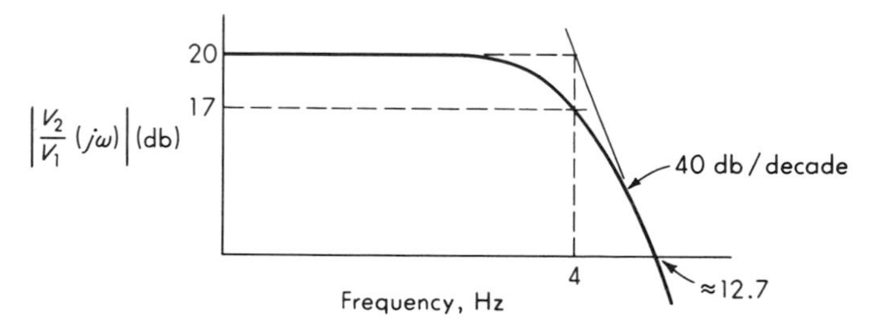

* The operational amplifier used in constructing this realization was a Burr-Brown Model 3003/15.

Circuit 5 Design procedure for the realization of a second-degree high-pass voltage transfer function using an operational amplifier realization for a current-inversion negative-immittance converter (INIC).

General circuit schematic

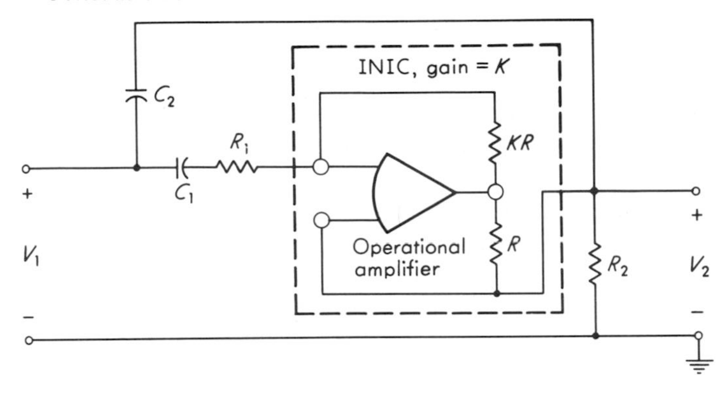

General transfer function The voltage transfer function in terms of the circuit elements and also in terms of the frequency-normalization constant ω_0 and the constant a is

$$\frac{V_2}{V_1} = \frac{p^2C_1C_2 + p(1/R_1)\overbrace{(C_2 - KC_1)}^{=0}}{p^2C_1C_2 + p[(C_1/R_2) + (1/R_1)\underbrace{(C_2 - KC_1)}_{=0}] + 1/R_1R_2}$$

$$= \frac{p^2}{p^2 + a\omega_0 p + \omega_0{}^2}$$

General circuit characteristics An idealized Bode plot illustrating the relative gain characteristics of the transfer function and of the (open-loop) operational amplifier is shown below:

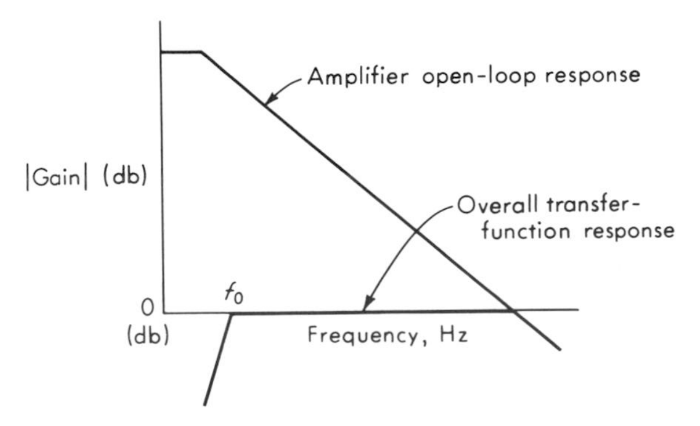

Design procedure Given ω_0, a:

1. Choose a convenient value of C_1 (farads)
2. Define the constant $b = C_1\omega_0$
3. Calculate (ohms and farads)

$$C_2 = C_1 \qquad R_1 = \frac{a}{b} \qquad R_2 = \frac{1}{ab} \qquad K = 1$$

[Note: R may be set to a convenient value. Ten kilohms works well in most applications.]

Example of Circuit 5 The realization of a typical high-pass maximally-flat-magnitude (Butterworth) voltage transfer function follows:

Given $f_0 = \dfrac{\omega_0}{2\pi} = 160$ Hz, $a = \sqrt{2}$:

$$C_1 = C_2 = 0.1\ \mu\text{F}$$
$$b = 1.007 \times 10^{-4}$$
$$R_1 = 14.1 \text{ kilohms} \qquad R_2 = 7.02 \text{ kilohms}$$

Transfer function for example problem

$$\frac{V_2}{V_1} = \frac{p^2}{p^2 + \sqrt{2} \times 10^3 p + 10^6}$$

*Circuit schematic for example problem**

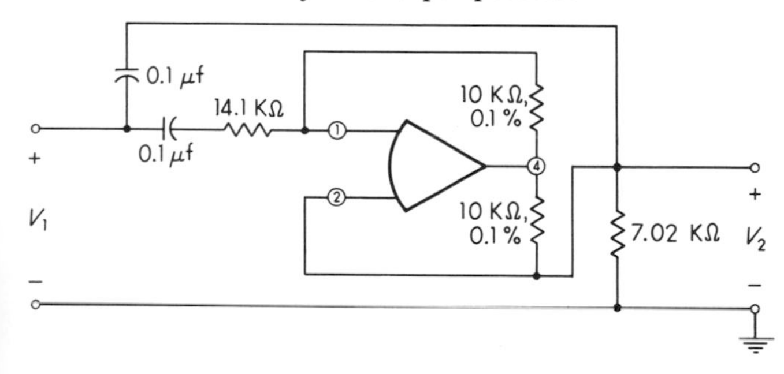

Circuit characteristic for example problem

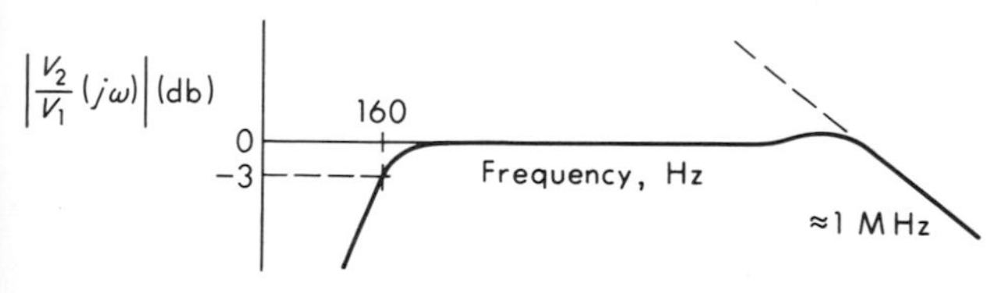

* The operational amplifier used in constructing this realization was a Burr-Brown Model 3003/15.

Circuit 6 Design procedure for the realization of a second-degree band-pass voltage transfer function using an operational amplifier realization for a current-inversion negative-immittance converter (INIC).

General circuit schematic

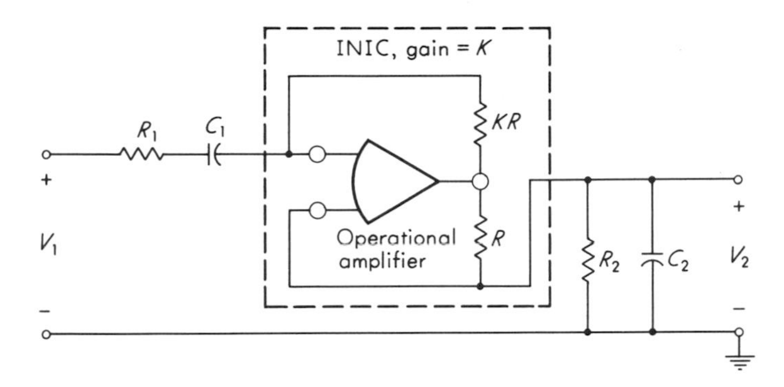

General transfer function The voltage transfer function in terms of the circuit elements and also in terms of the frequency-normalization constant ω_0 and the constant a is

$$\frac{V_2}{V_1} = \frac{-KC_1p/R_1}{p^2C_1C_2 + p[(C_2/R_1) + (C_1/R_2) - K(C_1/R_1)] + 1/R_1R_2}$$

$$= \frac{-H\omega_0 p}{p^2 + a\omega_0 p + \omega_0^2}$$

General circuit characteristics An idealized Bode plot illustrating the relative gain characteristics of the transfer function and of the (open-loop) operational amplifier is shown below:

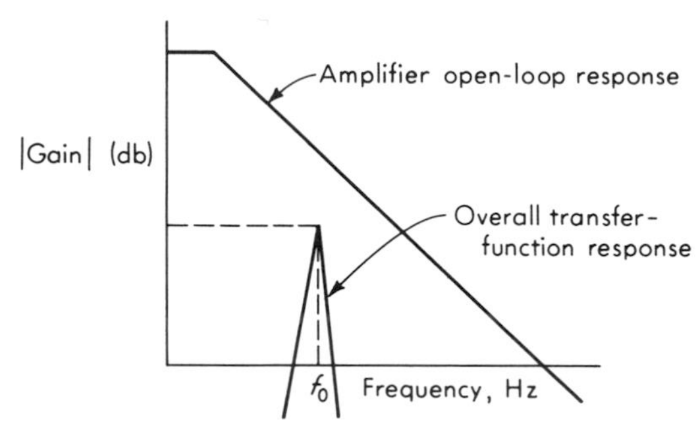

Design procedure Given ω_0, a:

1. Choose a convenient value of C_1 (farads)
2. Define the constant $b = C_1\omega_0$

3. Calculate (ohms and farads)

$$C_2 = C_1 \qquad R_1 = R_2 = \frac{1}{b}$$

$$K = 2 - a$$

[Note: The choice of R in the INIC is relatively arbitrary, but it should be near 10 kilohms for best results. ($R + KR$ can be a single trimming potentiometer of size 20 to 30 kilohms.)]

Example of Circuit 6 The realization of a typical bandpass voltage transfer function with a Q of approximately 100 follows:

Given $f_0 = \dfrac{\omega_0}{2\pi} = 80$ Hz, $a = 0.01$:

$$C_1 = C_2 = 0.1\ \mu\text{F} \qquad R_1 = R_2 = 19.9 \text{ kilohms}$$
$$b = 5.02 \times 10^{-5} \qquad K = 1.99$$

Transfer function for example problem

$$\frac{V_2}{V_1} = \frac{-10^3 p}{p^2 + 5.04p + 25.4 \times 10^4}$$

*Circuit schematic for example problem**

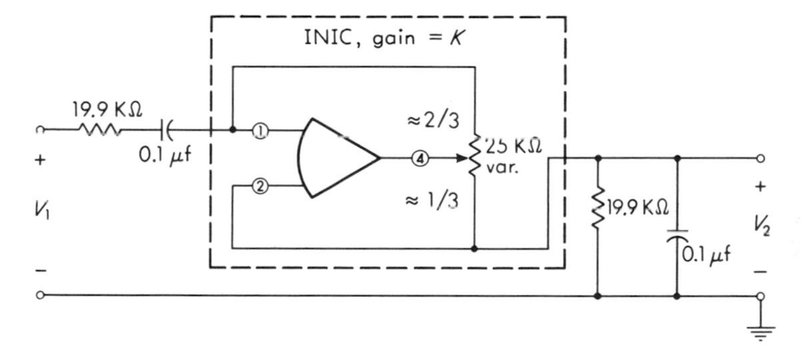

Circuit characteristic for example problem

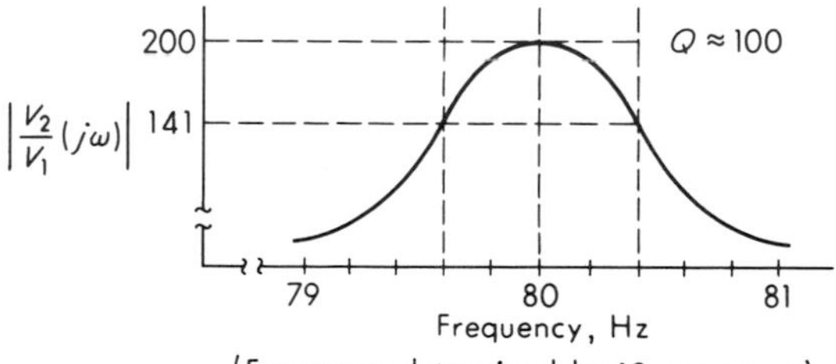

* The operational amplifier used in constructing this realization was a Burr-Brown Model 3003/15.

4.7 *Conclusion*

In this chapter we have discussed the general properties of a new type of active element, the NIC. It has been shown that the NIC may be used to realize completely general transfer functions. The realizations are easily optimized with respect to sensitivity. In addition, they may usually be constrained so as to minimize the number of elements required.

In summary then, NIC realizations provide an interesting addition to the active *RC* realization techniques which have been discussed so far. The mechanics of the process by means of which the element values are determined for a particular network function, in general, are simpler than those for the controlled-source case since they do not require the solution of a simultaneous set of nonlinear equations. This simplicity is readily apparent for the realization of higher-degree cases. Although these realizations do not have the low output impedance of the VCVS realizations and thus cannot be cascaded without suitable isolating amplifiers, they do provide an advantage over the controlled-source realizations in that various input voltages may be summed independently.

PROBLEMS

4.1 (*a*) Show that the realization given in Fig. 4.14 with the transfer function given in (12) can be realized with an optimum decomposition of the denominator with respect to the NIC gain. (*b*) If the denominator polynomial is given as

$$D(p) = p^2 + ap + 1$$

find expressions for the z parameters of the component networks.

4.2 Find an optimally insensitive realization using an INIC for the following network function:

$$\frac{V_2}{V_1} = \frac{10p}{p^2 + 0.1p + 1}$$

4.3 Find a realization using an INIC for the following low-pass function:

$$\frac{V_2}{V_1} = \frac{H}{p^3 + 2p^2 + 2p + 1}$$

Choose the value of H so as to simplify the realization. Let the polynomial $Q(p)$ of (21) have the factors $(p + 1)(p + 2)$.

4.4 Find an optimally insensitive realization using an INIC for the following function:

$$\frac{V_2}{V_1} = \frac{Hp}{p^2 + b_1 p + b_2}$$

where $b_1 = 0.01$, $b_2 = 1.0$, and H is chosen so as to simplify the realization. Find the sensitivity matrix defined in Sec. 2.5 in terms of the coefficients b_1 and b_2.

4.5 Find a realization using a single INIC for the following multiple-input transfer function:

$$V_2 = \frac{H_1 V_1 + H_2 p V_2 + H_3 p^2 V_3}{p^2 + 0.1p + 1}$$

Choose the constants H_1, H_2, and H_3 so as to simplify the resulting realization.

4.6 The network realization shown in Fig. 4.22 requires an INIC as the active element. Modify the realization so that a controlled source is used instead of the INIC.

4.7 If, as shown in Sec. 4.3, a controlled source is used to replace an NIC in a realization that is optimally insensitive to the gain of the NIC, will the resulting realization be optimally insensitive to the gain of the controlled source? Justify your answer.

4.8 Convert the realization obtained in Prob. 4.4 to a realization with a controlled source by the method of Sec. 4.3. Find the sensitivity matrix for the resulting realization.

4.9 Use the network configuration shown in Fig. 4.24 with the transfer function given in (28) to obtain an optimally insensitive realization for the following network function:

$$\frac{I_2}{I_1} = \frac{Hp}{p^2 + ap + 1}$$

Choose the constant H so as to simplify the resulting realization.

4.10 Use the network configuration shown in Fig. 4.25 with the transfer function given in (29) to obtain an optimally insensitive realization for the following network function:

$$\frac{V_2}{I_1} = \frac{Hp}{p^2 + ap + 1}$$

4.11 Use the nonideal voltage-controlled voltage source shown in Fig. P4.11 to find a circuit configuration that realizes an (ideal) INIC with unity gain.

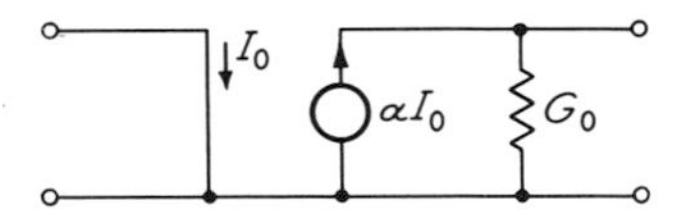

Figure P4.11

4.12 Find the transmission parameters of the circuit shown in Fig. P4.12. In the limit as the alphas of the transistors approach unity, what properties does this device have?*

* J. G. Linvill, *op. cit.*

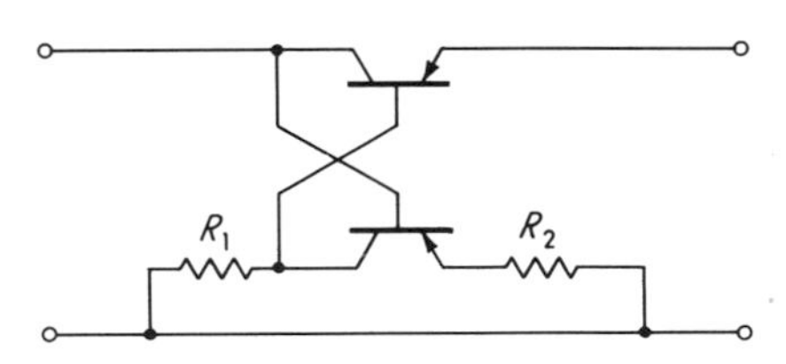

Figure P4.12

Chapter 5 Gyrator realizations

In the last two chapters, two general methods of realizing active RC circuits were discussed. The first of these used controlled sources as the active elements, the second used NICs. In this chapter we shall introduce the use of still another type of active device, the gyrator, and discuss its application in the realization of active RC circuits. We have already made references to the gyrator. For example, when we discussed the "sum" case of polynomial decomposition in Sec. 2.7, a simple realization using a gyrator was given as an example of such a decomposition (see Fig. 2.18). In this chapter we shall study gyrators and their application to active RC circuit realizations in detail. Thus, in Sec. 5.1 we will define the different types of gyrators and illustrate their properties. In Sec. 5.2 we shall present some approaches to the general theory of active RC circuit realizations using gyrators. In Sec. 5.3 we shall discuss the realization of some of the commonly encountered second-degree transfer functions. Finally, in Sec. 5.4 some methods of realizing gyrators will be presented.

5.1 Properties of the gyrator

A gyrator is a two-port device characterized by the property that the impedance seen at either port is the *reciprocal* (times a constant) of the impedance connected to the other port. Necessary and sufficient conditions for such behavior may be defined in terms of the $ABCD$ parameters for the two-port as

$$A = D = 0 \qquad \frac{B}{C} > 0 \tag{1}$$

where B and C are real, but may be positive or negative. Thus, such devices may be characterized by operating points that lie in the first and third quadrants of the BC plane, a plane with values of B plotted along the abscissa and values of C plotted along the ordinate. The BC plane and the regions of possible gyrator behavior are shown in Fig. 5.1.

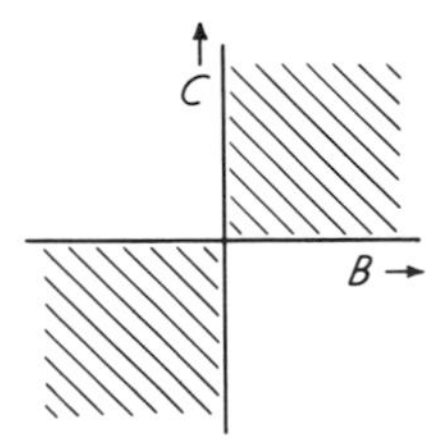

***Figure 5.1** Regions of gyration action in the BC plane.*

The conditions for a gyrator given in (1) may also be defined by the equations

$$\begin{aligned} I_1 &= G_1 V_2 \\ I_2 &= -G_2 V_1 \end{aligned} \tag{2}$$

where G_1 and G_2 are real and positive.* A consideration of actual realizations for gyrators leads one to consider, as a first type of gyrator, the case in which G_1 and G_2 are equal. If we let $G = G_1 = G_2$, we may define an *ideal gyrator* by the transmission parameters

$$\begin{bmatrix} 0 & \frac{1}{G} \\ G & 0 \end{bmatrix} \tag{3}$$

where G is referred to as the *gyration conductance*.† The loci of operating points for such a device are shown in Fig. 5.2. A circuit symbol for the ideal gyrator is shown in Fig. 5.3.

* The case in which G_1 and G_2 are real and negative simply represents an interchange of ports and therefore exhibits no different properties from this case.

† The ideal gyrator as a network element was first defined by B. D. H. Tellegen, The Gyrator, a New Electric Network Element, *Phillips Res. Rept.*, vol. 3, pp. 81–101, April, 1948.

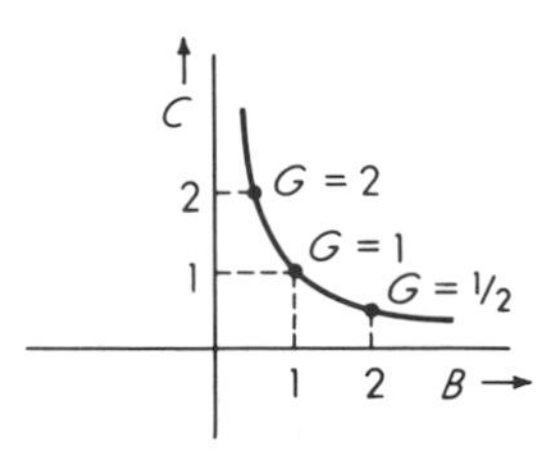

***Figure 5.2** Locus of operating points for the ideal gyrator.*

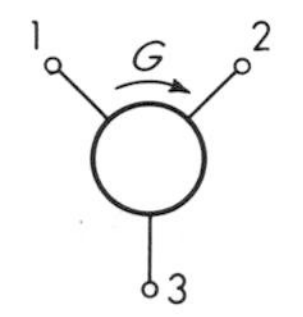

Figure 5.3 Circuit symbol for an ideal gyrator.

A second type of gyrator may be considered for the case in which G_1 and G_2 of (2) are not equal. Such a device will be referred to as a *perfect gyrator* and may be defined by the transmission parameters*

$$\begin{bmatrix} 0 & \dfrac{1}{G_2} \\ G_1 & 0 \end{bmatrix} \tag{4}$$

The loci of operating points for the case in which G_1 is varied and G_2 is held fixed and for the case in which G_2 is varied and G_1 is held fixed are shown in Fig. 5.4. A circuit symbol for the perfect gyrator is shown in Fig. 5.5.

The properties of gyrators may be determined in more detail by considering the general properties of the class of two-port networks characterized by the restriction on their transmission parameters that $A = D = 0$. First let us consider reciprocity. For such a class of devices, the condition

* This is an analogy to the designations used for transformers, where a transformer defined by a single parameter is referred to as an "ideal" transformer, and a transformer defined by two parameters is called a "perfect" transformer. See N. Balabanian, "Fundamentals of Circuit Theory," chap. 9, Allyn and Bacon, Inc., Englewood Cliffs, N.J , 1961.

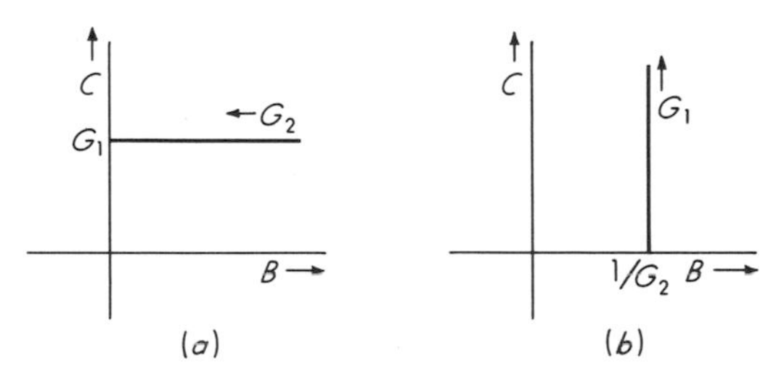

***Figure 5.4** (a) Locus of operating points for a perfect gyrator with G_1 constant. (b) Locus of operating points for a perfect gyrator with G_2 constant.*

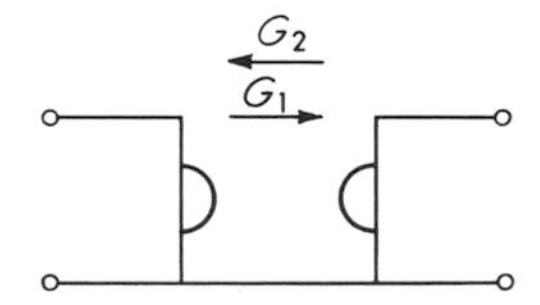

Figure 5.5 Circuit symbol for a perfect gyrator.

for reciprocity is

$$BC = -1 \tag{5}$$

The loci of all points on the BC plane satisfying (5) are shown in Fig. 5.6. If these loci are compared with the regions of gyration action shown in Fig. 5.1, it is easily verified that the gyrator is a nonreciprocal device.

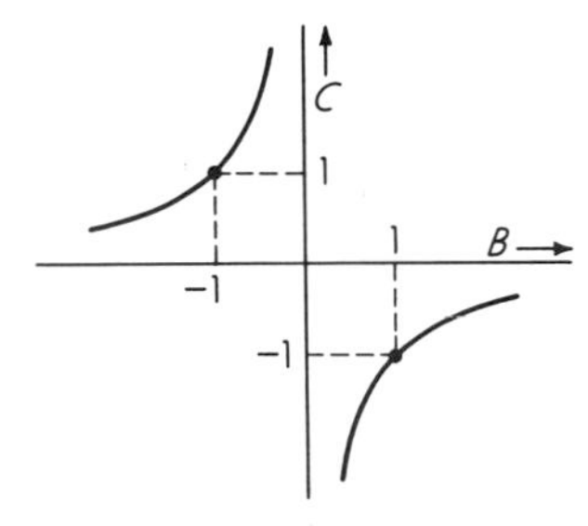

Figure 5.6 Loci of reciprocal two-port devices.

Now let us consider the impedance transformation properties of this class of devices. We may define an impedance transformation constant k_z as indicated in Fig. 5.7. It should be noted that, unlike the impedance

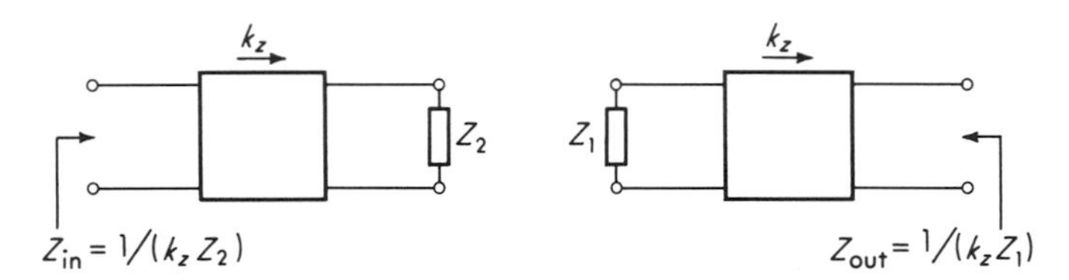

Figure 5.7 The impedance transformation constant k_z.

transformation properties of the class of two-port devices (including the NIC) discussed in the last chapter, the impedance transformation properties for this class of networks are the same in both directions. It is easily shown that $k_z = C/B$. A plot of lines of constant k_z is given in Fig. 5.8.

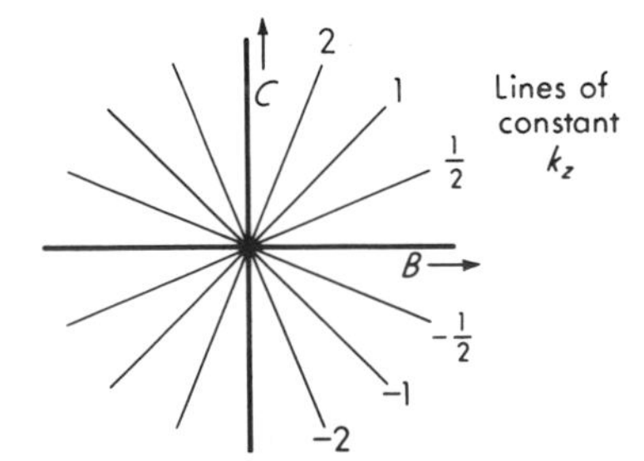

Figure 5.8 Loci of constant impedance transformation.

In a similar manner we may define a power transformation constant k_p as shown in Fig. 5.9. For this class of networks, $k_p = 1/BC$. A plot of lines of constant k_p is given in Fig. 5.10. From (3) we see that k_p for the ideal

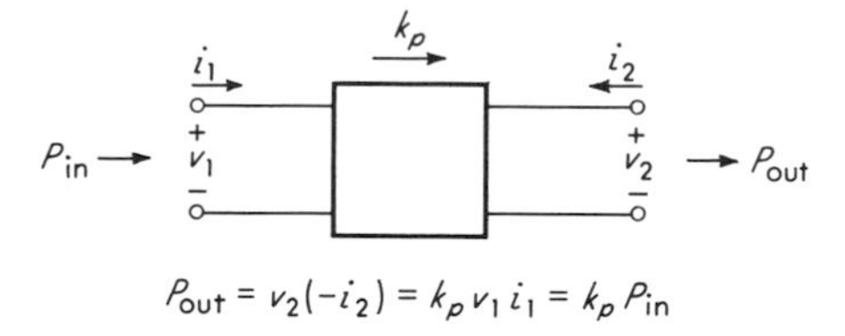

***Figure 5.9** The power transformation constant k_p.*

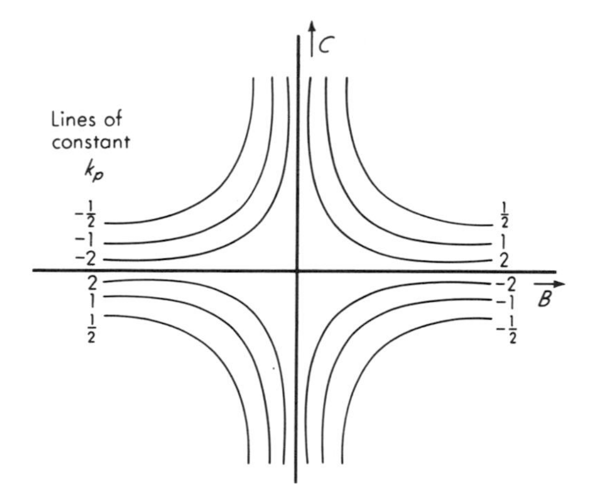

***Figure 5.10** Loci of constant power transformation.*

gyrator is unity. Therefore, the power flow into port 1 equals the power flow out of port 2. Thus, we see that the ideal gyrator, in terms of the power supplied to its ports, is a lossless device. The actual realization of a gyrator, however, inevitably requires the use of active elements. As a result, we shall consider it as an active element. In Fig. 5.11, the loci of constant k_z, constant k_p, and the loci of operating points for the ideal gyrator have been superimposed. It is readily apparent that as the gyration constant G is varied, the impedance transformation properties of the ideal gyrator change. Similarly, for the perfect gyrator, where G_1 is not equal to G_2, the power transfer characteristics of the device may be less than or greater than unity, depending on the relative values of G_1 and G_2. Thus, the perfect gyrator may act as an active or a passive device although categorically we shall consider it as an active one.

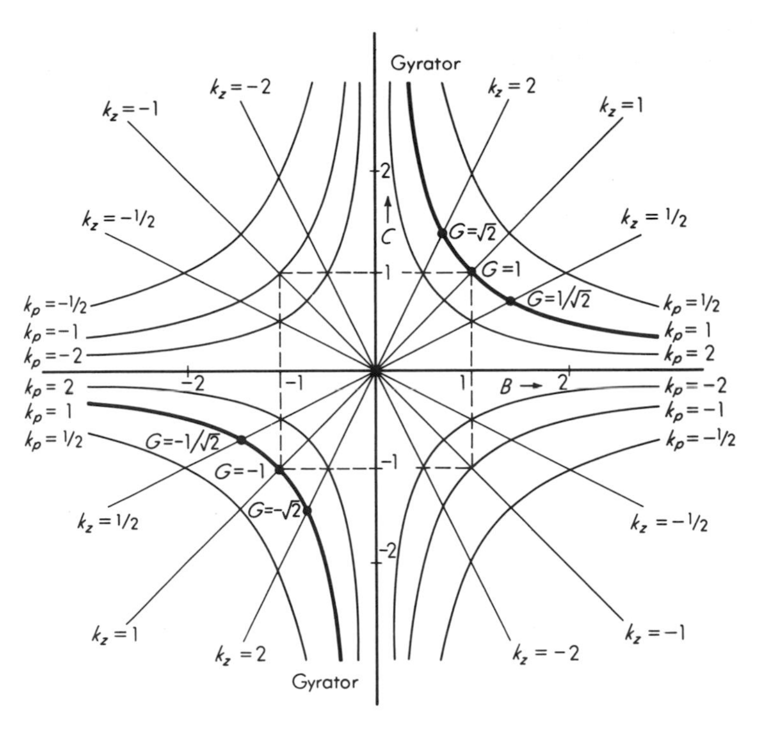

Figure 5.11 Characteristics of an ideal gyrator.

One of the characteristic properties of the three-terminal ideal gyrator shown in Fig. 5.3 and defined by the transmission parameters of (3) (which are based on the use of terminal 3 of the gyrator as a common ground for the two ports) is the fact that the device acts as an ideal gyrator independent of which terminal is used as the reference or ground terminal. To see this, consider the indefinite admittance matrix for the ideal gyrator. For the terminal numbering shown in Fig. 5.3, this is easily shown to be*

$$\begin{bmatrix} 0 & G & -G \\ -G & 0 & G \\ G & -G & 0 \end{bmatrix} \tag{6}$$

If terminal 3 is grounded, the admittance parameters of the resulting two-port network are found by deleting the third row and column of (6). The resulting device is a gyrator with gyration conductance G from terminal 1 to terminal 2. Similarly, if terminal 1 is grounded, the result is a gyrator with gyration conductance G from terminal 2 to terminal 3. Finally,

* See L. P. Huelsman, "Circuits, Matrices, and Linear Vector Spaces," chap. 3, McGraw-Hill Book Company, New York, 1963.

if terminal 2 is grounded, the result is a gyrator of gyration conductance G from terminal 1 to terminal 3. In each case, the grounded terminal forms the common terminal of the resulting two-port network.

Another property of the ideal gyrator which will be useful in future developments may be seen as follows: Consider an ideal gyrator with a

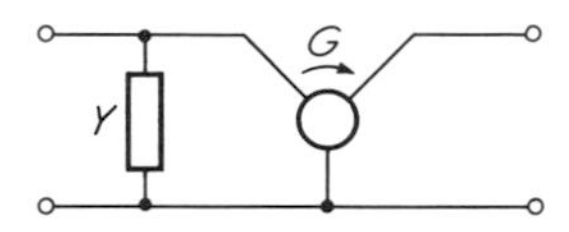

***Figure 5.12** An ideal gyrator and a shunt admittance.*

shunt admittance Y connected across its input port as shown in Fig. 5.12. The transmission parameter matrix of the overall two-port network is

$$\begin{bmatrix} 0 & \frac{1}{G} \\ G & \frac{Y}{G} \end{bmatrix} \tag{7}$$

Now consider an ideal gyrator with an impedance connected in series with

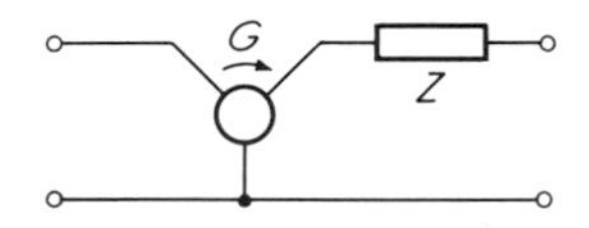

***Figure 5.13** An ideal gyrator and a series impedance.*

its output port as shown in Fig. 5.13. The transmission parameters of this network are given by the matrix

$$\begin{bmatrix} 0 & \frac{1}{G} \\ G & GZ \end{bmatrix} \tag{8}$$

Comparing (7) and (8), we conclude that the two networks have identical properties under the condition

$$Y = G^2Z \tag{9}$$

Thus, as shown in Fig. 5.14, a gyrator and a series inductor of value L

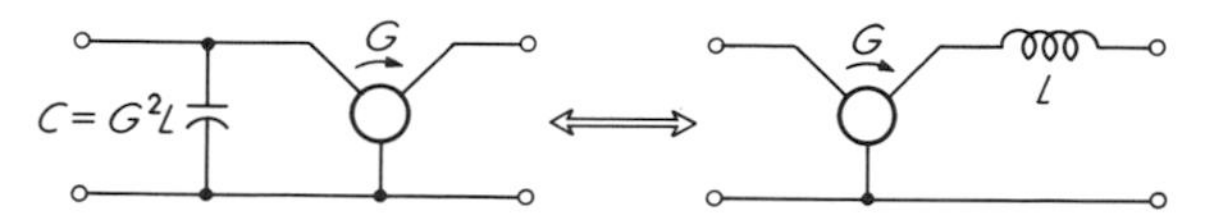

***Figure 5.14** A pair of equivalent two-port networks.*

may be replaced by a gyrator with a shunt capacitor of value C, where $C = G^2L$.

One final property of gyrators which will be of use to us results from the cascade connection of two gyrators. If two ideal gyrators, both of gyration conductance G, are connected in cascade, the transmission parameter matrix of the resulting two-port network is

$$\begin{bmatrix} 1 & 0 \\ 0 & 1 \end{bmatrix} \tag{10}$$

This is also the transmission parameter matrix of an ideal transformer of unity turns ratio. Thus, we may conclude that, as shown in Fig. 5.15, the

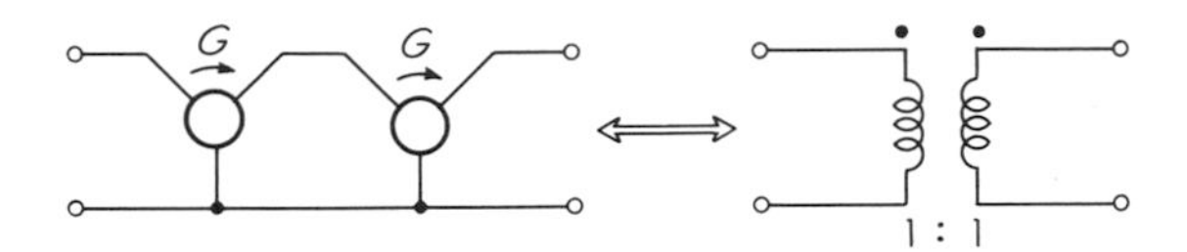

Figure 5.15 A pair of equivalent two-port networks.

cascade connection of two gyrators is equivalent to an ideal transformer. We shall see an application of this property in the next section.

It should be noted that it is also possible to define an ideal gyrator with a gyration admittance that is a function of the complex-frequency variable.* Such a device may be useful in specialized applications.

5.2 *The general theory of gyrator realizations*

As an introduction to the general properties of RC-gyrator network realizations, let us consider the case where an arbitrary four-port network described by its y parameters has an ideal gyrator defined by (3) connected

* L. P. Huelsman, *op. cit.*, Appendix B.

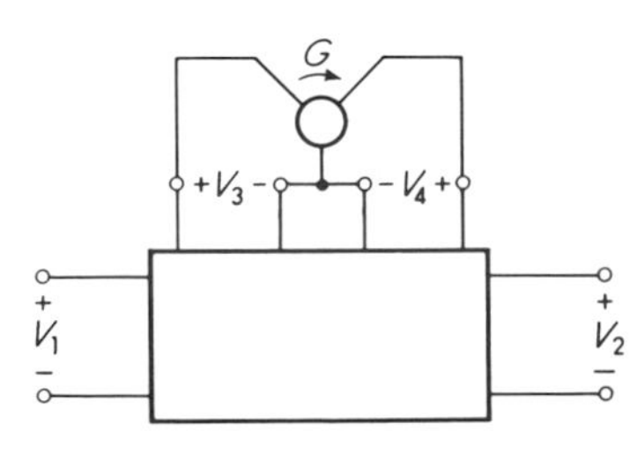

Figure 5.16 A four-port network and an ideal gyrator.

between ports 3 and 4, as shown in Fig. 5.16. The y parameters of the resulting two-port network may be expressed in terms of the y parameters of the four-port network, and the gyration constant G of the gyrator as

$$\begin{bmatrix} I_1 \\ I_2 \end{bmatrix} = \left\{ \begin{bmatrix} y_{11} & y_{12} \\ y_{21} & y_{22} \end{bmatrix} - \begin{bmatrix} y_{13} & y_{14} \\ y_{23} & y_{24} \end{bmatrix} \begin{bmatrix} y_{33} & y_{34} + G \\ y_{43} - G & y_{44} \end{bmatrix}^{-1} \begin{bmatrix} y_{31} & y_{32} \\ y_{41} & y_{42} \end{bmatrix} \right\} \begin{bmatrix} V_1 \\ V_2 \end{bmatrix} \tag{11}$$

The reduction of the above matrix expression leads to a relatively complicated and useless set of parameters. A significant feature of these parameters, however, is that they are *not* bilinear with respect to the gyration constant G of the gyrator. This is easily seen from the fact that the determinant of the middle matrix in the triple-matrix product produces an expression which is quadratic in G. Thus, the propositions based on the bilinear nature of network functions developed in Chap. 2 are, in general, not applicable to this class of networks. Several specific network configurations involving gyrators, however, may involve only G^2. In these cases the decomposition may be treated as linear with respect to G^2. The polynomial decomposition techniques described in Chap. 2 are readily applicable to such cases.

Two major uses may be made of gyrators in network realizations. The first of these is the use of gyrators and capacitors to replace inductors. Since a gyrator effectively inverts an immittance, a capacitive termination at one port of such a device results in the immittance of an inductance being present at the other port. Since the gyrator may be used to multiply as well as to invert immittance, it is theoretically possible to "gyrate" microfarads of capacitance into hundreds of henrys of effective inductance. In addition, such a synthetic inductor may be more usable than a real inductor since it will have the Q of the capacitor which was used as a termination, and it is usually possible to obtain higher Q's in capacitors than in inductors. Such an approach is attractive for producing filter characteristics at very low frequencies without having to use large values of reactive elements.

In using gyrator-capacitor elements for direct replacement of inductors there are two cases of interest. The first of these is the case in which the inductor to be replaced has one terminal grounded. In this situation, a gyrator and a capacitor, both grounded, may be used as a direct replacement as shown in Fig. 5.17. A more difficult situation occurs when the

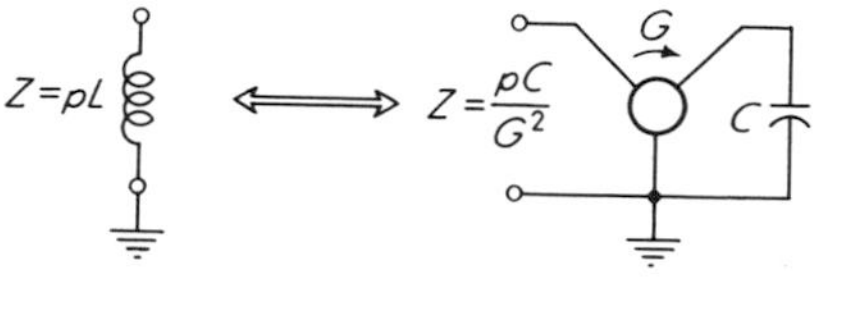

$Z = pL \iff Z = \dfrac{pC}{G^2}$

***Figure 5.17** A realization for a grounded inductor.*

inductor that is to be replaced has neither end grounded. The utilization of an ungrounded gyrator in such a case is usually not practical. Instead, a configuration of two grounded gyrators and a capacitor may be employed. To see this, first let us consider the two-port network consisting of a single series inductor of value L, shown in Fig. 5.18*a*. An equivalent two-port

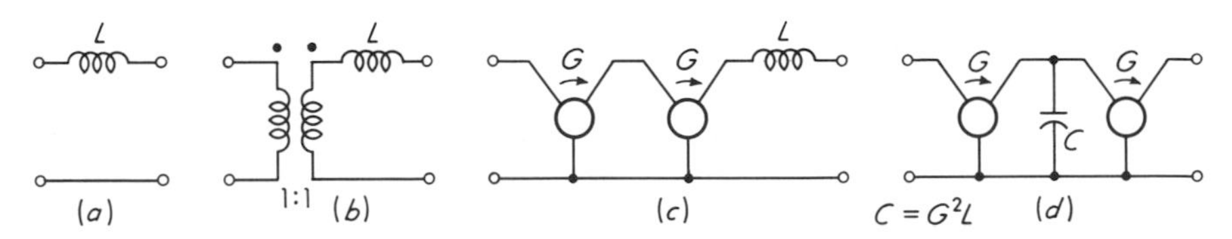

Figure 5.18 ***A realization for an ungrounded inductor.***

network may be formed by connecting an ideal transformer of unity turns ratio in cascade with one end of the inductor as shown in Fig. 5.18*b*. As was shown in the last section, such an ideal tranformer may be replaced by a cascade connection of two ideal gyrators as shown in Fig. 5.18*c*. Finally, as was also shown in the last section, the gyrator on the right and the series inductor may be replaced by a shunt capacitor and gyrator, yielding the network configuration shown in Fig. 5.18*d*. Thus, we see that an ungrounded inductor may be realized by a connection of two gyrators and a capacitor, all of which are grounded.*

For second-degree realizations using the direct substitution of capacitors and gyrators for inductors, the coefficients of the polynomials of the network functions will have the form indicated in properties 3 and 4 of Sec. 2.5 with respect to the passive elements and with respect to G^2 (the gyration conductance squared). Thus, the sensitivities of the coefficients will be less than or equal to unity in magnitude. An example of the use of gyrators and capacitors to replace inductors follows.

Example 5.1 As an example of the use of gyrator-capacitor elements for the direct replacement of inductors, consider the bandpass *RLC* circuit

* A. G. J. Holt and J. Taylor, Method of Replacing Ungrounded Inductors by Grounded Gyrators, *Electron. Letters*, vol. 1, no. 4, p. 105, June, 1965. For the case of a perfect gyrator, in which $G_1 \neq G_2$, it is pointed out in D. F. Sheahan, Gyrator-flotation Circuit, *Electron. Letters*, vol. 3, no. 1, pp. 39–40, that the resulting effect may be quite sensitive to variations in G_1 and G_2. The circuit may also be used to realize a pair of coupled coils. A second capacitor is required in this case. See B. D. Anderson, W. New, and R. W. Newcomb, Proposed Adjustable Tuned Circuits for Microelectronic Structures, *Proc. IEEE*, vol. 54, no. 3, p. 411, March, 1965. A circuit that requires only three operational amplifiers can also be used to provide an ungrounded inductor. See G. J. Deboo, Application of a Gyrator-type Circuit to Realize Ungrounded Inductors, *IEEE Trans. Circuit Theory*, vol. CT-14, no. 1, pp. 101–102, March, 1967.

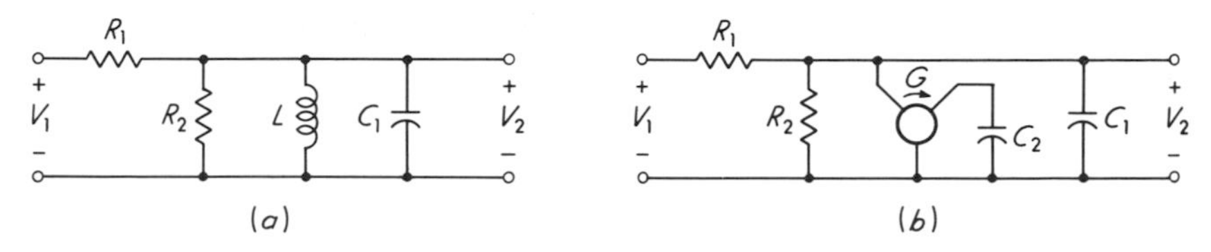

Figure 5.19 ***A bandpass realization.***

shown in Fig. 5.19*a*. The gyrator realization for this is shown in Fig. 5.19*b*. It has the following open-circuit voltage transfer function:

$$\frac{V_2}{V_1} = \frac{pS_1G_1}{p^2 + pS_1(G_1 + G_2) + G^2S_1S_2}$$

where S_1 and S_2 are the values of reciprocal capacitance. If we let $G_1 = G_2$ and write the transfer function in the form

$$\frac{V_2}{V_1} = \frac{pH}{p^2 + b_1p + b_2}$$

then, following the methods of Sec. 2.5 (see properties 3 and 4), the sensitivity matrix is easily shown to be

$$\begin{bmatrix} \Delta b_1^{(n)} \\ \Delta b_2^{(n)} \end{bmatrix} = \begin{bmatrix} \frac{1}{2} & \frac{1}{2} & 1 & 0 & 0 \\ 0 & 0 & 1 & 1 & 1 \end{bmatrix} \begin{bmatrix} \Delta G_1^{(n)} \\ \Delta G_2^{(n)} \\ \Delta S_1^{(n)} \\ \Delta S_2^{(n)} \\ \Delta G^{2(n)} \end{bmatrix}$$

Thus, it is independent of the values of b_1 and b_2 and thus independent of the Q of the realization.

One of the attractive features of *RC*-gyrator realizations resulting from the direct replacement of inductors by capacitor-gyrator elements is the fact that a vast range of results pertaining to passive *RLC* synthesis of network functions becomes directly available to the design of *RC*-gyrator networks. Of special interest are designs for flat-passband *LC* ladder filters operating between resistive source and load. If such a filter has the property that at the frequencies of minimum loss over the passband the source delivers its maximum available power into the load, then, as a first order approximation, the filter has zero magnitude sensitivity to component variations.* As an example of such a network let us again consider

* H. J. Orchard, Inductorless Filters, *Electron. Letters*, vol. 2, no. 6, pp. 224–225, June, 1966. See also J. Gorski-Popiel, Horowitz Minimum Sensitivity Decomposition, *Electron. Letters*, vol. 2, no. 9, pp. 334–335, Sept., 1966.

Fig. 5.19*a*. The voltage transfer function for the network shown in the figure, assuming $G_1 = G_2 = G_0$, is

$$N(p) = \frac{V_2}{V_1} = \frac{pG_0/C_1}{p^2 + p^2G_0/C_1 + 1/LC_1}$$

If we determine the classical sensitivity at resonance ($\omega_0 = 1/\sqrt{LC_1}$) with respect to variations in the inductor and the capacitor, we obtain

$$S_L{}^N(j\omega_0) = \left.\frac{dN/N}{dL/L}\right|_{p=j\omega_0} = -jQ$$

$$S_{C_1}{}^N(j\omega_0) = \left.\frac{dN/N}{dC_1/C_1}\right|_{p=j\omega_0} = -jQ$$

where Q ($= \omega_0C_1/2G_0$) is the Q of the network. In Sec. 2.1 it was shown that the real part of the classical sensitivity gives the normalized change in the magnitude of the network function. Thus, we see that for this type of network

$$\left.\frac{d|N|/|N|}{dL/L}\right|_{p=j\omega_0} = \left.\frac{d|N|/|N|}{dC_1/C_1}\right|_{p=j\omega_0} = 0$$

If the inductor of this network is realized by means of a gyrator and a capacitor, then (as shown in Fig. 5.19*b*) since $L = C_2/G^2$, we see that

$$\frac{d|N|/|N|}{d(G^2)/G^2} = 0$$

Thus, we see that we have obtained zero magnitude sensitivity with respect to changes in the gyration constant. This result is, of course, the same as that given by the sensitivity matrix as determined above for this example. It should be noted that, in some applications, it may be more desirable to minimize the phase sensitivity, in which case this type of realization might not be as attractive.

A second use of gyrators is their application to direct synthesis procedures. No practical general realization technique has yet been presented, but some specialized techniques have appeared in the literature. As an example of such a technique, consider the cascade of two passive RC net-

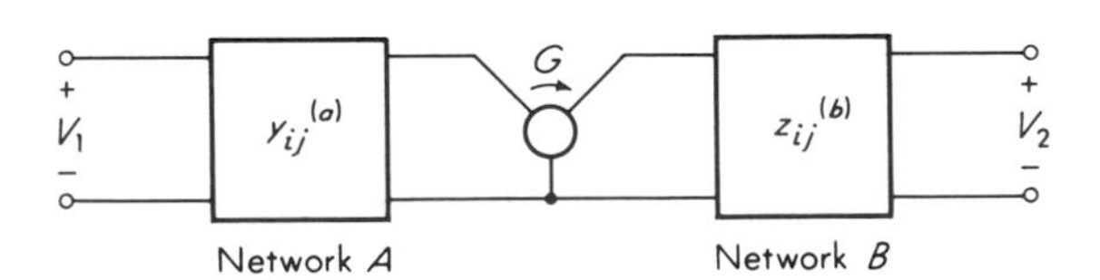

Figure 5.20 A cascade network configuration.

works separated by a gyrator as shown in Fig. 5.20. This cascade may be used to realize a certain class of voltage transfer function.* Let the network designated as network A in the figure be defined by its y parameters $y_{ij}^{(a)}$. Similarly, let network B be defined by its z parameters $z_{ij}^{(b)}$. The open-circuit voltage transfer function for the overall network is

$$\frac{V_2}{V_1} = \frac{N(p)}{D(p)} = \frac{-Gy_{21}^{(a)}z_{21}^{(b)}}{y_{22}^{(a)} + G^2z_{11}^{(b)}} \tag{12}$$

where G is the gyration constant of the gyrator. It is easily seen that the denominator is linear in G^2. Now let us assume that the poles of $y_{21}^{(a)}$ and $y_{22}^{(a)}$ are the same and that the poles of $z_{11}^{(b)}$ and $z_{21}^{(b)}$ are also the same. Then we may write

$$\begin{aligned} y_{22}^{(a)} &= \frac{n_{22}^{(a)}}{d^{(a)}} \qquad & z_{11}^{(b)} &= \frac{n_{11}^{(b)}}{d^{(b)}} \\ y_{21}^{(a)} &= \frac{n_{21}^{(a)}}{d^{(a)}} \qquad & z_{21}^{(b)} &= \frac{n_{21}^{(b)}}{d^{(b)}} \end{aligned} \tag{13}$$

Substituting these relations into (12), we obtain

$$\frac{V_2}{V_1} = \frac{N(p)}{D(p)} = \frac{-Gn_{21}^{(a)}n_{21}^{(b)}}{n_{22}^{(a)}d^{(b)} + G^2n_{11}^{(b)}d^{(a)}} \tag{14}$$

Thus, we see that we must consider the decomposition of $D(p)$ into the sum of two polynomials $n_{22}^{(a)}d^{(b)}$ and $G^2n_{11}^{(b)}d^{(a)}$, both of the latter having only negative-real zeros. Such a decomposition may be optimized by the methods discussed in Sec. 2.7. For such an optimum decomposition, the denominator of (14) must have the form

$$D(p) = a^2(p) + K^2b^2(p) \tag{15}$$

If we let the numerator of the desired voltage transfer function be expressed as a product of factors, we may write

$$N(p) = KN_1(p)N_2(p) \tag{16}$$

The original voltage transfer function may now be expressed as

$$\frac{V_2}{V_1} = \frac{N(p)}{D(p)} = \frac{-KN_1(p)N_2(p)}{a^2(p) + K^2b^2(p)} = \frac{-KN_1(p)N_2(p)/b(p)a(p)}{a(p)/b(p) + K^2b(p)/a(p)} \tag{17}$$

It was shown in Sec. 2.7 that $a(p)/b(p)$ is realizable as a passive RC driving-point admittance and that $b(p)/a(p)$ is realizable as a passive RC

* B. A. Shenoi, Practical Realization of a Gyrator Circuit and *RC*-gyrator Filters, *IEEE Trans. Circuit Theory*, vol. CT-12, no. 3, pp. 374–380, Sept., 1965.

driving-point impedance. Thus, comparing (12) and (17), we see that if we let

$$\begin{aligned} y_{22}^{(a)} &= \frac{a(p)}{b(p)} & z_{11}^{(b)} &= \frac{b(p)}{a(p)} \\ y_{21}^{(a)} &= \frac{N_1(p)}{b(p)} & z_{21}^{(b)} &= \frac{N_2(p)}{a(p)} \\ & G = K \end{aligned} \tag{18}$$

the desired voltage transfer function is realized. It should be noted that it may be possible to realize the desired transfer immittances only within a multiplicative constant. Thus, the gain constant of the numerator of (14) may not be equal to the constant K in the numerator of (17). Obviously, any convenient factoring of $N(p)$ into the product $N_1(p)N_2(p)$ may be chosen since the zeros of passive RC transfer immittances are relatively unrestricted. If complex conjugate zeros are required, bridged-T or twin-T networks will be required. A discussion of these will be given in the following chapter.

5.3 *The second-degree case*

In this section we shall illustrate the RC-gyrator synthesis technique introduced in the last section for some specific second-degree network functions. As a first illustration, we will consider the realization of a low-pass open-circuit frequency-normalized voltage transfer function of the form

$$\frac{V_2}{V_1} = \frac{N(p)}{D(p)} = \frac{H}{p^2 + 2ap + 1} \tag{19}$$

where $0 < a < 1$. The denominator polynomial of (19) may be decomposed according to the procedure given in Sec. 2.7. Thus, we obtain

$$D(p) = (p + a)^2 + (1 - a^2) \tag{20}$$

From (18) we see that the parameters of the component networks may be found to be

$$\begin{aligned} y_{22}^{(a)} &= p + a & z_{11}^{(b)} &= \frac{1}{p + a} \\ y_{21}^{(a)} &= H_1 & z_{21}^{(b)} &= \frac{H_2}{p + a} \end{aligned} \tag{21}$$

where H_1 and H_2 are constants resulting from the realization of the transfer immittances and where the nominal value of G is assumed to be $\sqrt{1 - a^2}$.

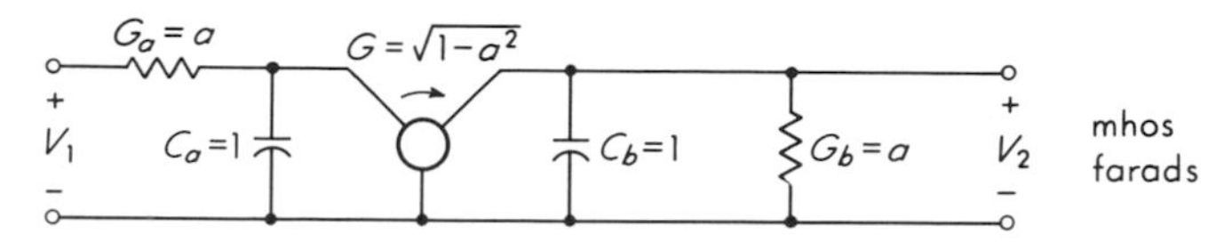

Figure 5.21 A low-pass network realization.

A network realization incorporating the y and z parameters of (21) is shown in Fig. 5.21. For this network the actual voltage transfer function is

$$\frac{V_2}{V_1} = \frac{a\sqrt{1-a^2}}{(p+a)^2 + (1-a^2)} \tag{22}$$

To permit a comparison of this realization with the realizations for comparable low-pass networks made in previous chapters, let us consider the synthesis of the voltage transfer function

$$\frac{V_2}{V_1} = \frac{H}{p^2 + b_1 p + b_2} \tag{23}$$

In terms of the elements shown in Fig. 5.21, the voltage transfer function may be written in the form

$$\frac{V_2}{V_1} = \frac{GG_aS_aS_b}{p^2 + p(G_aS_a + G_bS_b) + (G_aG_b + G^2)S_aS_b} \tag{24}$$

The following properties may be noted with respect to this transfer function:

1. It is bilinear with respect to G^2 and with respect to the passive elements.
2. The decomposition of the denominator with respect to G^2 is a sum decomposition which is optimized by means of the procedure given in Sec. 2.7.
3. Since the denominator decomposition is of the type given in case 7 of Table 2.1, the realization is stable for all values of G.
4. The low-frequency (passband) gain is $GG_a/(G_aG_b + G^2)$. Thus, the constant H in (23) is positive.

The following comments apply to the elements of the sensitivity matrix that results for the realization:

1. The sensitivities for the b_1 coefficient of (23) with respect to the elements G_a, G_b, S_a, and S_b are positive and less than unity (see property 4, Sec. 2.5).
2. The sensitivities for the b_2 coefficient of (23) with respect to the elements S_a and S_b are unity; with respect to G^2 and to the elements G_a and G_b, they are positive and less than unity (see properties 3 and 4, Sec. 2.5).

The above conclusions are easily verified by an example.

Example 5.2 As an example of the use of the network shown in Fig. 5.21 to realize a low-pass function by the decomposition shown as case 7 of Table 2.1, consider the maximally-flat-magnitude voltage transfer function

$$\frac{V_2}{V_1} = \frac{H}{p^2 + \sqrt{2}\,p + 1}$$

A suitable choice of element values is

$$\begin{aligned} G_a &= \frac{1}{\sqrt{2}} \text{ mho} \qquad & S_a &= 1 \text{ daraf} \\ G_b &= \frac{1}{\sqrt{2}} \text{ mho} \qquad & S_b &= 1 \text{ daraf} \\ & & G &= \frac{1}{\sqrt{2}} \text{ mho} \end{aligned} \tag{25}$$

The sensitivity matrix for such a realization is easily found by the techniques of Sec. 2.5. Thus, in terms of the coefficients of (23), we obtain

$$\begin{bmatrix} \Delta b_1^{(n)} \\ \\ \Delta b_2^{(n)} \end{bmatrix} = \begin{bmatrix} \frac{1}{2} & \frac{1}{2} & \frac{1}{2} & \frac{1}{2} & 0 \\ \\ \frac{1}{2} & \frac{1}{2} & 1 & 1 & \frac{1}{2} \end{bmatrix} \begin{bmatrix} \Delta G_a^{(n)} \\ \Delta G_b^{(n)} \\ \Delta S_a^{(n)} \\ \Delta S_b^{(n)} \\ \Delta G^{2(n)} \end{bmatrix} \tag{26}$$

For this realization, the constant H of (23) is 0.5. Thus, the low-frequency (passband) gain is also 0.5.

The RC-gyrator cascade synthesis technique may also be used to realize a second-degree bandpass frequency-normalized open-circuit voltage transfer function of the form

$$\frac{V_2}{V_1} = \frac{Hp}{p^2 + 2ap + 1} \tag{27}$$

The optimum decomposition of (20) may again be applied. The parameters of the resulting component networks for the case in which $G = \sqrt{1 - a^2}$ thus become

$$\begin{aligned} y_{22}^{(a)} &= p + a \qquad & z_{11}^{(b)} &= \frac{1}{p + a} \\ y_{21}^{(a)} &= H_1 p \qquad & z_{21}^{(b)} &= \frac{H_2}{p + a} \end{aligned} \tag{28}$$

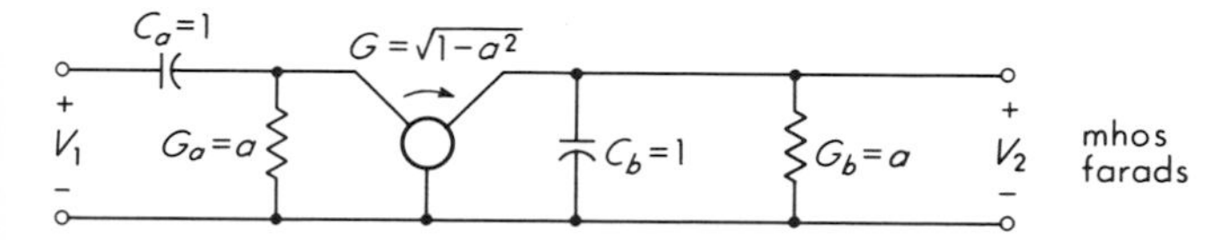

Figure 5.22 A bandpass network realization.

The realization for the network is shown in Fig. 5.22. For this circuit the actual voltage transfer function is

$$\frac{V_2}{V_1} = \frac{p\sqrt{1-a^2}}{(p+a)^2 + (1-a^2)} \tag{29}$$

This is of the general form

$$\frac{V_2}{V_1} = \frac{Hp}{p^2 + b_1p + b_2} \tag{30}$$

In terms of the elements shown in Fig. 5.22, the voltage transfer function may also be written in the form

$$\frac{V_2}{V_1} = \frac{pGS_b}{p^2 + p(G_aS_a + G_bS_b) + (G_aG_b + G^2)S_aS_b} \tag{31}$$

The following properties may be noted with respect to this transfer function:

1. It is bilinear with respect to G^2 and with respect to the passive elements.
2. The decomposition of the denominator with respect to G^2 is a sum decomposition which is optimized by means of the procedure given in Sec. 2.7.
3. Since the denominator decomposition is of the type given in case 7 of Table 2.1, the realization is stable for all values of G.
4. The gain at resonance is $GS_b/(G_aS_a + G_bS_b)$. Thus, the constant H in (30) is positive.
5. Changes in the gyration conductance G will change the resonant frequency without changing the bandwidth.

The following comments apply to the elements of the sensitivity matrix that results for the realization:

1. The sensitivities for the b_1 coefficient of (30) with respect to the elements G_a, G_b, S_a, and S_b are positive and less than unity (see property 4, Sec. 2.5).

2. The sensitivities for the b_2 coefficient of (30) with respect to the elements S_a and S_b are unity; with respect to G^2 and to the elements G_a and G_b, they are positive and less than unity (see properties 3 and 4, Sec. 2.5).

The above conclusions are easily verified by an example.

Example 5.3 As an example of the use of the network shown in Fig. 5.22 to realize a bandpass function by the decomposition shown as case 7 of Table 2.1, consider the transfer function

$$\frac{V_2}{V_1} = \frac{Hp}{p^2 + 0.1p + 1}$$

A suitable choice of element values is

$$\begin{array}{ll} G_a = 0.05 \text{ mho} & S_a = 1 \text{ daraf} \\ G_b = 0.05 \text{ mho} & S_b = 1 \text{ daraf} \\ \multicolumn{2}{c}{G^2 = 0.9975 \text{ (mho)}^2} \end{array} \qquad (32)$$

The sensitivity matrix relating the change in the coefficients b_1 and b_2 of (30) to the changes in the elements is

$$\begin{bmatrix} \Delta b_1^{(n)} \\ \Delta b_2^{(n)} \end{bmatrix} = \begin{bmatrix} 0.5 & 0.5 & 0.5 & 0.5 & 0 \\ 0.0025 & 0.0025 & 1.0 & 1.0 & 0.9975 \end{bmatrix} \begin{bmatrix} \Delta G_a^{(n)} \\ \Delta G_b^{(n)} \\ \Delta S_a^{(n)} \\ \Delta S_b^{(n)} \\ \Delta G^{2(n)} \end{bmatrix} \qquad (33)$$

For this realization, the constant H of (30) is approximately equal to 1. Thus, the gain in the passband is approximately 10.

Finally, it should be noted that it is possible to choose polynomial decompositions other than the optimum one if it is desired to realize the network functions with configurations other than those illustrated.

5.4 *Circuit realizations for gyrators*

In the preceding sections we have discussed the application of gyrators to the synthesis of network functions. In this section we shall discuss the realization of the gyrator itself. There are two basic ways in which a gyrator may be realized. The first of these is by means of one of the previously defined active devices. For example, it was pointed out in Chap. 4 that the NIC is a nonreciprocal device; therefore, with suitable compensation, it may be used to realize a gyrator. A circuit for doing this is shown

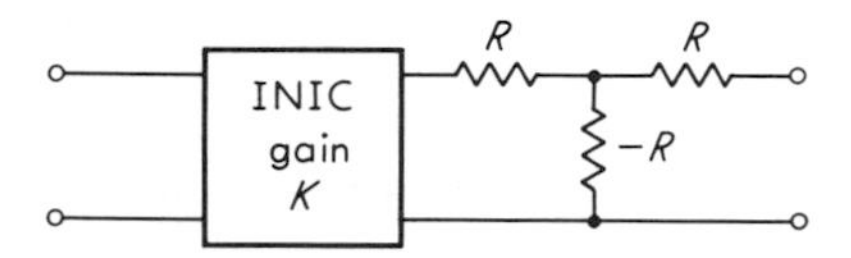

***Figure 5.23** A realization for an ideal gyrator.*

in Fig. 5.23.* The circuit requires the use of two NICs, one of which must be an INIC of gain K as shown; the other is simply used to produce the negative-valued resistance. Analysis of this circuit yields the transmission parameters

$$\begin{bmatrix} 0 & \frac{1}{G} \\ \frac{G}{K} & 0 \end{bmatrix} \tag{34}$$

If the gain K of the INIC is set equal to unity, this circuit realizes an ideal gyrator. Several variations of this circuit are possible. For example, if the

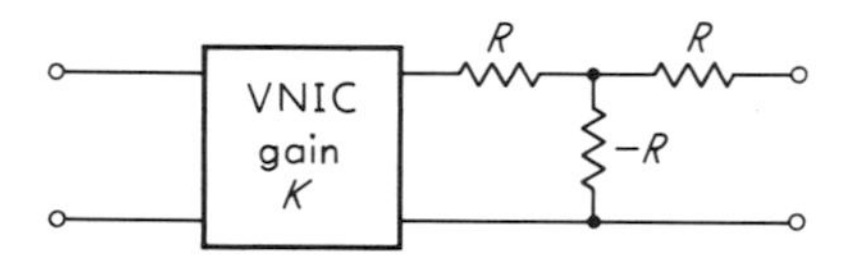

***Figure 5.24** A realization for an ideal gyrator.*

INIC is replaced by a VNIC as shown in Fig. 5.24, we obtain the transmission parameters

$$\begin{bmatrix} 0 & \frac{-1}{GK} \\ -G & 0 \end{bmatrix} \tag{35}$$

where K is the gain of the VNIC. For a unity-gain VNIC, such a device represents an ideal gyrator with a gyration conductance of the opposite polarity to the device shown in Fig. 5.3. Some other variations of this circuit are possible. For example, the T of resistors shown in Fig. 5.23 may be replaced by a "pi" network of resistors as shown in Fig. 5.25. The result, for a unity-gain INIC, is again a realization for an ideal gyrator. Other variations of this circuit are easily derived.

* Although this circuit configuration is usually attributed to H. W. Bode, only the T configuration of positive- and negative-valued resistors appears in Bode's book, "Network Analysis and Feedback Amplifier Design," D. Van Nostrand Company, Inc., Princeton, N.J., 1945. R. W. Newcomb has pointed out that this T also appears in A. C. Bartlett, Boucherot's Constant-current Networks and Their Relation to Electric Wave Filters, *J. IEE*, vol. 65, no. 363, pp. 373–376, March, 1927. It is, of course, the addition of the INIC to the T that produces the ideal gyrator action.

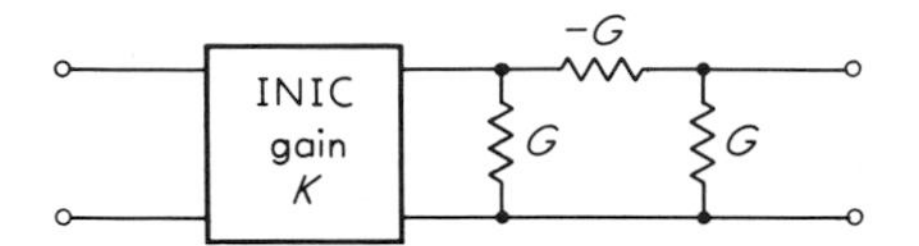

Figure 5.25 A realization for an ideal gyrator.

Another active device which may be used to realize a gyrator is an infinite-gain VCVS, that is, an operational amplifier. For example, consider the circuit involving two operational amplifiers shown in Fig. 5.26.*

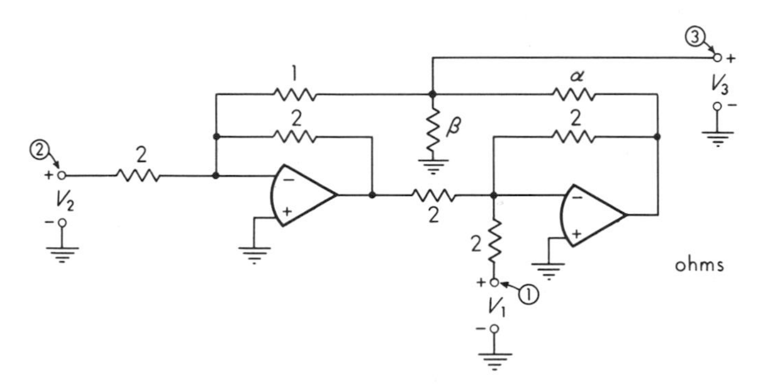

Figure 5.26 A circuit with two operational amplifiers.

Considering this circuit as a three-port network, we find that the admittance parameters are given by

$$\begin{bmatrix} I_1 \\ I_2 \\ I_3 \end{bmatrix} = \begin{bmatrix} \frac{1}{2} & 0 & 0 \\ 0 & \frac{1}{2} & 0 \\ \frac{1}{\alpha} & \frac{-1}{\alpha} & 1 + \frac{1}{\beta} - \frac{1}{\alpha} \end{bmatrix} \begin{bmatrix} V_1 \\ V_2 \\ V_3 \end{bmatrix} \tag{36}$$

If two such identical circuits are interconnected by paralleling two of

* A. S. Morse and L. P. Huelsman, Gyrator Realization Using Operational Amplifiers, *IEEE Trans. Circuit Theory*, vol. CT-11, no. 2, p. 277, June, 1964.

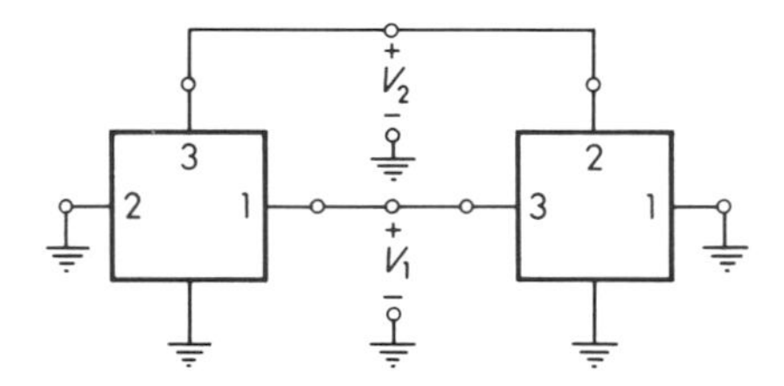

Figure 5.27 An interconnection of two of the circuits shown in Fig. 5.26.

their ports and shorting the third port in the manner indicated in Fig. 5.27, the resulting network may be considered as a two-port network, as indicated. For this overall network, the admittance parameters are defined by the equations

$$\begin{bmatrix} I_1 \\ I_2 \end{bmatrix} = \begin{bmatrix} \frac{3}{2} + \frac{1}{\beta} - \frac{1}{\alpha} & \frac{-1}{\alpha} \\ \frac{1}{\alpha} & \frac{3}{2} + \frac{1}{\beta} - \frac{1}{\alpha} \end{bmatrix} \begin{bmatrix} V_1 \\ V_2 \end{bmatrix} \tag{37}$$

If the constants α and β are chosen so as to make the terms on the main diagonal equal to zero, the result is an ideal gyrator with transmission parameters

$$\begin{bmatrix} 0 & \frac{-1}{G} \\ -G & 0 \end{bmatrix} \tag{38}$$

where $G = 1/\alpha$. An example of such a gyrator realization is given in Fig. 5.28. For the indicated choice of elements, the gyration constant G equals

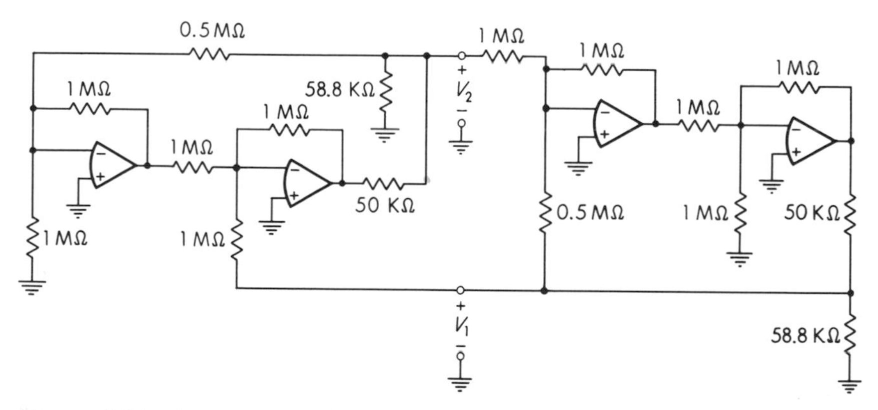

Figure 5.28 An operational amplifier realization for an ideal gyrator.

0.2×10^{-4}. Such a circuit will gyrate 1 μF of capacitance into 2500 henrys of inductance!

A second approach to the realization of gyrators is the use of basic physical active elements, for example, transistors. Several such realizations of gyrators have appeared in the literature. As an example of this

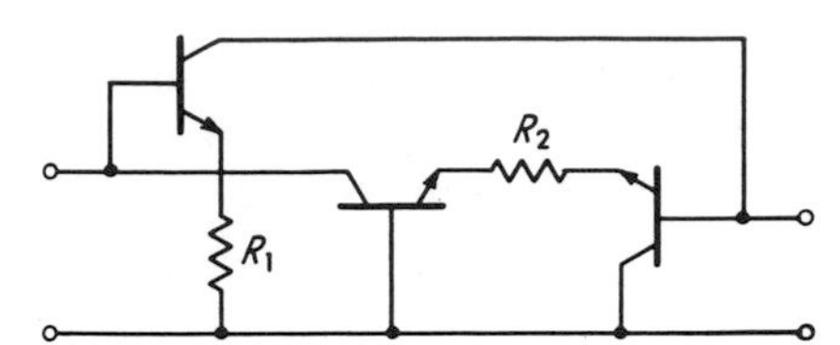

***Figure 5.29** A simple gyrator realization.*

type of realization, consider the circuit shown in Fig. 5.29.* For convenience in analyzing the circuit, only the dominant elements have been shown, and the details of the biasing networks have been deleted. It is readily verified that in the limit as the alphas of the transistors approach unity, the transmission parameters for this circuit become

$$\begin{bmatrix} 0 & -R_1 \\ \frac{-1}{R_2} & 0 \end{bmatrix} \tag{39}$$

Thus, for equal values of R_1 and R_2, this circuit realizes an ideal gyrator. Realizations involving many more active components than the one shown in Fig. 5.29 and which are more suitable for integration have also been reported in the literature. Such a realization is shown in Fig. 5.30.† It basically consists of two voltage-controlled current sources, satisfying the relations

$$\begin{aligned} V_1 &= -R_b I_2 \\ V_2 &= R_a I_1 \end{aligned}$$

A slightly modified version of this circuit has been integrated.‡ A photomicrograph of the integrated version is shown in the frontpiece of this book.

In addition to the circuit realizations for gyrators which have been

* B. A. Shenoi, A 3-transistor Gyrator Circuit with Variable Gyration Resistance, *Proc. 2nd Ann. Allerton Conf. Circuit and System Theory*, pp. 728–801, 1964. See also B. A. Shenoi, Practical Realization of a Gyrator Circuit and *RC*-Gyrator Filters, *IEEE Trans. Circuit Theory*, vol. CT-12, no. 3, pp. 374–380, Sept., 1965.

† T. N. Rao and R. W. Newcomb, Direct-coupled Gyrator Suitable for Integrated Circuits and Time Variation, *Electron. Letters*, vol. 2, no. 7, pp. 250–251, July, 1966. See also W. New and R. W. Newcomb, An Integratable Time-variable Gyrator, *Proc. IEEE*, vol. 53, no. 12, pp. 2161–2162, Dec., 1965. A realization utilizing eight active elements has been described in D. J. Sheahan and H. J. Orchard, Integratable Gyrator Using M.O.S. and Bipolar Transistors, *Electron. Letters*, vol. 2, no. 10, pp. 390–391, Oct., 1966. See also D. F. Sheahan and H. J. Orchard, High Quality Transistorized Gyrator, *Electron. Letters*, vol. 2, p. 274, July, 1966.

‡ H. T. Chua and R. W. Newcomb, Integrated Direct-coupled Gyrator, *Electron. Letters*, vol. 5, no. 5, pp. 182–184, May, 1967.

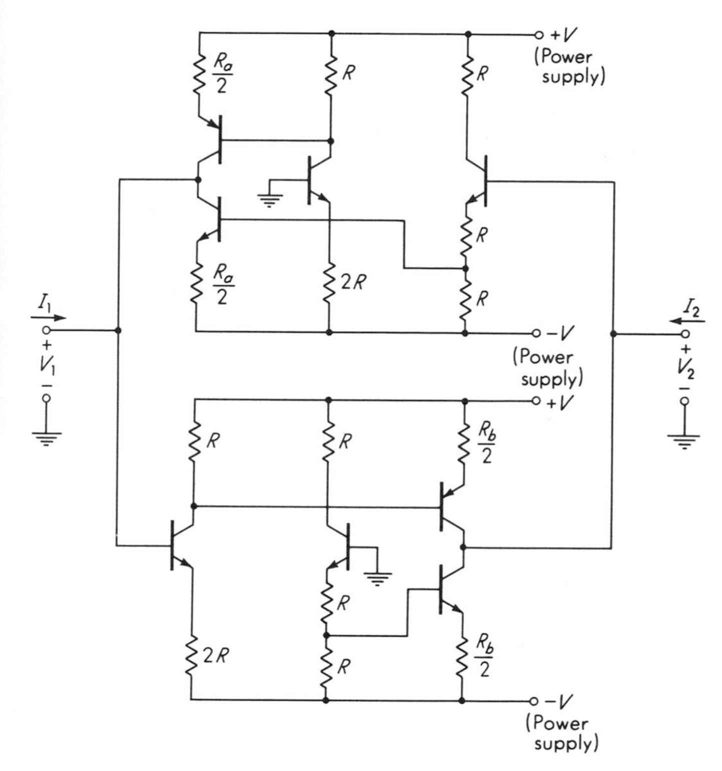

Figure 5.30 Schematic for a gyrator realization.

discussed in this section, it should be pointed out that other approaches may be used to produce gyration properties. For example, a gyrator has been produced using the Hall effect in a semiconductor.* Similarly, at microwave frequencies, the Faraday effect in ferrites has been applied.† In electromechanical devices, it has been shown that a piezoelectric device may be mechanically coupled to a piezomagnetic device to produce gyrator action, and several realizations of such effects have been reported.‡ Most of these approaches, however, yield gyrators with a limited range of application which may be far from ideal, especially with respect to the presence of parasitic elements.

* W. P. Mason, W. H. Hewitt, and R. F. Wick, Hall Effect Modulators and Gyrators Employing Magnetic Field Independent Orientations in Germanium, *J. Appl. Phys.*, vol. 24, pp. 166–175, Feb., 1953.

† C. L. Hogan, The Ferromagnetic Effect at Microwave Frequencies and Its Application; the Microwave Gyrator, *Bell System Tech. J.*, vol. 31, pp. 1–31, Jan., 1952.

‡ See, for example, M. Onoe and M. Sawabe, A Piezoelectric-Piezomagnetic Gyrator, *Proc. IRE*, vol. 50, no. 9, pp. 1967–1973, Sept., 1962.

5.5 Conclusion

In this chapter, the use of yet another type of active element, namely the gyrator, has been considered. Although, in general, network functions realized by means of a gyrator are not bilinear with respect to the gyration conductance, many realization techniques provide functions which are bilinear with respect to the square of the conductance. In these cases it is possible to apply the optimization techniques described in Chap. 2. Unlike the situation discussed for the controlled-source realizations and for the NIC realizations, the optimization of gyrator realizations requires a sum decomposition of the type discussed in Sec. 2.7.

Considered as a class, *RC*-gyrator realizations have several distinct advantages. Because such realizations are based on sum decompositions rather than difference decompositions, they tend to have lower sensitivities than comparable realizations using controlled sources or NICs as the active element. This does not provide a great advantage in low-pass or high-pass realizations with their low-Q poles, but it can be of considerable significance in the realization of bandpass functions which usually require pole locations close to the $j\omega$ axis. In addition, gyrator realizations for second-degree functions are frequently found to be of such a nature that changes in the gyration conductance will not produce instability in the network.

There are also some disadvantages connected with *RC*-gyrator realizations. First of all, they are usually operated as lossless devices with respect to their terminal behavior. As a result, realizations involving gyrators do not normally provide large amounts of gain. Second, an efficient gyrator realization may require the use of more active elements than a realization for a controlled source or an NIC. Finally, since gyrator realizations do not provide low output impedance, isolating amplifiers must be employed if such realizations are to be cascaded. Despite these disadvantages, the advantage of low sensitivity may still make the gyrator realization a very attractive one.

PROBLEMS

5.1 What active device is represented by the abscissa of the *BC* plane? By the ordinate?

5.2 Can an ideal gyrator of gyration conductance G be represented by an ideal gyrator of unity gyration conductance cascaded with an ideal transformer? Prove your conclusion.

5.3 Show that an ideal voltage-controlled current source with a gain G_0 may be used to realize an ideal gyrator if suitable positive- and negative-valued compensating resistors are used.

5.4 Can a cascade connection of two gyrators be used to realize an ideal transformer with a nonunity turns ratio? Prove your conclusion.

5.5 Derive the y parameters given in (11) for the two-port network shown in Fig. 5.16.

5.6 Find an RC-gyrator realization for the network shown in Fig. P5.6 for the following transfer function. All capacitors should be grounded.

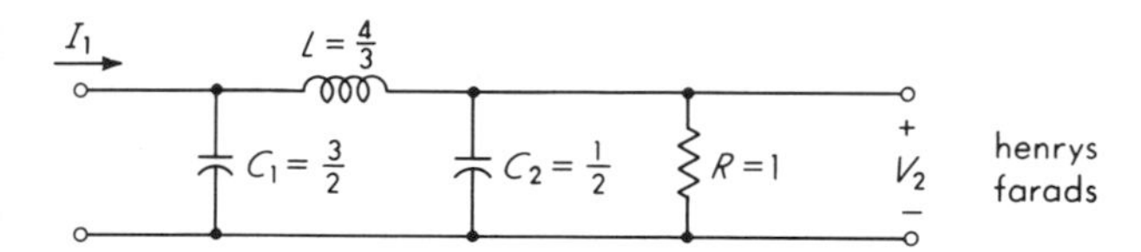

Figure P5.6

Use G_a and G_b as the gyration constants of the two gyrators. Find the sensitivity matrix for the coefficients of the denominator in terms of the elements of the network.

$$\frac{V_2}{I_1} = \frac{H}{p^3 + 2p^2 + 2p + 1}$$

5.7 Derive the voltage transfer function given in (12) for the network shown in Fig. 5.20.

5.8 A pair of coupled coils may be represented as shown in Fig. P5.8. Find an equivalent two-port network consisting only of gyrators and capacitors.

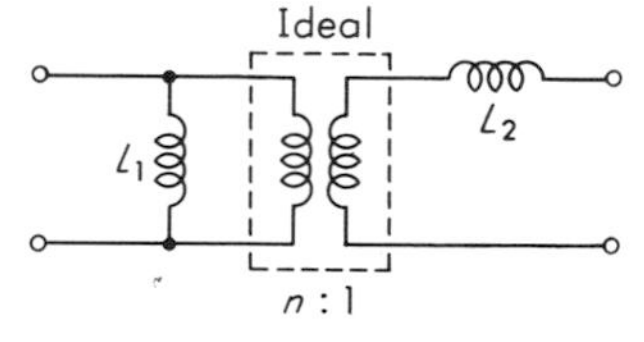

Figure P5.8

5.9 Find the values of K and α for which the network shown in Fig. P5.9 will realize an ideal gyrator.

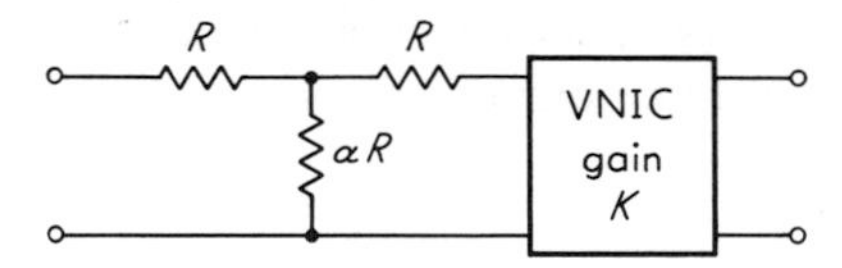

Figure P5.9

5.10 Find an NIC realization for the network function realized in Example 5.1 (Sec. 5.2). Show that if an optimum decomposition is used, such a realization has a classical sensitivity (with respect to the NIC gain) that is purely real when evaluated at resonance.

Chapter 6 *Infinite-gain realizations*

In the previous chapters the realization of active *RC* circuits using controlled sources, NICs, and gyrators as the active elements was discussed. In this chapter, realizations using still another type of active element, an infinite-gain element, will be described. Although there are several types of such elements, we shall confine our discussion mainly to the application of the most common type, the operational amplifier. We have already made reference to such a device. For example, in Sec. 3.7 we presented ways in which the operational amplifier could be used to realize noninverting and inverting controlled sources (see Figs. 3.21 and 3.25). Similarly, in Sec. 4.5 we showed how operational amplifiers could be used to realize NICs (see Fig. 4.35), and in Sec. 5.4 we showed how they could be used to realize gyrators (see Fig. 5.28). In addition, the detailed design procedures and example realizations given in Secs. 3.8 and 4.6 are based on the use of operational amplifiers. In this chapter we shall study the application of infinite-gain devices in general (and the operational amplifier in particular) and their use in the realization of active *RC* circuits. Thus, in Sec. 6.1 we shall define various types of infinite-gain devices and demonstrate in what way they are equivalent. In Secs. 6.2 and 6.3 we shall describe some specific types of infinite-gain realizations and apply them to the realization of low-pass, high-pass, and bandpass voltage transfer functions. In Sec. 6.4, we shall demonstrate some general realization techniques using operational amplifiers. In Sec. 6.5, the use of state-variable feedback is presented as a general realization technique. Finally, in Sec. 6.6, detailed realization techniques, complete with design formulas and numerical examples for the types of realizations presented in Secs. 6.2 and 6.3, are given.

6.1 The equivalence of infinite-gain devices

Any of the four types of ideal sources discussed in Sec. 3.1 may be considered as infinite-gain devices by taking the limiting case as their respective gains go to infinity. Thus, we may consider an infinite-input-impedance zero-output-impedance infinite-gain device similar to a VCVS, a zero-input-impedance infinite-output-impedance infinite-gain device similar to an ICIS, etc. Let us first consider the effect of embedding a VCVS with infinite gain in an arbitrary four-port network described by its y parameters as indicated in Fig. 6.1. The constraints imposed by the

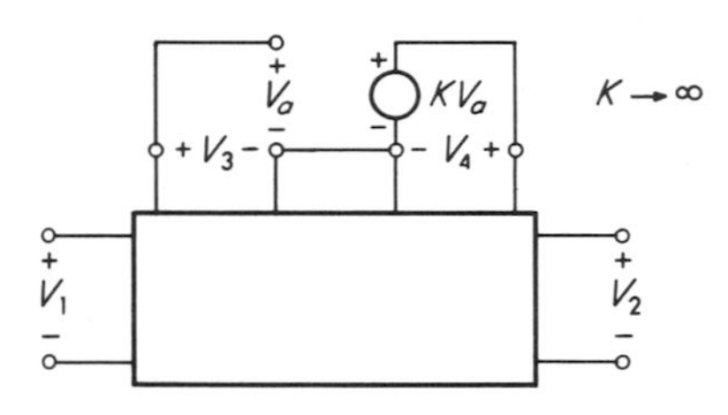

Figure 6.1 A four-port network and an infinite-gain VCVS.

VCVS, in the limit as K approaches infinity, yield the following admittance parameters for the resulting two-port network.*

$$\begin{bmatrix} I_1 \\ I_2 \end{bmatrix} = \begin{bmatrix} y_{11} - \dfrac{y_{14}y_{31}}{y_{34}} & y_{12} - \dfrac{y_{14}y_{32}}{y_{34}} \\ y_{21} - \dfrac{y_{24}y_{31}}{y_{34}} & y_{22} - \dfrac{y_{24}y_{32}}{y_{34}} \end{bmatrix} \begin{bmatrix} V_1 \\ V_2 \end{bmatrix} \tag{1}$$

Now let us consider the effect of embedding an ICIS in a four-port network in the manner shown in Fig. 6.2. Analysis of the circuit shows that in

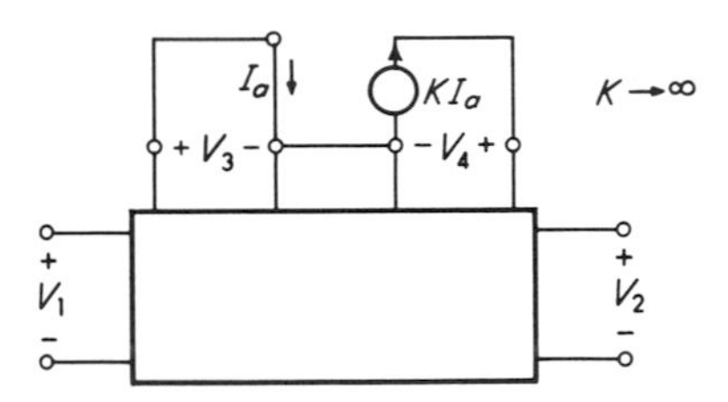

Figure 6.2 A four-port network and an infinite-gain ICIS.

the limit as K approaches infinity, the admittance parameters of the resulting two-port network are again given by (1). In similar fashion, the

* A. Nathan, Matrix Analysis of Networks Having Infinite-gain Operational Amplifiers, *Proc. IRE*, vol. 49, no. 10, pp. 1577–1578, Oct., 1961.

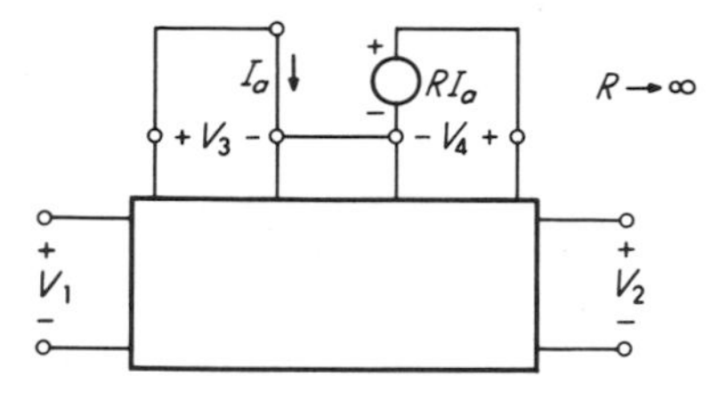

Figure 6.3 A four-port network and an infinite-gain ICVS.

use of an ICVS as shown in Fig. 6.3, or a VCIS as shown in Fig. 6.4, yields the same two-port parameters for the overall network in the limit as the

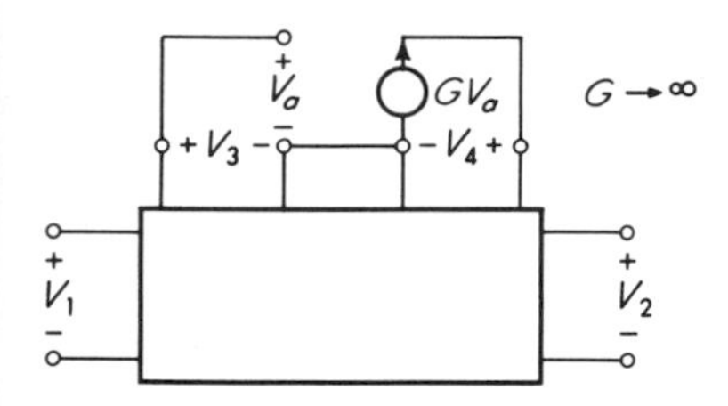

Figure 6.4 A four-port network and an infinite-gain VCIS.

gain of the active element approaches infinity. We conclude that any network realization employing an infinite-gain active element yields the same characteristics independent of the type of active element which is used, i.e., independent of whether it is a VCVS, ICIS, VCIS, or ICVS.*

The infinite-input-impedance zero-output-impedance infinite-gain active device (similar to a VCVS) is, of course, also referred to as an *operational amplifier*. We have previously considered the use of such a device to realize other types of active elements. For example, in Sec. 3.7 we discussed its use in the realization of inverting and noninverting VCVSs of low, i.e., finite, gain. A brief discussion of the properties of the operational amplifier was given in this section. Similarly, in Sec. 4.5 it was pointed out how the operational amplifier may be used to realize an INIC. In this chapter, we shall consider the use of the operational amplifier as a typical infinite-gain element which may be used directly for the realization of network functions. From the preceding paragraphs we have seen that in such a capacity it may be replaced by any other type of infinite-gain element.

Since the operational amplifier has zero output impedance, it is desirable from the standpoint of possible cascading of networks to use its output terminals as the output port of the two-port network. Thus, we may modify the configuration shown in Fig. 6.1 involving a four-port network

* This was pointed out by A. S. Morse, The Use of Operational Amplifiers in Active Network Theory, Master of Science thesis, University of Arizona, 1963.

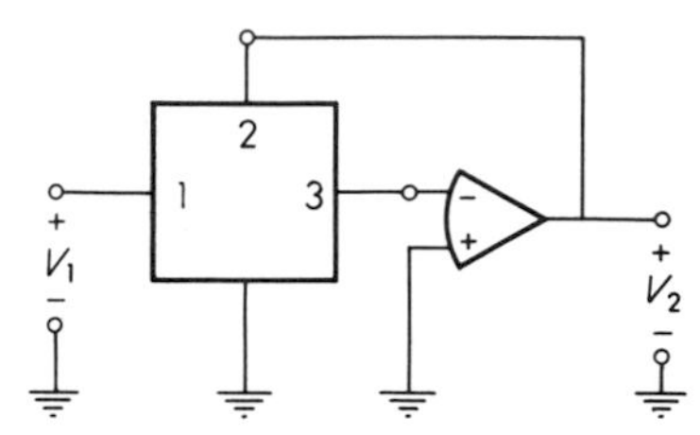

Figure 6.5 A three-port network and an inverting operational amplifier.

to that shown in Fig. 6.5 where, for practicality, we have assumed that all of the ports of the network have a common ground. It is easily shown that the voltage transfer function for this circuit, in terms of the y parameters of the three-port network, is

$$\frac{V_2}{V_1} = \frac{-y_{31}}{y_{32}} \tag{2}$$

where it has been assumed that the positive input terminal of the operational amplifier has been grounded; i.e., it functions as an inverting VCVS of infinite gain (the symbol used for the operational amplifier is defined further in Sec. 3.7). If the denominators of both of the transfer admittances of (2) are the same, the poles of the network function are determined by the zeros of the transfer admittance y_{32}, whereas the zeros of the network function are determined by the zeros of the transfer admittance y_{31}. Since transfer admittances for passive RC networks with a common ground may have zeros located anywhere on the complex-frequency plane except the positive-real axis, we see that the voltage transfer function resulting from a passive RC network and an operational amplifier may have poles and zeros which are quite general in nature. In practice, to simplify the structure of the passive RC network, it is usually expedient to restrict the configuration of the three-port passive network shown in Fig. 6.5 to a less general configuration. Several of the more usual configurations will be discussed in the following sections of this chapter.

6.2 *Infinite-gain single-feedback realizations*

In this section we shall consider the use of an operational amplifier and passive RC networks to realize a voltage transfer function. Such an investigation will serve to illustrate the techniques that may be used for this type of active device. The extension of the methods to the realization of other types of infinite-gain active elements is easily justified from the development of the preceding section. To increase the practicality of our realization, the general network configuration shown in Fig. 6.5 will be restricted to the configuration shown in Fig. 6.6, utilizing two three-

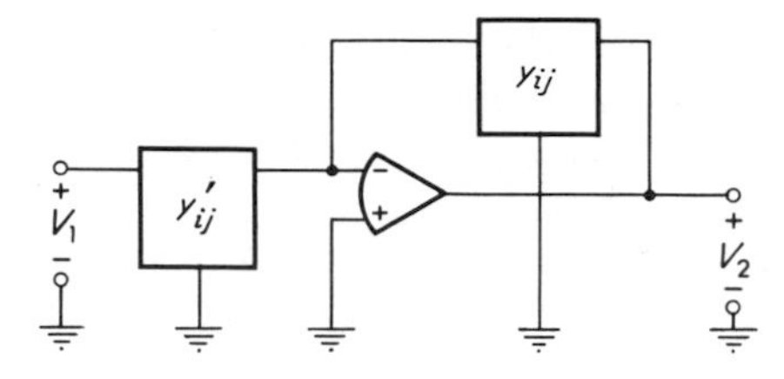

Figure 6.6 The realization of a voltage transfer function with an operational amplifier.

terminal networks with y parameters y'_{ij} and y_{ij} as shown. The network with the y_{ij} parameters shown in this figure may be considered as a feedback network from the output to the input of the operational amplifier. Since the feedback is made to a single point, we shall refer to this network configuration as an *infinite-gain single-feedback configuration.* It is easily shown that the voltage transfer function for this circuit is

$$\frac{V_2}{V_1} = \frac{-y'_{21}}{y_{12} + (1/K)(y'_{22} + y_{11})} \tag{3}$$

In the limit as K approaches minus infinity, the voltage transfer function becomes

$$\frac{V_2}{V_1} = \frac{-y'_{21}}{y_{12}} \tag{4}$$

In general, the two networks will be realized with the same natural frequencies. Thus, the zeros of their transfer admittances will determine the poles and zeros of the voltage transfer function. It should be noted that this type of network configuration is easily adapted to produce a summing

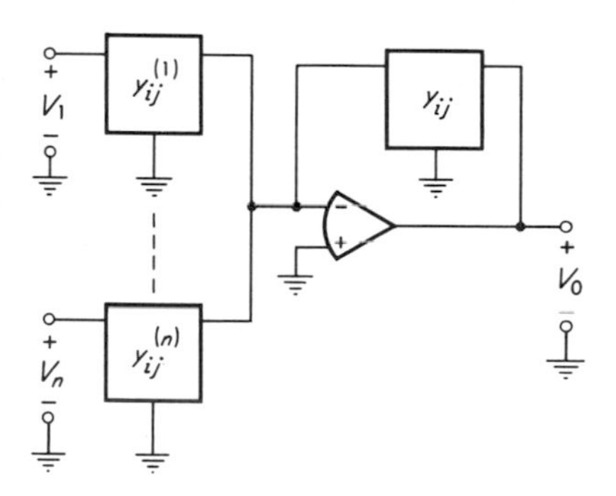

Figure 6.7 The use of an operational amplifier to produce a summing function.

function. A configuration to accomplish this is shown in Fig. 6.7. For the network shown in this figure, we may write

$$V_0 = -\sum_{i=1}^{n} \frac{y_{21}{}^{(i)}}{y_{12}} V_i \tag{5}$$

It is apparent from the above discussion that the realization of specific network functions by means of the infinite-gain single-feedback active *RC* network configuration quickly resolves itself into a problem of the synthesis of the component passive networks. A detailed discussion of techniques, by means of which such networks are realized, may be found in many modern texts and will not be duplicated here.* For the sake of completeness, however, realizations that have been found useful for some of the more common network cases are given in Table 6.1, together with some relations for determining the network elements. It should be noted that the bridged-T network shown as type 4 is not normally capable of satisfactorily producing transmission zeros close to the $j\omega$ axis without an unduly large spread of element values. This network will usually prove satisfactory over a range of the constant a indicated in the table. The twin-T network shown as type 5 also deserves some comment. As the zeros of the second-degree factor of the numerator of the transfer admittance approach the $j\omega$ axis, i.e., as a becomes small, the values of the terms σ_1 and σ_2 determining the location of the finite poles approach unity. For such a case it may be assumed that the negative-real zero of the numerator very nearly cancels one of these poles, and, within a good approximation, the transfer admittance may be considered to be

$$y_{12} = \frac{-(p^2 + ap + 1)}{p + 1} \tag{6}$$

For such a realization, it is easily shown that the movement of the zeros in a direction normal to the $j\omega$ axis is affected most strongly by changes in the elements C_3 and G_3.†

In terms of the networks given in Table 6.1, realizations are easily found for the more common low-order network functions. For example, for a low-pass network function of the type

$$\frac{V_2}{V_1} = \frac{H}{p^2 + b_1 p + b_2} \tag{7}$$

we need merely choose a type 1 network from Table 6.1 for the network

* A general discussion of the synthesis of passive *RC* networks may be found in N. Balabanian, "Network Synthesis," chap. 7, Prentice-Hall, Inc., Englewood Cliffs, N.J., 1958. Design charts may be found in app. 5 of C. J. Savant, Jr., "Control System Design," 2d ed., McGraw-Hill Book Company, New York, 1964. A simplified method for the design of twin-T networks with transmission zeros in the right half of the complex-frequency plane may be found in B. A. Shenoi, A New Technique for Twin-T *RC* Network Synthesis, *IEEE Trans. Circuit Theory*, vol. CT-11, no. 3, pp. 435–436, Sept., 1964.

† A discussion of the adjustment problem in twin-T networks is given by K. Posel, A New Treatment of the *RC* Parallel-T Network, *Proc. IEE (England)*, vol. 110, no. 1, pp. 126–138, Jan., 1963.

with the y'_{ij} parameters of Fig. 6.6 and a type 4 network for the network with the y_{ij} parameters. The location of the negative-real poles as determined by the constant a must, of course, be the same for both networks. The value of a may be chosen to satisfy the desired approximation criteria. The constant H of (7) will be negative. The form of the overall realization is shown in Fig. 6.8. An example of such a low-pass realization follows.

Table 6.1 Some simple networks and their transfer admittances

Type	Configuration	Transfer admittance	Element values (mhos & farads)
1	Series G, series C	$y_{12} = \dfrac{-kp}{p+a}$	$k = G$; $a = \dfrac{G}{C}$
2	Series G_1, shunt C, series G_2	$y_{12} = \dfrac{-k}{p+a}$	$k = \dfrac{G_1G_2}{C}$; $a = \dfrac{G_1+G_2}{C}$
3	Series C_1, shunt G, series C_2	$y_{12} = \dfrac{-kp^2}{p+a}$	$k = \dfrac{C_1C_2}{C_1+C_2}$; $a = \dfrac{G}{C_1+C_2}$
4	Bridged-T: C_1 bridging series G_1, G_2; shunt C_2	$y_{12} = \dfrac{-(p^2+ap+1)}{p+a}$, $\frac{1}{2} < a < 2$	$G_1 = 2.5 - a$; $G_2 = \dfrac{1}{a - 1/G_1}$; $C_1 = 1$; $C_2 = G_1G_2$
5	C_1, C_2, G_1, G_2, C_3, G_3	$y_{12} = \dfrac{-(p+1)(p^2+ap+1)}{(p+\sigma_1)(p+\sigma_2)}$, $a < 1$	$G_1 = (2.5-a)\dfrac{1+a}{2+a}$; $G_2 = \dfrac{G_1}{G_1-1}$; $G_3 = \dfrac{G_1G_2}{1+a}$; $C_1 = G_1$; $C_2 = G_2$; $C_3 = G_3$

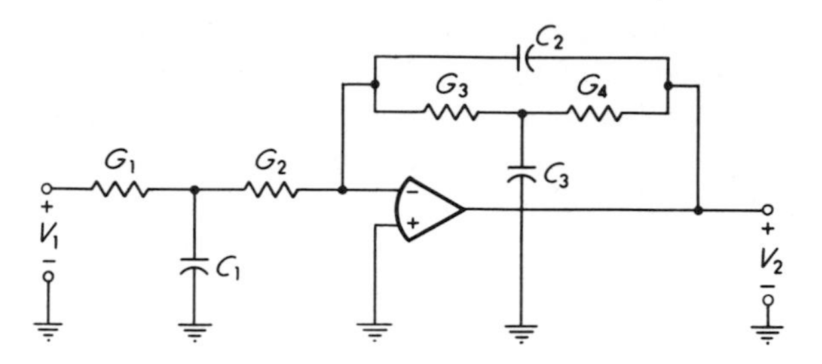

Figure 6.8 A low-pass network realization.

Example 6.1 As an example of the use of the network configuration shown in Fig. 6.8 to realize a low-pass function, consider the frequency-normalized function

$$\frac{V_2}{V_1} = \frac{-10}{p^2 + \sqrt{2}\,p + 1}$$

From a consideration of (4) and the network configurations shown in Table 6.1, we find the following transfer admittances for the component networks:

$$-y'_{21} = \frac{10}{p + \sqrt{2}} \qquad -y_{12} = \frac{p^2 + \sqrt{2}\,p + 1}{p + \sqrt{2}}$$

In terms of the elements shown in Fig. 6.8, we find the element values as follows:

$$\begin{aligned} G_1 &= 14.14 \text{ mhos} & C_1 &= 20.0 \text{ farads} \\ G_2 &= 14.14 \text{ mhos} & C_2 &= 1.0 \text{ farad} \\ G_3 &= 1.086 \text{ mhos} & C_3 &= 2.201 \text{ farads} \\ G_4 &= 2.027 \text{ mhos} \end{aligned}$$

In terms of the coefficients of (7) and for an open-loop operational amplifier gain $K = -1000$, we find the following sensitivities (for convenience, we have presented the matrix of sensitivities in a tabular array):

	$\Delta G_1{}^{(n)}$	$\Delta G_2{}^{(n)}$	$\Delta G_3{}^{(n)}$	$\Delta G_4{}^{(n)}$	$\Delta C_1{}^{(n)}$	$\Delta C_2{}^{(n)}$	$C_3{}^{(n)}$	$\Delta K^{(n)}$
$\Delta b_1{}^{(n)}$	0	0	0.35	0.65	0.01	−0.01	−1.0	−0.01
$\Delta b_2{}^{(n)}$	0	0	1.0	1.0	0.01	1.0	−1.0	−0.01

A detailed design procedure for the low-pass, infinite-gain, single-feedback network shown in Fig. 6.8 is given in Sec. 6.6 as circuit 7.

A process similar to the one described above may be used to realize a high-pass network function. For example, for a function of the type

$$\frac{V_2}{V_1} = \frac{Hp^2}{p^2 + b_1 p + b_2} \tag{8}$$

we need merely choose a type 3 network for the network with the y'_{ij} parameters of Fig. 6.6 and a type 4 network for the network with the y_{ij} parameters. The constant H of (8) will be negative. The form of the overall realization is shown in Fig. 6.9. An example of such a high-pass realization follows.

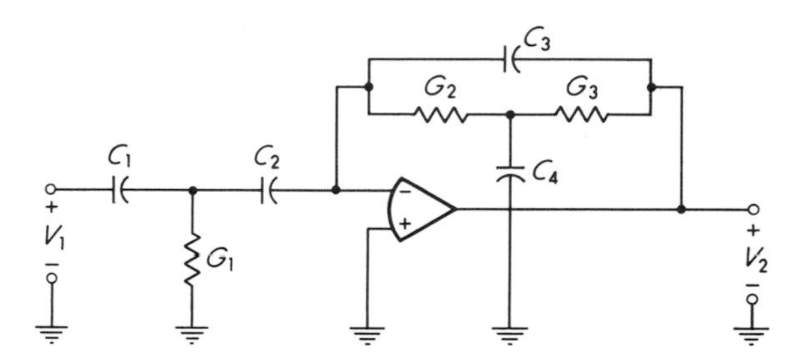

***Figure 6.9** A high-pass network realization.*

Example 6.2 As an example of the use of the network configuration shown in Fig. 6.9 to realize a high-pass function, consider the frequency-normalized function

$$\frac{V_2}{V_1} = \frac{-10p^2}{p^2 + \sqrt{2}\,p + 1}$$

The transfer admittances for the component networks shown in Fig. 6.6 are

$$-y'_{21} = \frac{10p^2}{p + \sqrt{2}} \qquad -y_{12} - \frac{p^2 + \sqrt{2}\,p + 1}{p + \sqrt{2}}$$

In terms of the elements shown in Fig. 6.9, we find the following element values:

$$\begin{aligned} G_1 &= 56.56 \text{ mhos} & C_1 &= 20 \text{ farads} \\ G_2 &= 1.086 \text{ mhos} & C_2 &= 20 \text{ farads} \\ G_3 &= 2.027 \text{ mhos} & C_3 &= 1.0 \text{ farad} \\ & & C_4 &= 2.201 \text{ farads} \end{aligned}$$

For an operational amplifier gain $K = -1000$ we may find the sensitivities for the coefficients of the denominator of (8). These are presented in the following tabular array:

	$\Delta G_1^{(n)}$	$\Delta G_2^{(n)}$	$\Delta G_3^{(n)}$	$\Delta C_1^{(n)}$	$\Delta C_2^{(n)}$	$\Delta C_3^{(n)}$	$\Delta C_4^{(n)}$	$\Delta K^{(n)}$
$\Delta b_1^{(n)}$	0.009	0.34	0.65	−0.005	−0.005	0.002	−1.0	−0.0001
$\Delta b_2^{(n)}$	0.0007	1.0	1.0	0.005	0.005	−1.0	−1.0	−0.007

A detailed design procedure for the high-pass infinite-gain single-feedback network shown in Fig. 6.9 is given in Sec. 6.6 as circuit 8.

Now let us consider the use of the general network configuration shown in Fig. 6.6 to realize a bandpass network function. For the second-degree case, such a function will have the general form

$$\frac{V_2}{V_1} = \frac{Hp}{p^2 + b_1 p + b_2} \tag{9}$$

It may be realized by using a type 1 network from Table 6.1 for the network with the y'_{ij} parameters of Fig. 6.6 and a type 5 network for the network with the y_{ij} parameters. The value of a must be the same for both networks and will be determined by the coefficient b_1 in (9). The constant H of (9) will be negative. The network configuration will have the form shown in Fig. 6.10. An example of such a realization follows.

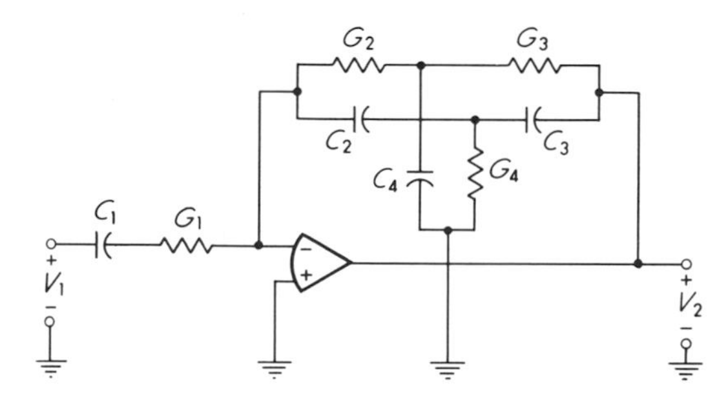

Figure 6.10 A bandpass network realization.

Example 6.3 As an example of the use of the network configuration shown in Fig. 6.10 to realize a bandpass function, consider the frequency-normalized function

$$\frac{V_2}{V_1} = \frac{-10p}{p^2 + 0.1p + 1}$$

The transfer admittances for the component networks shown in Fig. 6.6 are

$$-y'_{21} = \frac{10p}{p+1} \qquad -y_{12} = \frac{p^2 + 0.1p + 1}{p+1}$$

where cancellation of a numerator and denominator factor of approximately $p + 1$ has been made for $-y_{12}$. From Table 6.1, in terms of the elements shown in Fig. 6.10, we find the following element values:

$$\begin{aligned} G_1 &= 10 \text{ mhos} & C_1 &= 10 \text{ farads} \\ G_2 &= 1.2571 \text{ mhos} & C_2 &= 1.2571 \text{ farads} \\ G_3 &= 4.8875 \text{ mhos} & C_3 &= 4.8875 \text{ farads} \\ G_4 &= 5.5854 \text{ mhos} & C_4 &= 5.5854 \text{ farads} \end{aligned}$$

For an operational amplifier gain $K = -1000$ we may find the sensitivities for the coefficients of the denominator of (9). These are presented in the following tabular array:

	$\Delta G_1^{(n)}$	$\Delta G_2^{(n)}$	$\Delta G_3^{(n)}$	$\Delta G_4^{(n)}$	$\Delta C_1^{(n)}$	$\Delta C_2^{(n)}$	$\Delta C_3^{(n)}$	$\Delta C_4^{(n)}$	$\Delta K^{(n)}$
$\Delta b_1^{(n)}$	0.043	1.438	4.198	−4.708	0.047	0.508	3.627	−5.163	−0.112
$\Delta b_2^{(n)}$	−0.005	0.935	0.597	0.4757	0.005	−0.935	−0.594	−0.479	0

A detailed design procedure for the bandpass infinite-gain single-feedback network shown in Fig. 6.10 is given in Sec. 6.6 as circuit 9.

In general, realizations made using the infinite-gain single-feedback procedure require considerably more elements than do comparable realizations made by means of other techniques. As an example of this, compare the number of elements used in the realization for the second-degree bandpass function given in Fig. 3.15 with the one given in Fig. 6.10. This disadvantage is the natural result of having to realize separate networks, each with its own set of natural frequencies. It should be noted, however, that the infinite-gain single-feedback realization is capable of realizing very high-Q network functions. In addition, such realizations will normally be quite stable since the pole locations are determined completely by the zeros of the passive networks, rather than by the value of the gain of the active element.

One other point that is characteristic of this type of realization deserves mention. This is the fact that the admittance levels of the two component passive networks may be adjusted independently. Thus, it is possible to raise or lower the magnitude of the gain constant H in (7), (8), or (9) by an appropriate admittance normalization of the elements of either network, without changing the frequency characteristics of the network.

6.3 *Infinite-gain multiple-feedback realizations*

In this section we shall consider the use of a single infinite-gain element of the VCVS (operational amplifier) type, together with passive RC network elements, to realize voltage transfer functions. The difference between the approach used in this section and that used in the previous section will be that feedback connections will be made to more than one point in the passive network from the output of the operational amplifier. Thus, this approach will provide a different example of a specific technique based on the general realization configuration given in Fig. 6.5. The passive network will take the form shown in Fig. 6.11, where each of the blocks

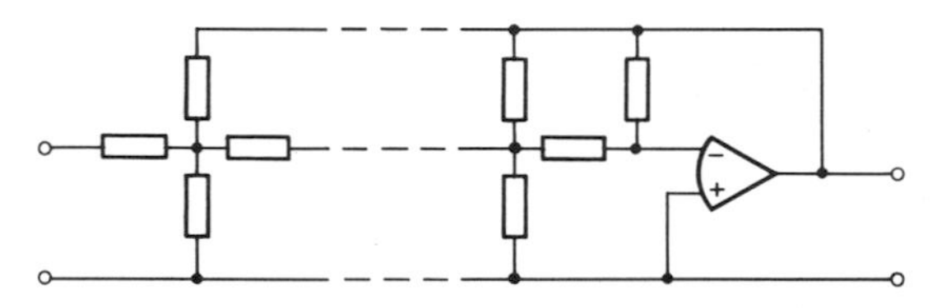

***Figure 6.11** A multiple-feedback operational amplifier configuration.*

represents a single two-terminal element, either a resistor or a capacitor. Explicit algorithms have been written for determining the relation between the network elements and the desired network function. Here we shall consider the less general configuration shown in Fig. 6.12, involving

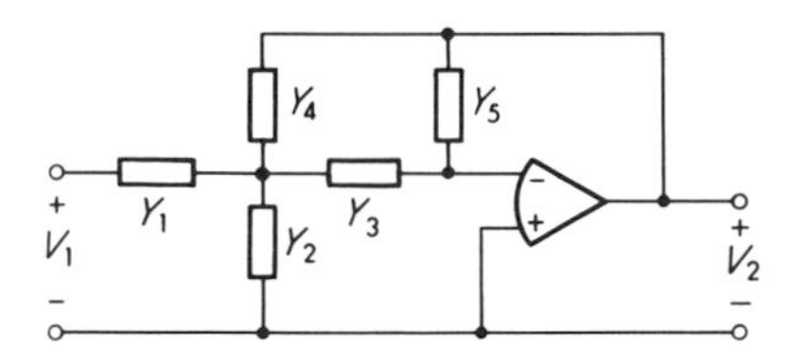

***Figure 6.12** An infinite-gain multiple-feedback configuration for second-degree voltage transfer functions.*

only five elements, and see how it may be used to realize second-degree voltage transfer functions.

The open-circuit voltage transfer function for the circuit shown in Fig. 6.12 is easily shown to be

$$\frac{V_2}{V_1} = \frac{-Y_1Y_3}{Y_5(Y_1 + Y_2 + Y_3 + Y_4) + Y_3Y_4 - (1/K)[(Y_3 + Y_5)(Y_1 + Y_2 + Y_4) + Y_3Y_5]} \tag{10}$$

In the limiting case as K approaches minus infinity, we obtain

$$\frac{V_2}{V_1} = \frac{-Y_1Y_3}{Y_5(Y_1 + Y_2 + Y_3 + Y_4) + Y_3Y_4} \tag{11}$$

In the following paragraphs we shall show how the five elements may be chosen so as to realize low-pass, high-pass, and bandpass network functions.

We shall now apply the configuration shown in Fig. 6.12 to the realization of a frequency-normalized low-pass voltage transfer function of the type given in (7). If we compare the numerators of (7) and (11), we observe that both the elements Y_1 and Y_3 must be resistors. From the denominators of the two expressions, we see that Y_2 and Y_5 must be capacitors (to obtain the second-degree term), and Y_4 must be a resistor (to generate the zero-degree term). The network configuration resulting from these choices

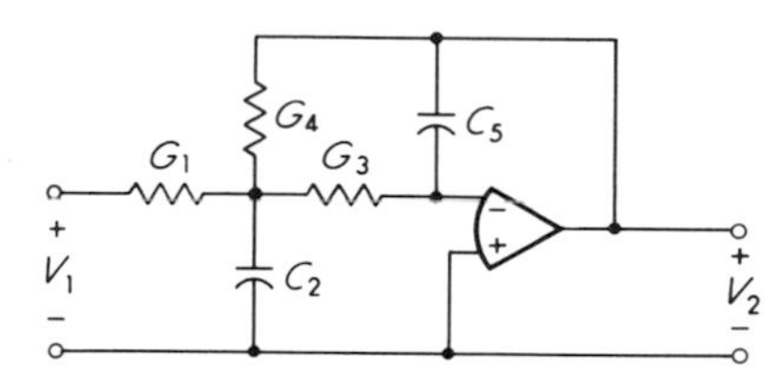

***Figure 6.13** A low-pass network realization.*

is shown in Fig. 6.13.* The voltage transfer function may be expressed in terms of the network elements as

$$\frac{V_2}{V_1} = \frac{-G_1G_3}{p^2C_2C_5 + pC_5(G_1 + G_3 + G_4) + G_3G_4} \tag{12}$$

The sensitivity matrix for the elements of this realization has the following properties:

1. The sensitivities for the b_1 coefficient of (7) will be positive and less than unity for the elements G_1, G_3, and G_4. For the element C_2 the sensitivity will be -1 (see properties 2, 3, and 4, Sec. 2.5).

2. The sensitivities for the b_2 coefficient of (7) with respect to the elements G_3 and G_4 will be unity; with respect to the elements C_2 and C_5 they will be -1 (see properties 2 and 3, Sec. 2.5).

An example of such a low-pass realization follows.

* This low-pass configuration is also sometimes referred to as a *Rausch filter* and was introduced by M. H. Nichols and L. Rausch, "Radio Telemetry," p. 396, John Wiley & Sons, Inc., New York, 1956. Extensive tables giving the element values for the two-pole and three-pole case for Butterworth, Chebychev, and Bessel approximating criteria may be found in E. J. Foster, Active Low-pass Filter Design, *IEEE Trans. Audio*, vol. AU-13, no. 5, pp. 104–111, Sept./Oct., 1965.

Example 6.4 As an example of the use of the network configuration shown in Fig. 6.13 to realize a low-pass function, consider the frequency-normalized function

$$\frac{V_2}{V_1} = \frac{-10}{p^2 + \sqrt{2}\,p + 1}$$

In terms of the elements shown in Fig. 6.13, we find the following element values:

$$\begin{aligned} G_1 &= 3.01 \text{ mhos} & G_4 &= 0.301 \text{ mho} \\ C_2 &= 4.69 \text{ farads} & C_5 &= 0.213 \text{ farad} \\ G_3 &= 3.32 \text{ mhos} \end{aligned}$$

In terms of the coefficients of (7), assuming the gain of the operational amplifier is infinite, we find the following sensitivities:

$$\begin{bmatrix} \Delta b_1{}^{(n)} \\ \\ \Delta b_2{}^{(n)} \end{bmatrix} = \begin{bmatrix} 0.454 & -1.0 & 0.500 & 0.045 & 0 \\ \\ 0 & -1.0 & 1.0 & 1.0 & -1.0 \end{bmatrix} \begin{bmatrix} \Delta G_1{}^{(n)} \\ \Delta C_2{}^{(n)} \\ \Delta G_3{}^{(n)} \\ \Delta G_4{}^{(n)} \\ \Delta C_5{}^{(n)} \end{bmatrix}$$

A more accurate although considerably more complicated determination of the sensitivities may be made by including the effects of the operational amplifier, using (10). For such a determination, for an operational amplifier gain $K = -1000$ we find the following sensitivities:

$$\begin{bmatrix} \Delta b_1{}^{(n)} \\ \\ \Delta b_2{}^{(n)} \end{bmatrix} = \begin{bmatrix} 0.499 & -1.0 & 0.506 & 0.045 & -0.01 & -0.01 \\ \\ 0.01 & -1.0 & 1.0 & 1.0 & 1.0 & -0.01 \end{bmatrix} \begin{bmatrix} \Delta G_1{}^{(n)} \\ \Delta C_2{}^{(n)} \\ \Delta G_3{}^{(n)} \\ \Delta G_4{}^{(n)} \\ \Delta C_5{}^{(n)} \\ \Delta K^{(n)} \end{bmatrix}$$

It is easily noted that for large values of K, quite accurate determinations of the sensitivities may be made without considering K, and that the effect of changes in K upon the coefficients of the denominator of (7) is small.

A detailed design procedure for the low-pass, infinite-gain, multiple-feedback network shown in Fig. 6.13 is given in Sec. 6.6 as circuit 10.

Similar considerations lead to the proper choices of the type of elements shown in the general configuration of Fig. 6.12 so that a high-pass voltage transfer function is realized. For the second-degree case, the frequency-normalized transfer function will be of the form given in (8). The network

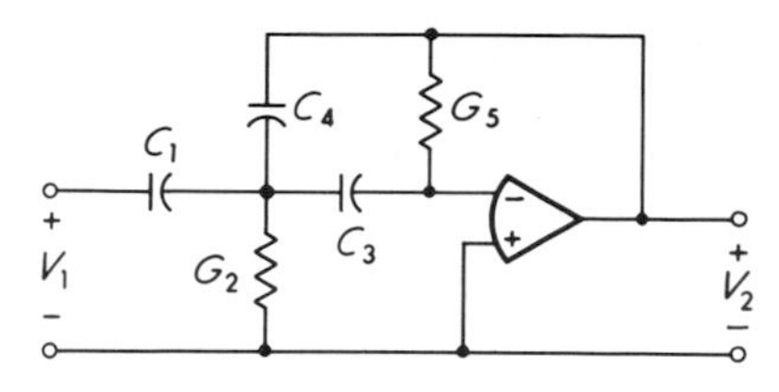

Figure 6.14 *A high-pass network realization.*

configuration for this case is shown in Fig. 6.14. For the elements shown in this figure, the voltage transfer function may be written explicitly as

$$\frac{V_2}{V_1} = \frac{-p^2C_1C_3}{p^2C_3C_4 + pG_5(C_1 + C_3 + C_4) + G_2G_5} \tag{13}$$

The sensitivity matrix for the elements of this realization has the following properties:

1. The sensitivities for the b_1 coefficient of (8) with respect to the elements C_1, C_3, and C_4 will be less than unity in magnitude; for the element G_5 the sensitivity is unity (see properties 2, 3, and 4, Sec. 2.5).
2. The sensitivities for the b_2 coefficient of (8) with respect to the elements G_2 and G_5 are unity; with respect to the elements C_3 and C_4, they are -1 (see properties 2 and 3, Sec. 2.5).

An example of such a high-pass realization follows.

Example 6.5 As an example of the use of the network configuration shown in Fig. 6.14 to realize a high-pass function, consider the frequency-normalized function

$$\frac{V_2}{V_1} = \frac{-10p^2}{p^2 + \sqrt{2}\,p + 1}$$

In terms of the elements shown in Fig. 6.14, we find the following element values:

$$\begin{aligned} C_1 &= 3.01 \text{ farads} & C_4 &= 0.301 \text{ farad} \\ G_2 &= 4.69 \text{ mhos} & G_5 &= 0.213 \text{ mho} \\ C_3 &= 3.32 \text{ farads} \end{aligned}$$

In terms of the coefficients of (8), assuming the gain of the operational amplifier is infinite, we find the following sensitivities:

$$\begin{bmatrix} \Delta b_1^{(n)} \\ \Delta b_2^{(n)} \end{bmatrix} = \begin{bmatrix} 0.454 & 0 & -0.5 & -0.955 & 1.0 \\ 0 & 1.0 & -1.0 & -1.0 & 1.0 \end{bmatrix} \begin{bmatrix} \Delta C_1^{(n)} \\ \Delta G_2^{(n)} \\ \Delta C_3^{(n)} \\ \Delta C_4^{(n)} \\ \Delta G_5^{(n)} \end{bmatrix}$$

A more accurate determination of the sensitivities may be made by including the effects of the operational amplifier, using (10). For such a determination, for an operational amplifier gain $K = -1000$, we find the following sensitivity matrix:

$$\begin{bmatrix} \Delta b_1^{(n)} \\ \Delta b_2^{(n)} \end{bmatrix} = \begin{bmatrix} 0.439 & 0.01 & -0.5 & -0.955 & 0.989 & -0.001 \\ 0.01 & 1.0 & 1.0 & 1.0 & 1.0 & 0.01 \end{bmatrix} \begin{bmatrix} \Delta C_1^{(n)} \\ \Delta G_2^{(n)} \\ \Delta C_3^{(n)} \\ \Delta C_4^{(n)} \\ \Delta G_5^{(n)} \\ \Delta K^{(n)} \end{bmatrix}$$

A detailed design procedure for finding the element values for the high-pass, infinite-gain, multiple-feedback network shown in Fig. 6.14 is given in Sec. 6.6 as circuit 11.

There are several configurations of five elements which may be used to realize a frequency-normalized bandpass voltage transfer function of the

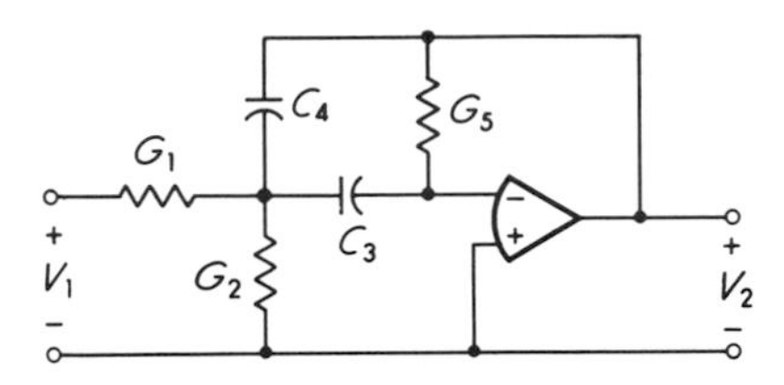

***Figure 6.15** A bandpass network realization.*

type given in (9). One of the more practical configurations is the one shown in Fig. 6.15. For this configuration the voltage transfer function is

$$\frac{V_2}{V_1} = \frac{-pG_1C_3}{p^2C_3C_4 + pG_5(C_3 + C_4) + G_5(G_1 + G_2)} \tag{14}$$

The sensitivity matrix for the elements of this realization has the following properties:

1. The sensitivities for the b_1 coefficient of (9) with respect to the elements C_3 and C_4 will be negative and less than unity in magnitude; with respect to the element G_5, the sensitivity is unity (see properties 3, 4, and 5, Sec. 2.5).
2. The sensitivities for the b_2 coefficient of (9) with respect to the elements G_1 and G_2 will be positive and less than unity; with respect to the elements C_3 and C_4, they will be -1; and with respect to the element G_5, the sensitivity is unity (see properties 3, 4, and 5, Sec. 2.5).

An example of such a bandpass realization follows.

Example 6.6 As an example of the use of the network configuration shown in Fig. 6.15 to realize a bandpass function, consider the frequency-normalized function

$$\frac{V_2}{V_1} = \frac{-10p}{p^2 + 0.1p + 1}$$

In terms of the elements shown in Fig. 6.15, we find the following element values:

$$G_1 = 10 \text{ mhos} \qquad C_4 = 1 \text{ farad}$$
$$G_2 = 10 \text{ mhos} \qquad G_5 = 0.05 \text{ mho}$$
$$C_3 = 1 \text{ farad}$$

In terms of the coefficients of (9), assuming infinite operational amplifier gain, we find the following sensitivity matrix:

$$\begin{bmatrix} \Delta b_1^{(n)} \\ \Delta b_2^{(n)} \end{bmatrix} = \begin{bmatrix} 0 & 0 & -0.5 & -0.5 & 1.0 \\ 0.5 & 0.5 & -1.0 & -1.0 & 1.0 \end{bmatrix} \begin{bmatrix} \Delta G_1^{(n)} \\ \Delta G_2^{(n)} \\ \Delta C_3^{(n)} \\ \Delta C_4^{(n)} \\ \Delta G_5^{(n)} \end{bmatrix}$$

A more accurate determination of the sensitivities may be made by including the effects of the operational amplifier gain using (10). For such a determination, for $K = -1000$, we find the following sensitivity matrix:

$$\begin{bmatrix} \Delta b_1^{(n)} \\ \Delta b_2^{(n)} \end{bmatrix} = \begin{bmatrix} 0.083 & 0.083 & -0.421 & -0.589 & 0.833 & -0.168 \\ 0.5 & 0.5 & -1.0 & -1.0 & 1.0 & 0 \end{bmatrix} \begin{bmatrix} \Delta G_1^{(n)} \\ \Delta G_2^{(n)} \\ \Delta C_3^{(n)} \\ \Delta C_4^{(n)} \\ \Delta G_5^{(n)} \\ \Delta K^{(n)} \end{bmatrix}$$

The actual value of the coefficient b is 0.12 in this case.

A detailed design procedure for finding the element values for the bandpass, infinite-gain, multiple-feedback network shown in Fig. 6.15 is given in Sec. 6.6 as circuit 12.

It is possible to extend the configuration shown in Fig. 6.12 to include more network elements and thus to have the capacity for the realization of higher-degree network functions. Because of the nonlinear nature of the equations relating the network elements to the coefficients in the numerator and denominator polynomials of the network function, solutions for the values of the network elements become considerably more difficult in these higher-degree cases. Some of the more common cases have appeared in the literature, and the interested reader is referred to these.*

The infinite-gain multiple-feedback circuits introduced in this section have the advantage that they usually require a minimum number of elements. In the realizations shown in this section, five elements are used. In some cases, element values may be so selected that four elements will suffice. Another advantage of this type of circuit is that its output impedance is that of the operational amplifier, i.e., very low. Thus, network realizations of this type may be cascaded to realize more complicated network functions without appreciable interaction occurring between the cascaded networks. These realizations also have a disadvantage although it is not readily apparent. If it is desired to realize poles that are close to the $j\omega$ axis, the techniques described, in general, require large spreads of element values. The same is true if it is desired to realize large values of the gain constant H. In these cases, this type of realization becomes considerably less attractive.

6.4 *Infinite-gain general realization techniques*

The techniques using infinite-gain active elements proposed in the last two sections have some limitations on the locations of the zeros of the resulting transfer functions. In general, these are the result of the limitations on the permissible locations of the zeros of the transfer functions of the component passive RC networks. In this section we shall present two techniques using infinite-gain active elements which are completely general in the sense that they will realize any rational function. In addition, the synthesis procedures will be shown to be exceedingly straightforward; specifically, they do not require the solution of a set of nonlinear simultaneous equations to determine the element values. The approaches are similar to the one used for the general NIC synthesis method for voltage transfer functions introduced in Sec. 4.3.

Let us consider the realization of the general voltage transfer function

$$\frac{V_2}{V_1} = \frac{Q(p)}{P(p)} \tag{15}$$

* L. K. Wadhwa, Simulation of Third-order Systems with One Operational Amplifier, *Proc. IRE*, vol. 50, no. 2, pp. 201–202, Feb., 1962; also, by the same author, Simulation of Third-order Systems with Simple-Lead Using One Operational Amplifier, *Proc. IRE*, vol. 50, no. 4, part I, p. 456, April, 1962, and Simulation of Third-order Systems with Double-Lead Using One Operational Amplifier, *Proc. IRE*, vol. 50, no. 6, pp. 1538–1539, June, 1962.

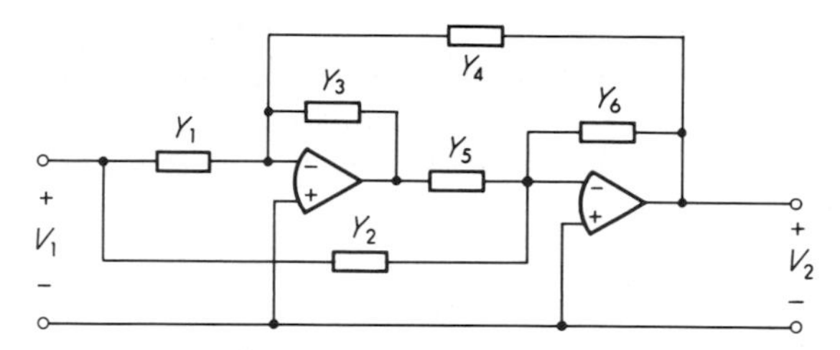

Figure 6.16 ***A general network realization configuration.***

For the infinite-gain active element, we shall use the operational amplifier. If two such amplifiers are used in the general network configuration shown in Fig. 6.16, the overall voltage transfer function is*

$$\frac{V_2}{V_1} = \frac{Y_1Y_5 - Y_2Y_3}{Y_3Y_6 - Y_4Y_5} \tag{16}$$

If we let the elements Y_3 and Y_5 be resistive and have unity value, then (16) becomes

$$\frac{V_2}{V_1} = \frac{Y_1 - Y_2}{Y_6 - Y_4} \tag{17}$$

Now let us divide the numerator and denominator polynomials of (15) by a polynomial $W(p)$ having simple negative-real zeros and of degree 1 less than the degree of $Q(p)$ or $P(p)$, whichever is greater. Comparing the result with (17), we obtain

$$\begin{aligned} \frac{Q(p)}{W(p)} &= Y_1 - Y_2 \\ \frac{P(p)}{W(p)} &= Y_6 - Y_4 \end{aligned} \tag{18}$$

Each of the rational functions $Q(p)/W(p)$ and $P(p)/W(p)$ may be expanded in the form

$$k_\infty p + k_0 + \sum_i \frac{k_i p}{p + \sigma_i} \tag{19}$$

* W. P. Lovering, Analog Computer Simulation of Transfer Functions, *Proc. IEEE*, vol. 53, no. 3, pp. 306–307, March, 1965.

where the various k's will be real but may be positive or negative. The positive terms in such expansions may be associated with Y_1 and Y_6, and the negative terms with Y_2 and Y_4. Thus, the admittances Y_i in Fig. 6.16 are all realizable by passive RC networks whose values are easily found, and the realization is complete.

Example 6.7 As an example of this type of realization, consider the voltage transfer function

$$\frac{V_2}{V_1} = \frac{(p-1)^2}{(p+1)^2}$$

This is an all-pass function. In addition, the zeros on the positive-real axis are not realizable by the techniques discussed in the preceding sections of this chapter unless passive RC networks without a common ground are used. In applying the method of this section, we may choose $W(p) = p + 1$. Thus, we obtain

$$\frac{Q(p)}{W(p)} = \frac{(p-1)^2}{p+1} = p + 1 - \frac{4p}{p+1} = Y_1 - Y_2$$
$$\frac{P(p)}{W(p)} = \frac{(p+1)^2}{p+1} = p + 1 = Y_6$$

Note that we have chosen $W(p)$ in such a manner as to eliminate Y_4, thus simplifying our realization. Such a simplification is frequently possible. The overall network realization for the all-pass function is shown in Fig. 6.17.

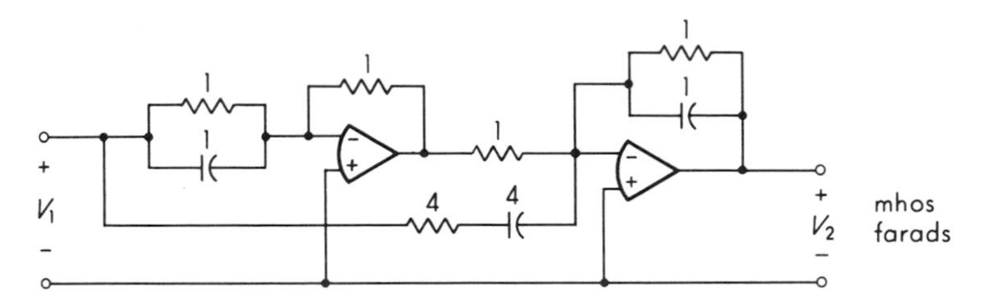

Figure 6.17 ***Realization of an all-pass network function.***

A second general realization technique for voltage transfer functions is possible with the use of a single differential-input operational amplifier as

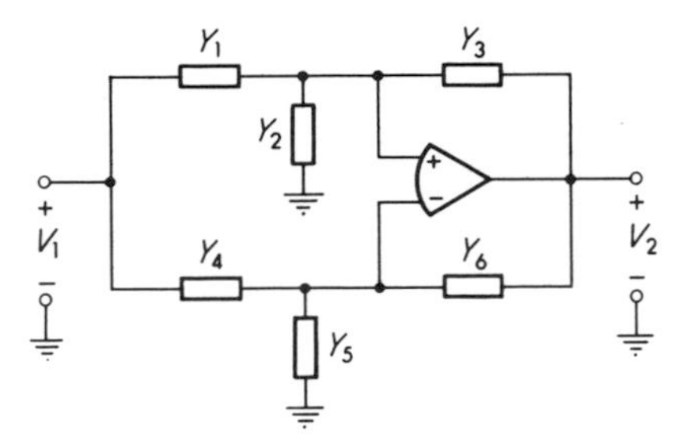

Figure 6.18 A general network realization configuration.

the active element. To see this, consider the circuit shown in Fig. 6.18.* The voltage transfer function for this circuit is

$$\frac{V_2}{V_1} = \frac{Y_1(Y_4 + Y_5 + Y_6) - Y_4(Y_1 + Y_2 + Y_3)}{Y_6(Y_1 + Y_2 + Y_3) - Y_3(Y_4 + Y_5 + Y_6)} \tag{20}$$

If the admittances are chosen so that

$$Y_1 + Y_2 + Y_3 = Y_4 + Y_5 + Y_6 \tag{21}$$

then the voltage transfer function given in (21) becomes

$$\frac{V_2}{V_1} = \frac{Y_1 - Y_4}{Y_6 - Y_3} \tag{22}$$

For a desired voltage transfer function, the admittances Y_1, Y_4, Y_6, and Y_3 may be found by the same method as was used for the previous circuit. The synthesis procedure is completed by selecting Y_2 and Y_5 according to the relations

$$\begin{aligned} Y_2 &= Y_4 + Y_6 \\ Y_5 &= Y_1 + Y_3 \end{aligned} \tag{23}$$

It should be noted that any common terms in the right-hand members of (23) may be subtracted, reducing the complexity of Y_2 and Y_5.

As an example of this realization technique, let us again realize the all-pass function given in Example 6.7. The partial-fraction expansions are the same as those which were made for the realization using two opera-

* J. S. Brugler, *RC* Synthesis with Differential Input Operational Amplifiers, in "Papers on Integrated Circuit Synthesis" (compiled by R. Newcomb and T. Rao), *Stanford Electron. Labs. Rept. No.* 6560-4, June, 1966.

tional amplifiers. Thus, we see that

$$Y_1 = p + 1 \qquad Y_4 = \frac{4p}{p+1}$$
$$Y_3 = 0 \qquad Y_6 = p + 1$$

In addition, after subtracting common factors, we obtain

$$Y_2 = \frac{4p}{p+1} \qquad Y_5 = 0$$

The final realization is shown in Fig. 6.19.

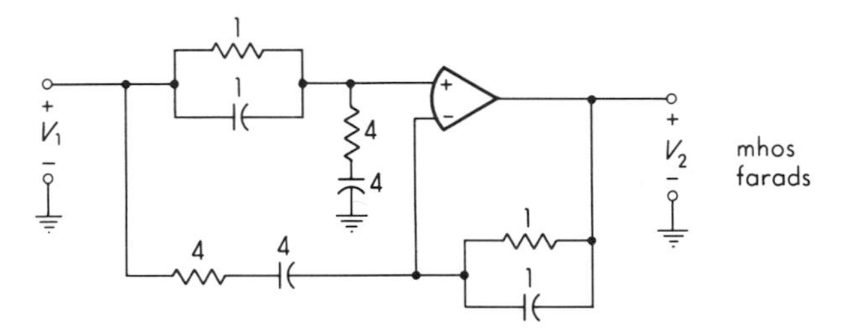

Figure 6.19 Realization of an all-pass network function.

In addition to providing more generality in the types of network functions that are to be realized, it should be noted that the synthesis methods (as given in this section) also retain many of the advantages of the other infinite-gain realizations that have been discussed. First of all, the resulting realization is relatively independent of the gain of the active element; thus, the sensitivity problem is minimized. Secondly, the output impedance of the network is the output impedance of the operational amplifier. This is very nearly equal to zero. Thus, realizations of this type can be cascaded without appreciable interaction occurring between the cascaded networks.

6.5 *A state-variable infinite-gain realization*

In the preceding section some general infinite-gain realization techniques were presented. Another general method of synthesis using operational amplifiers may be set up through the use of state variables. To see this, consider the open-circuit voltage transfer function

$$\frac{V_2}{V_1} = \frac{a_0 + a_1 p + \cdots + a_{n-1}p^{n-1} + a_n p^n}{b_0 + b_1 p + \cdots + b_{n-1}p^{n-1} + b_n p^n} \tag{24}$$

where the coefficients a_i and b_i are real but may be positive or negative (or zero). We shall assume that the usual requirements of stability are met. Let us now write this function in the following form

$$\frac{V_2}{V_1} = \frac{(a_0 x/p^n) + (a_1 x/p^{n-1}) + \cdots + (a_{n-1}x/p) + a_n x}{(b_0 x/p^n) + (b_1 x/p^{n-1}) + \cdots + (b_{n-1}x/p) + b_n x} \tag{25}$$

where we have multiplied the numerator and denominator of (24) by the parameter x/p^n. The quantities x/p^i may be identified as state variables.* Finally, we may write the function (25) as two separate equations in

* A set of state variables provides sufficient information to characterize the behavior of a given network at any instant of time. Such a set of variables is usually expressed by an equation of the form $\dot{\mathbf{x}} = \mathbf{Ax} + \mathbf{Bu}$, where $\mathbf{x}$ is the state vector, $\dot{\mathbf{x}}$ is the derivative of the state vector, $\mathbf{A}$ is a matrix determined by the system properties, and the matrix product $\mathbf{Bu}$ represents the inputs to the network. The reader who is unfamiliar with the concepts of state variables may consult any of several modern texts in this area. See, for example, P. M. DeRusso, R. J. Roy, and C. M. Close, "State Variables for Engineers," chap. 6, John Wiley & Sons, Inc., New York, 1965.

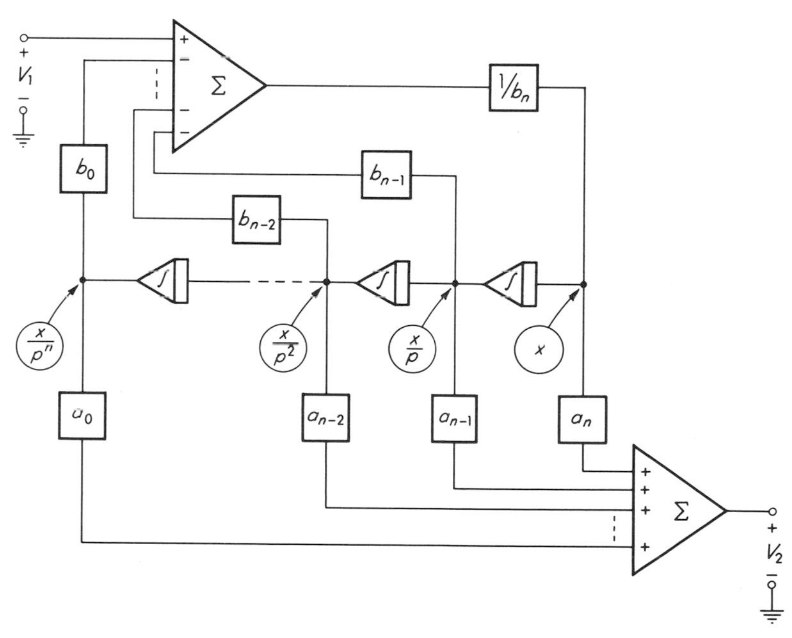

Figure 6.20 A state-variable infinite-gain network configuration.

the form

$$
\begin{aligned}
b_n x &= V_1 - \frac{b_0 x}{p^n} - \frac{b_1 x}{p^{n-1}} - \cdots - \frac{b_{n-1} x}{p} \\
V_2 &= \frac{a_0 x}{p^n} + \frac{a_1 x}{p^{n-1}} + \cdots + \frac{a_{n-1} x}{p} + a_n x
\end{aligned}
\tag{26}
$$

These equations may be realized by means of the interconnection of n integrators (each realized by an operational amplifier, a resistor, and a capacitor) and two summers (each also requiring an operational amplifier). The overall configuration is shown in Fig. 6.20. In this figure, it has been assumed for convenience that the integrators are noninverting. Modification of the circuit for the case where the more conventional inverting integrators are used is easily made. It should be noted that such a realization requires only n capacitors and a maximum of $n + 2$ operational amplifiers.*

The realizations for the integrator and summer blocks in Fig. 6.20 are easily achieved. A schematic for an integrator is shown in Fig. 6.21. For

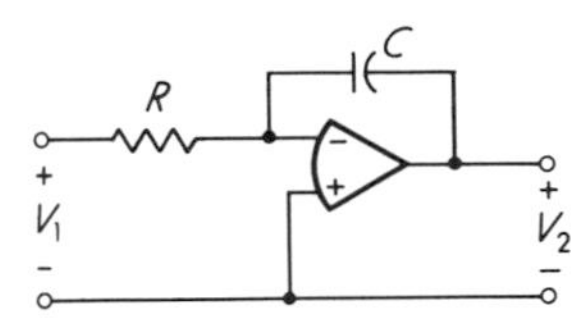

Figure 6.21 An integrator.

this circuit, the voltage transfer function (in the limit as the gain K of the operational amplifier approaches infinity) is

$$
\frac{V_2}{V_1} = \frac{-1}{pRC} \tag{27}
$$

It is also possible to use an operational amplifier to realize a noninverting integrator. Such an active device is shown in Fig. 6.22. For this circuit

* W. J. Kerwin, L. P. Huelsman, and R. W. Newcomb, State-variable Synthesis for Insensitive Integrated Circuit Transfer Functions, *IEEE J., Solid State Circuits,* vol. SC-2, no. 3, pp. 87–92, Sept., 1967.

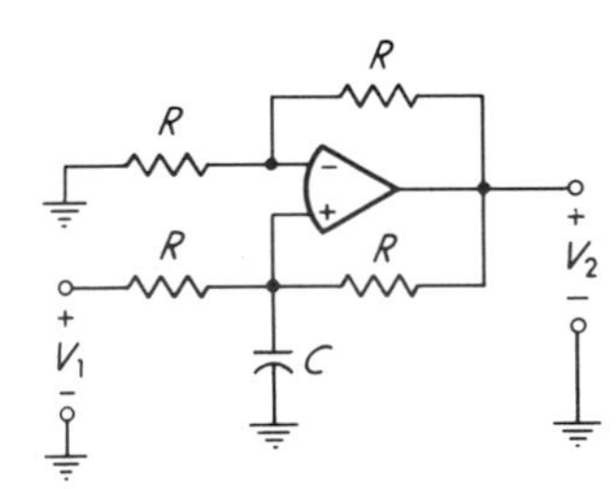

Figure 6.22 A noninverting integrator.

the voltage transfer function is*

$$\frac{V_2}{V_1} = \frac{2}{pRC} \tag{28}$$

An additional feature of the circuit shown in Fig. 6.22 is that the capacitor is grounded. This is frequently of advantage if the design is to be inte-

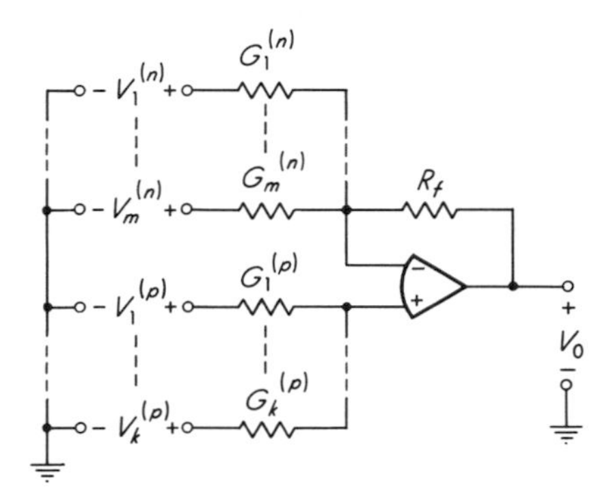

Figure 6.23 *A summer.*

grated. A schematic for a summer is given in Fig. 6.23. For this circuit, for infinite gain, we obtain

$$V_0 = \sum_{i=1}^{k} \frac{G_i^{(p)}}{G_0^{(p)}} (1 + R_f G_0^{(p)}) V_i^{(p)} - R_f \sum_{i=1}^{m} G_i^{(n)} V_i^{(n)} \tag{29}$$

where

$$G_0^{(p)} = \sum_{i=1}^{k} G_i^{(p)} \tag{30}$$

and

$$G_0^{(n)} = \sum_{i=1}^{m} G_i^{(n)} \tag{31}$$

An implementation of the above technique for the second-degree case is of interest. The schematic is shown in Fig. 6.24. For a low-pass realization, the output is taken from the terminals marked V_{lp}. In this case, the voltage transfer function in terms of the elements shown in the figure is

$$\frac{V_{lp}}{V_1} = \frac{G_1G_2G_3S_1S_2(G_5 + G_6)/G_6(G_3 + G_4)}{p^2 + p[G_1G_4S_1(G_5 + G_6)/G_6(G_3 + G_4)] + G_1G_2S_1S_2} \tag{32}$$

* G. J. DeBoo, A Novel Integrator, *Electron. Design*, no. 110, June 7, 1967.

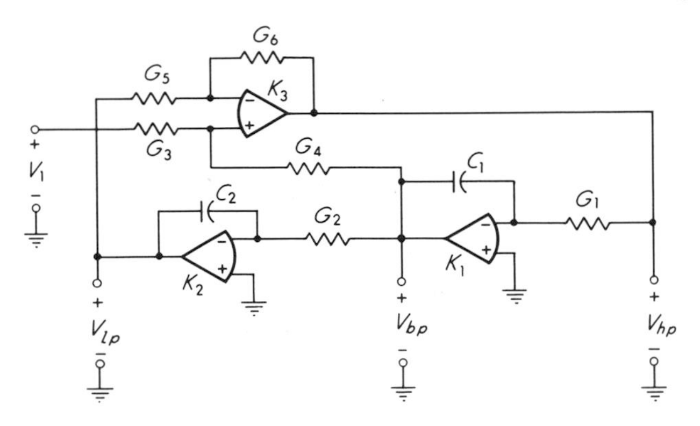

Figure 6.24 A second-degree state-variable realization.

The same circuit may be used to obtain a bandpass realization. In this case, the output is taken from the terminals marked V_{bp} in Fig. 6.24. The bandpass voltage transfer function is

$$\frac{V_{bp}}{V_1} = \frac{-pG_1G_3S_1(G_5 + G_6)/G_6(G_3 + G_4)}{p^2 + p[G_1G_4S_1(G_5 + G_6)/G_6(G_3 + G_4)] + G_1G_2S_1S_2} \tag{33}$$

Finally, if an output is taken from the terminals marked V_{hp}, we obtain the high-pass voltage transfer function

$$\frac{V_{hp}}{V_1} = \frac{p^2G_3(G_5 + G_6)/G_6(G_3 + G_4)}{p^2 + p[G_1G_4S_1(G_5 + G_6)/G_6(G_3 + G_4)] + G_1G_2S_1S_2} \tag{34}$$

Obviously, a summing amplifier can be added to produce any other desired numerator for the voltage transfer function. It should also be noted that all of the above pairs of output terminals have zero output impedance. Thus, the circuit may be readily cascaded with other circuits.

It is of interest to study the sensitivity of the coefficient of the first-degree term in the denominator of the above network transfer functions. A more detailed analysis of the integrator circuit shown in Fig. 6.21 yields the result

$$\frac{V_2}{V_1} = \frac{-K}{1 + (1 + K)pRC} \qquad K > 0 \tag{35}$$

where K is the magnitude of the gain of the operational amplifier. If we let K_1 be the magnitude of the gain of the amplifier associated with R_1 and C_1 in Fig. 6.24, let K_2 be the magnitude of the gain of the amplifier associated with R_2 and C_2, and call b_1 the coefficient of the first-degree term in the denominator of (32) through (34), we find that

$$b_1 = \frac{(G_5 + G_6)G_4}{G_6(G_3 + G_4)} \frac{K_1 G_1 S_1}{(1 + K_1)} + \frac{G_1 S_1}{(1 + K_1)} + \frac{G_2 S_2}{(1 + K_2)} \tag{36}$$

Now let us consider the case in which the network functions of (32) through (34) are frequency-normalized to unity; i.e., the coefficient of the zero-degree term in the denominator is set equal to unity. This is conveniently done by choosing $G_1 = S_1 = G_2 = S_2 = 1$. For this normalization $b_1 = 1/Q$. Thus, for large Q, b_1 must be small. From (36) we see that for small values of b_1, the term $G_4(G_5 + G_6)/G_6(G_3 + G_4)$ must also be small. Therefore, contrary perhaps to first impressions, all *three* terms in (36) must be considered in computing the sensitivity. To determine the sensitivity of b_1 to K_1, we calculate

$$S_{K_1}{}^{b_1} = \frac{\partial b_1}{\partial K_1} \frac{K_1}{b_1} = \frac{\partial b_1}{\partial K_1} K_1 Q \approx \frac{-Q}{K_1} \tag{37}$$

Similarly, it may be shown that

$$S_{K_2}{}^{b_1} = \frac{\partial b_1}{\partial K_2} \frac{K_2}{b_1} \approx \frac{-Q}{K_2} \tag{38}$$

For the low-Q case, in which the first term in the expression for b_1 in (36) is dominant, it may be shown that

$$S_{K_1}{}^{b_1} \approx \frac{-1}{K_1} \qquad S_{K_2}{}^{b_1} \approx \frac{-1}{K_2} \tag{39}$$

From (37) and (38), we see that, for cases in which the gains K_1 and K_2 are large, very large values of Q may be realized with quite reasonable sensitivities. Experimental results have shown that this circuit can be made to operate reliably with Q's in the range of 500 to 1000. It may be shown that the theoretical upper limit of the Q for this circuit is $K_1K_2/(K_1 + K_2)$, where K_1 and K_2 are the magnitudes of the gain of the operational amplifiers used in the realization.* If, in addition to choosing $G_1 = S_1 = G_2 = S_2 = 1$, we also choose $G_3 = G_5 = G_6 = 1$, the expression for G_4 (for the high-Q case) is

$$G_4 \approx \frac{1}{2}\left(b_1 - \frac{1}{K_1} - \frac{1}{K_2}\right) \tag{40}$$

* W. J. Kerwin, L. P. Huelsman, and R. W. Newcomb, *op. cit.*

For these values, the gain in the passband is $-G_3/G_4$. An example of a high-Q realization follows.

Example 6.8 As an example of the use of the state-variable configuration shown in Fig. 6.24 to realize the bandpass transfer function

$$\frac{V_2}{V_1} = \frac{-Hp}{p^2 + b_1 p + b_2}$$

for the high-Q case in which $b_1 = 0.005$ and $b_2 = 1$, we may choose the following element values:

$$\begin{array}{ll} G_1 = 1.0 \text{ mho} & G_5 = 1.0 \text{ mho} \\ G_2 = 1.0 \text{ mho} & G_6 = 1.0 \text{ mho} \\ G_3 = 1.0 \text{ mho} & C_1 = 1.0 \text{ farad} \\ G_4 = 0.0015 & C_2 = 1.0 \text{ farad} \end{array}$$
$$K_1 = K_2 = K_3 = 1000$$

From these values of elements we see that even at low values of operational amplifier gain, excellent results are obtained. This is verified by the following sensitivity matrix (for convenience a tabular format is used):

	$\Delta G_1^{(n)}$	$\Delta G_2^{(n)}$	$\Delta G_3^{(n)}$	$\Delta G_4^{(n)}$	$\Delta G_5^{(n)}$	$\Delta G_6^{(n)}$	$\Delta C_1^{(n)}$	$\Delta C_2^{(n)}$	$\Delta K_1^{(n)}$	$\Delta K_2^{(n)}$	$\Delta K_3^{(n)}$
$\Delta b_1^{(n)}$	0.8	0.2	−0.6	0.6	0.3	−0.3	−0.8	−0.2	−0.2	−0.2	0.0012
$\Delta b_2^{(n)}$	1.0	1.0	0	0	1.0	−1.0	−1.0	−1.0	0.001	0.001	0.002

To see the improved effects of increased gain, we may also consider the case where the $K_i = 10{,}000$ ($i = 1, 2,$ and 3). The element values are the same as the preceding case except for $G_4 = 0.0024$. The sensitivities in this case are

	$\Delta G_1^{(n)}$	$\Delta G_2^{(n)}$	$\Delta G_3^{(n)}$	$\Delta G_4^{(n)}$	$\Delta G_5^{(n)}$	$\Delta G_6^{(n)}$	$\Delta C_1^{(n)}$	$\Delta C_2^{(n)}$	$\Delta K_1^{(n)}$	$\Delta K_2^{(n)}$	$\Delta K_3^{(n)}$
$\Delta b_1^{(n)}$	1.0	0.02	−0.96	0.98	0.48	−0.48	−1.0	−0.02	−0.02	−0.02	0.0002
$\Delta b_2^{(n)}$	1.0	1.0	0	0	1.0	−1.0	−1.0	−1.0	0.0001	0.0001	0.0002

It should be noted that although the sensitivities for the operational amplifier gains are lower, some of the passive element sensitivities have been increased by the use of higher gains.

6.6 *Realization procedures and design information*

In this chapter we have considered the use of operational amplifiers as the active element for the realization of network functions. In the following pages, design information and actual numerical examples of circuit realizations for second-degree low-pass, high-pass, and bandpass network functions are given. These are titled circuits 7 through 12. Circuits 7 to 9 illustrate realizations using the single-feedback method discussed in Sec. 6.2. Circuits 10 to 12 provide corresponding information for the multiple-feedback techniques presented in Sec. 6.3. The network function which is realized in each case is a voltage transfer function. In each circuit, a general design procedure is described in terms of the circuit elements shown in the schematic. In addition, a specific numerical example is given illustrating the application of the design procedure. It should be noted that in all these circuits the impedance normalization constant is free to be chosen. Thus, in all of the design procedures, there will be one step in which some element is set to a convenient value. Once this value is chosen, the correct impedance normalization is achieved for all the remaining elements. It should also be noted that the examples presented in the following pages have actually been constructed and tested. Thus, the frequency-response curves indicated are those found by actual measurement.*

* The circuit diagrams and the design information given in the diagrams are reproduced through the permission of the copyright owner, the Burr-Brown Research Corporation of Tucson, Arizona, from their publication, "Handbook of Operational Amplifier RC Networks."

Circuit 7 Design procedure for the realization of a second-degree low-pass voltage transfer function using an operational amplifier in a single-feedback connection.

General circuit schematic

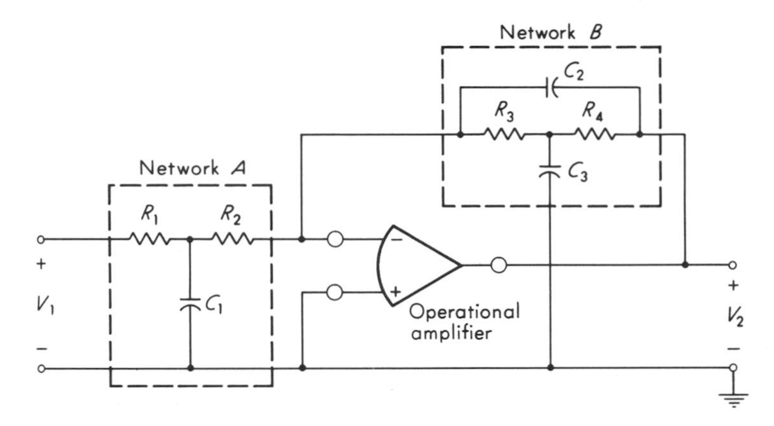

General transfer function The voltage transfer function in terms of the frequency-normalization constant ω_0 and the constant a is

$$\frac{V_2}{V_1} = \frac{-H\omega_0^2}{p^2 + a\omega_0 p + \omega_0^2}$$

General circuit characteristics An idealized Bode plot illustrating the relative gain characteristic of the transfer function and of the (open-loop) operational amplifier is shown below:

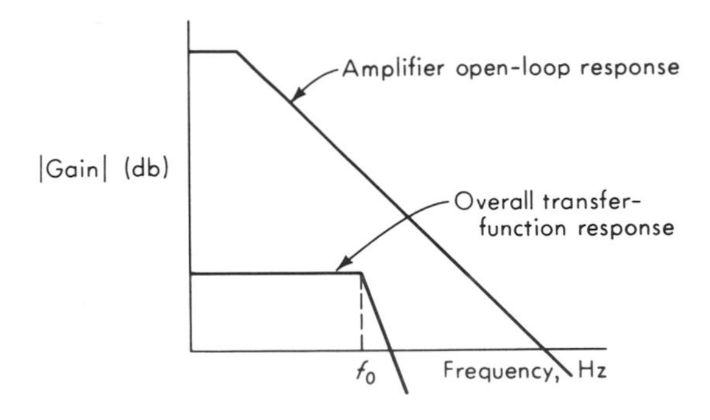

Design procedure Given a, ω_0, H:

1. Define $d = 2.5 - a$
2. Choose a convenient value of C_2 (farads) (this will usually be the smallest of the three capacitors)
3. Define $b = C_2\omega_0$

4. Calculate (ohms and farads)

$$R_1 = R_2 = \frac{a}{2Hb} \qquad C_1 = \frac{4HC_2}{a^2}$$

$$R_3 = \frac{1}{db} \qquad C_3 = \frac{d^2C_2}{ad - 1}$$

$$R_4 = \frac{a - (1/d)}{b}$$

Example of Circuit 7 The realization of a typical low-pass maximally-flat-magnitude (Butterworth) transfer function follows:

Given $f_0 = \frac{\omega_0}{2\pi} = 200$ Hz, $a = \sqrt{2}$, $H = 100$

$$C_2 = 0.00796\ \mu\text{F}$$

$b = 10^{-5}$	$R_1 = R_2 = 707$ ohms
$d = 1.086$	$R_3 = 92.1$ kilohms
$C_1 = 1.59\ \mu\text{F}$	$R_4 = 49.3$ kilohms
$C_3 = 0.0175\ \mu\text{F}$	

Transfer function for example problem

$$\frac{V_2}{V_1} = \frac{-1.58 \times 10^8}{p^2 + \sqrt{2} \times 1.256 \times 10^3 p + 1.58 \times 10^6}$$

*Circuit schematic for example problem**

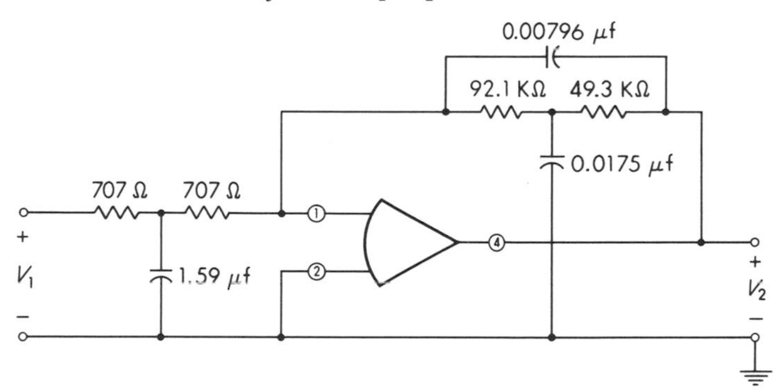

Circuit characteristic for example problem

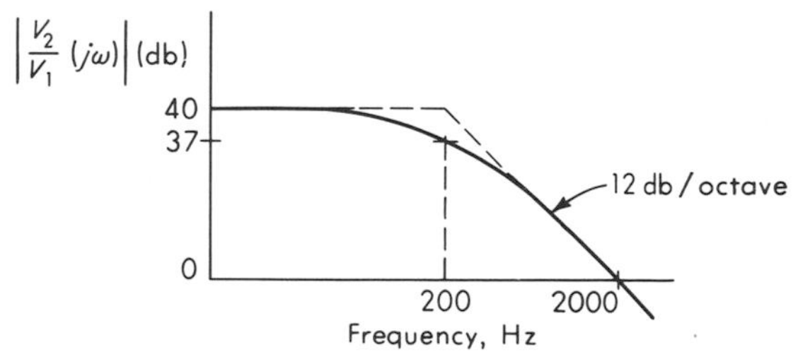

* The operational amplifier used in constructing this realization was a Burr-Brown Model 3003/15.

Circuit 8 Design procedure for the realization of a second-degree high-pass voltage transfer function using an operational amplifier in a single-feedback connection.

General circuit schematic

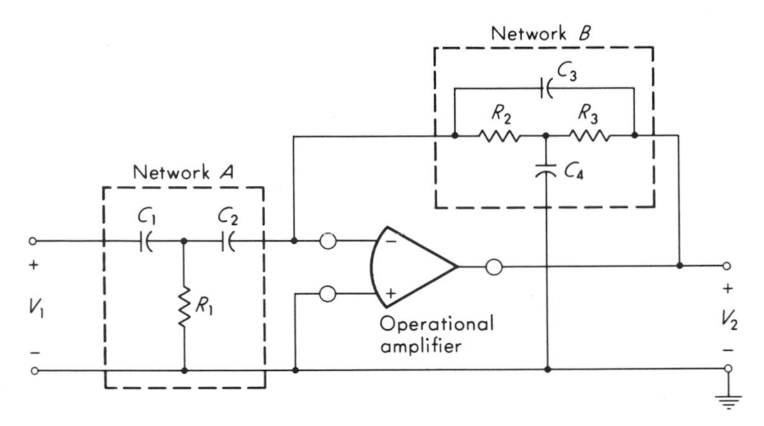

General transfer function The voltage transfer function in terms of the frequency-normalization constant ω_0 and the constant a is

$$\frac{V_2}{V_1} = \frac{-Hp^2}{p^2 + a\omega_0 p + \omega_0^2}$$

General circuit characteristics An idealized Bode plot illustrating the relative gain characteristics of the transfer function and of the (open-loop) operational amplifier is shown below:

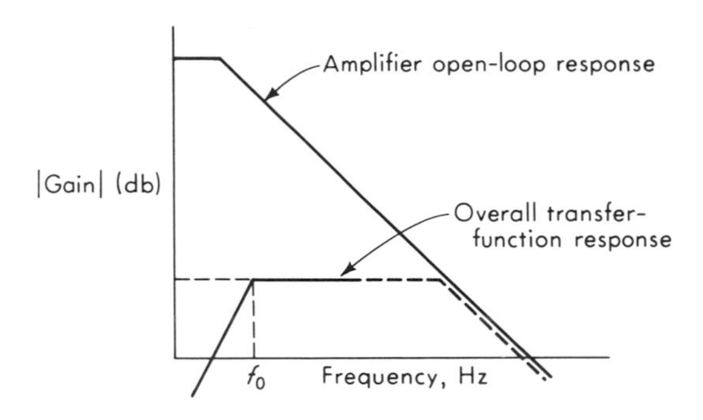

Design procedure Given a, ω_0, H:

1. Define $d = 2.5 - a$

2. Choose a convenient value of C_3 (farads) (this will usually be the smallest of the four capacitors)

3. Define $b = C_3\omega_0$

4. Calculate (ohms and farads)

$$C_1 = C_2 = 2HC_3$$

$$C_4 = \frac{d^2C_3}{ad - 1} \qquad R_2 = \frac{1}{db}$$

$$R_1 = \frac{1}{4Hab} \qquad R_3 = \frac{a - (1/d)}{b}$$

Example of Circuit 8 The realization of a typical high-pass maximally-flat-magnitude (Butterworth) transfer function follows:

Given $f_0 = \frac{\omega_0}{2\pi} = 20$ Hz, $H = 10$, $a = \sqrt{2}$

$$C_3 = 0.0796\ \mu\text{F}$$

$b = 10^{-5}$ $\qquad R_1 = 1.77$ kilohms
$d = 1.086$ $\qquad R_2 = 92.1$ kilohms
$C_1 = C_2 = 1.592\ \mu$F $\qquad R_3 = 49.3$ kilohms
$C_4 = 0.175\ \mu$F

Transfer function for example problem

$$\frac{V_2}{V_1} = \frac{-10p^2}{p^2 + \sqrt{2} \times 1.256 \times 10^2 p + 1.58 \times 10^4}$$

*Circuit schematic for example problem**

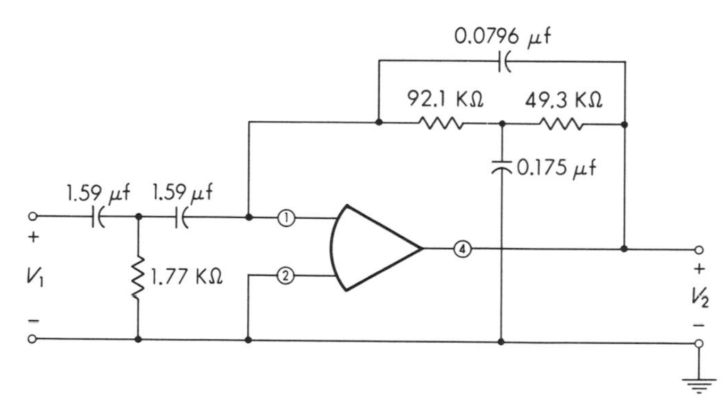

Circuit characteristic for example problem

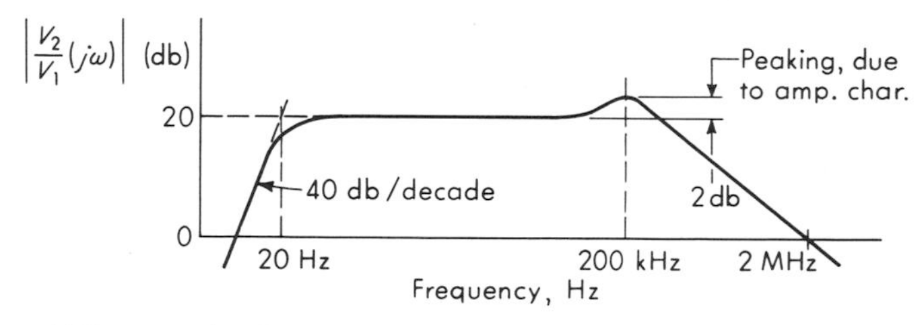

* The operational amplifier used in constructing this realization was a Burr-Brown Model 1552/15.

Circuit 9 Design procedure for the realization of a second-degree band-pass voltage transfer function using an operational amplifier in a single-feedback connection.

General circuit schematic

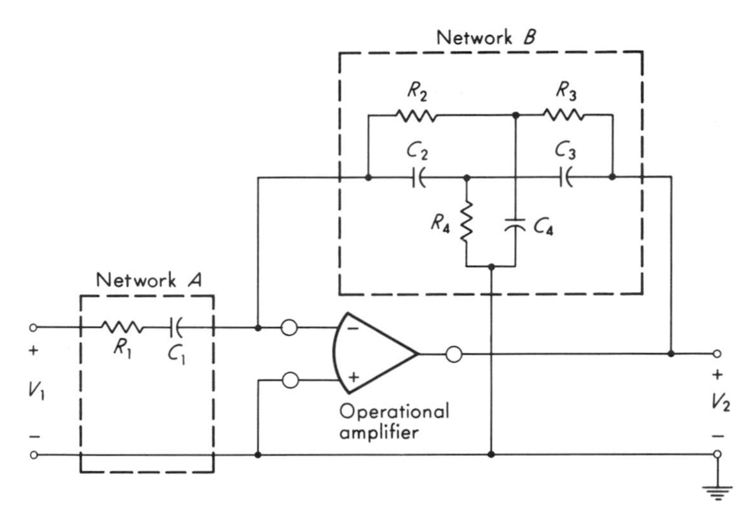

General transfer function The voltage transfer function in terms of the frequency-normalization constant ω_0 and the constant a is

$$\frac{V_2}{V_1} = \frac{-H\omega_0 p}{p^2 + a\omega_0 p + \omega_0^2}$$

General circuit characteristics An idealized Bode plot illustrating the relative gain characteristics of the transfer function and of the (open-loop) operational amplifier is shown below:

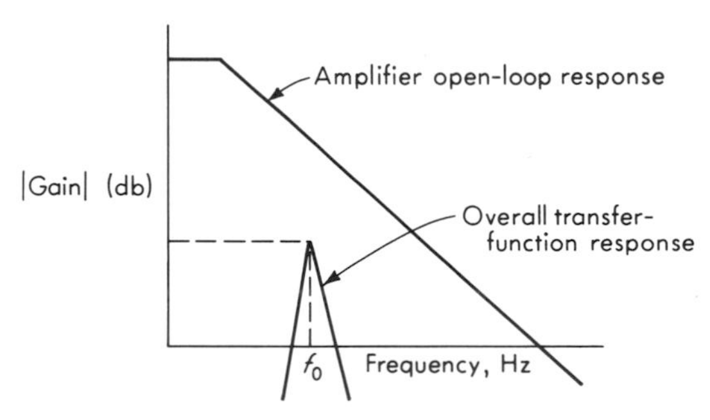

Design procedure Given a, ω_0, H:

1. Define $d = (2.5 - a)\dfrac{1 + a}{2 + a}$
2. Choose a convenient value of C_2
3. Define $b = C_2\omega_0/d$
4. Calculate (ohms and farads)

$$C_1 = \frac{Hb}{\omega_0} \qquad R_1 = \frac{1}{Hb}$$
$$C_3 = \frac{db}{(d-1)\omega_0} \qquad R_2 = \frac{1}{db}$$
$$C_4 = \frac{d}{1+a} C_3 \qquad R_3 = \frac{d-1}{db}$$
$$R_4 = \frac{(a+1)}{d} R_3$$

Example of Circuit 9 The realization of a typical bandpass function with a Q of 10 follows:

Given $f_0 = \omega_0/2\pi = 100$ Hz, $a = 0.1$, $H = 1$

$$C_2 = 0.2\ \mu\text{F}$$

$b = 10^{-4}$	$R_1 = 10$ kilohms
$C_1 = 0.159\mu\text{F}$	$R_2 = 7.96$ kilohms
$C_3 = 0.778\mu\text{F}$	$R_3 = 2.04$ kilohms
$C_4 = 0.888\mu\text{F}$	$R_4 = 1.79$ kilohms

Transfer function for example problem

$$\frac{V_2}{V_1} = \frac{-6.28 \times 10^2 p}{p^2 + 62.8p + 39.5 \times 10^4}$$

*Circuit schematic for example problem**

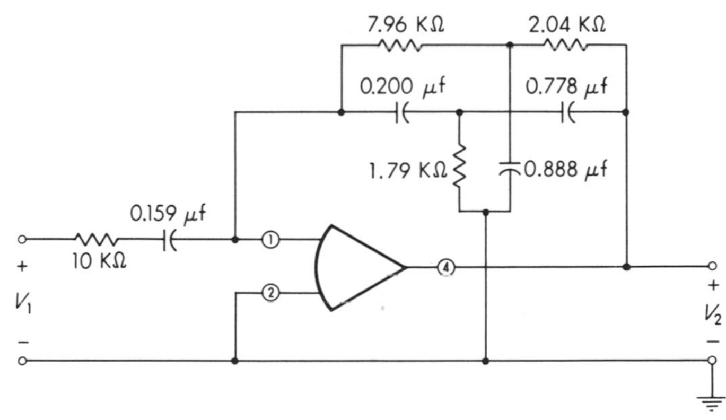

Circuit characteristic for example problem

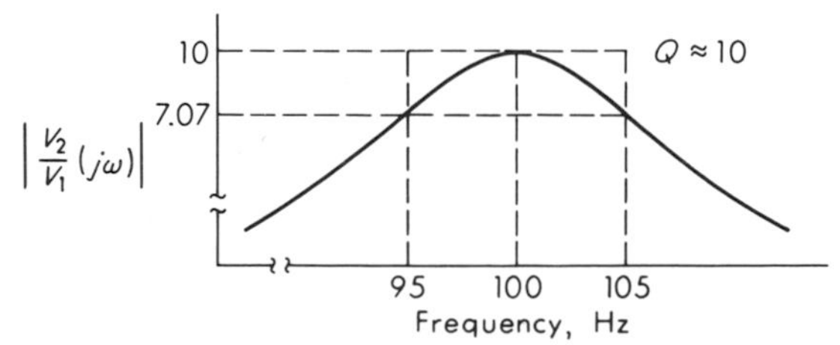

* The operational amplifier used in constructing this realization was a Burr-Brown Model 1552/15.

Circuit 10 Design procedure for the realization of a second-degree low-pass voltage transfer function using an operational amplifier in a multiple-feedback connection.

General circuit schematic

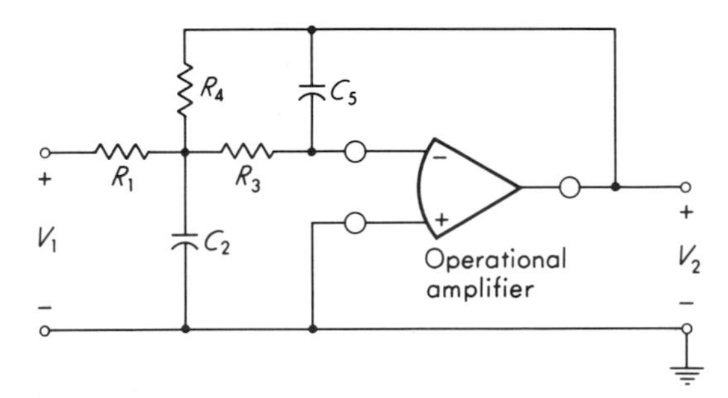

General transfer function The voltage transfer function in terms of the circuit elements and also in terms of the frequency-normalization constant ω_0 and the constant a is

$$\frac{V_2}{V_1} \approx \frac{-1/R_1R_3}{p^2C_2C_5 + pC_5[(1/R_1) + (1/R_3) + (1/R_4)] + 1/R_3R_4} = \frac{-H\omega_0^2}{p^2 + a\omega_0 p + \omega_0^2}$$

General circuit characteristics An idealized Bode plot illustrating the relative gain characteristics of the transfer function and of the (open-loop) operational amplifier is shown below:

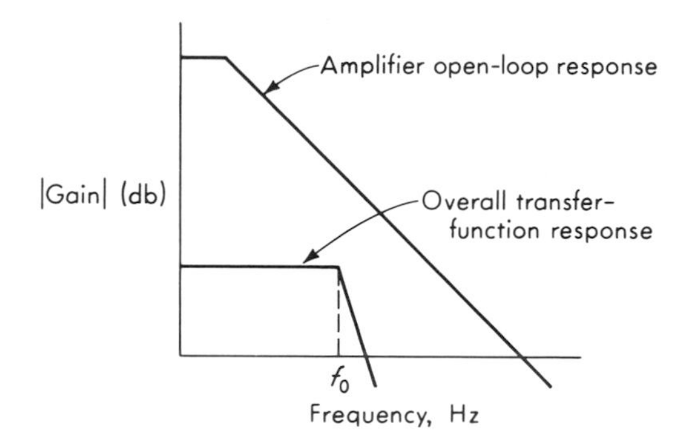

Design procedures Given a, ω_0, H:

1. Choose a convenient value of C_5
2. Define the constant $b = \omega_0 C_5$

3. Calculate (ohms and farads)

$$C_2 = \frac{4}{a^2}(H + 1)C_5 \qquad R_1 = \frac{a}{2Hb}$$

$$R_3 = \frac{a}{2(H + 1)b} \qquad R_4 = \frac{a}{2b}$$

Example of Circuit 10 The realization of a typical low-pass maximally-flat-magnitude (Butterworth) transfer function follows:

Given $f_0 = \frac{\omega_0}{2\pi} = 100$ Hz, $H = 10$, $a = \sqrt{2}$

$$C_5 = 0.1\mu F$$

$$b = 6.28 \times 10^{-5} \qquad R_1 = 1125 \text{ ohms}$$

$$C_2 = 2.2\mu F \qquad R_3 = 1020 \text{ ohms}$$

$$R_4 = 11.25 \text{ kilohms}$$

Transfer function for example problem

$$\frac{V_2}{V_1} = \frac{-39.5 \times 10^5}{p^2 + 8.9 \times 10^2 p + 39.5 \times 10^4}$$

*Circuit schematic for example problem**

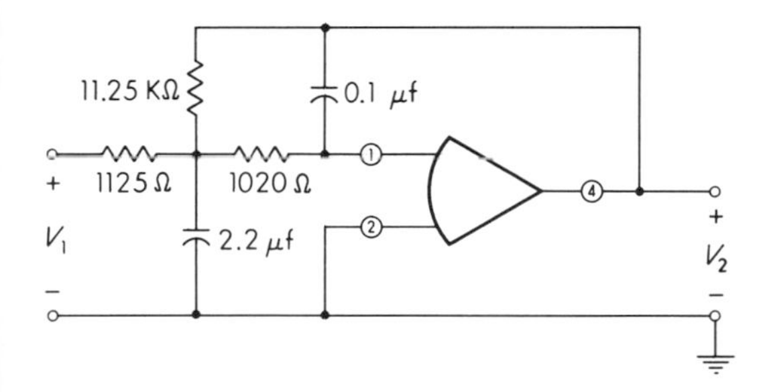

Circuit characteristic for example problem

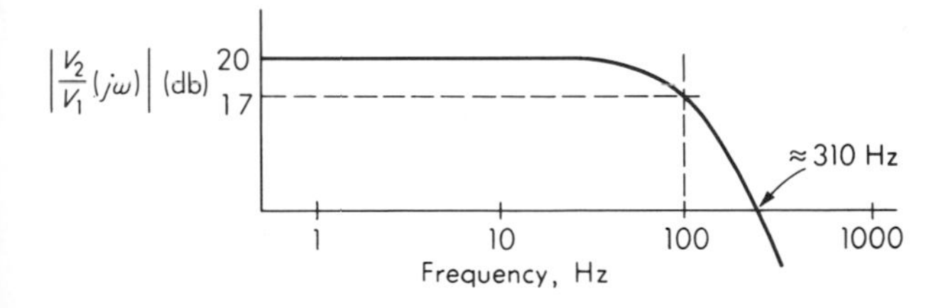

* The operational amplifier used in constructing this realization was a Burr-Brown Model 3003/15.

Circuit 11 Design procedure for the realization of a second-degree high-pass voltage transfer function using an operational amplifier in a multiple-feedback connection.

General circuit schematic

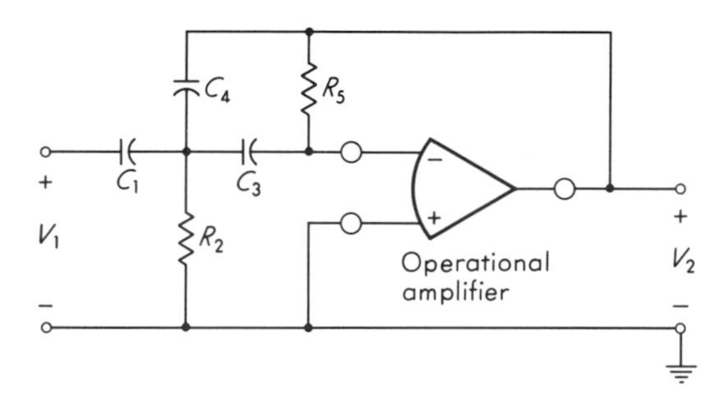

General transfer function The voltage transfer function in terms of the circuit elements and also in terms of the frequency-normalization constant ω_0 and the constant a is

$$\frac{V_2}{V_1} \approx \frac{-p^2 C_1 C_3}{p^2 C_3 C_4 + p(1/R_5)(C_1 + C_3 + C_4) + 1/R_2 R_5} = \frac{-Hp^2}{p^2 + a\omega_0 p + \omega_0^2}$$

General circuit characteristics An idealized Bode plot illustrating the relative gain characteristics of the transfer function and of the (open-loop) operational amplifier is shown below:

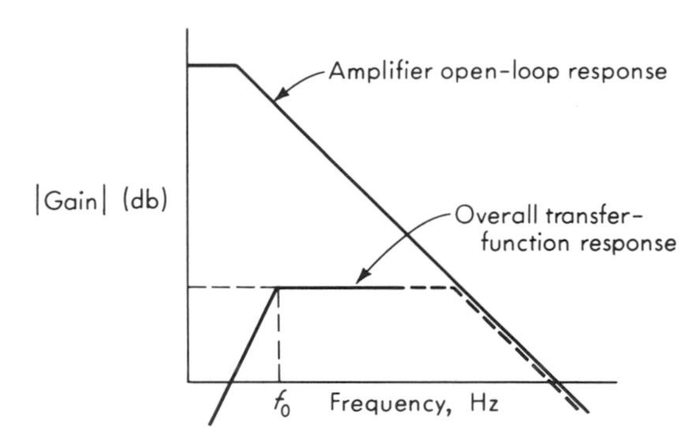

Design procedure Given a, ω_0, H:

1. Choose a convenient value of C_1
2. Define the constant $b = C_1\omega_0$

3. Calculate (ohms and farads)

$$C_3 = C_1 \qquad R_2 = \frac{a}{b[2 + (1/H)]}$$

$$C_4 = \frac{C_1}{H} \qquad R_5 = \frac{H[2 + (1/H)]}{ab}$$

Example of Circuit 11 The realization of a typical high-pass maximally-flat-magnitude (Butterworth) transfer function follows:

Given $f_0 = \frac{\omega_0}{2\pi} = 0.1$ Hz, $a = \sqrt{2}$, $H = 1$

$$C_1 = 10\ \mu\text{F}$$

$$b = 6.28 \times 10^{-6} \qquad R_2 = 75.2 \text{ kilohms}$$

$$C_3 = 10\ \mu\text{F} \qquad R_3 = 338 \text{ kilohms}$$

$$C_4 = 10\ \mu\text{F}$$

Transfer function for example problem

$$\frac{V_2}{V_1} = \frac{-p^2}{p^2 + 0.89p + 0.395}$$

*Circuit schematic for example problem**

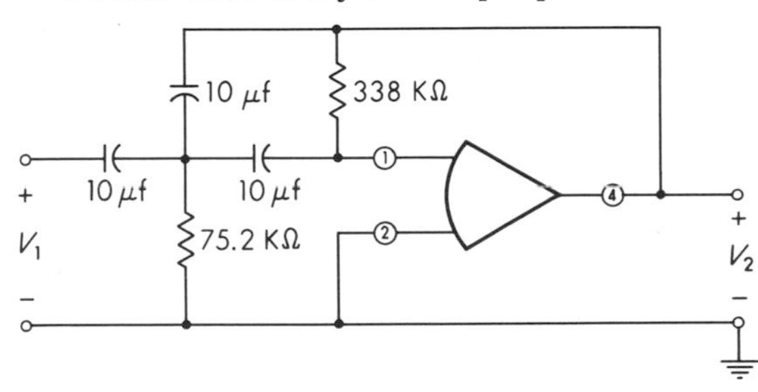

Circuit characteristic for example problem

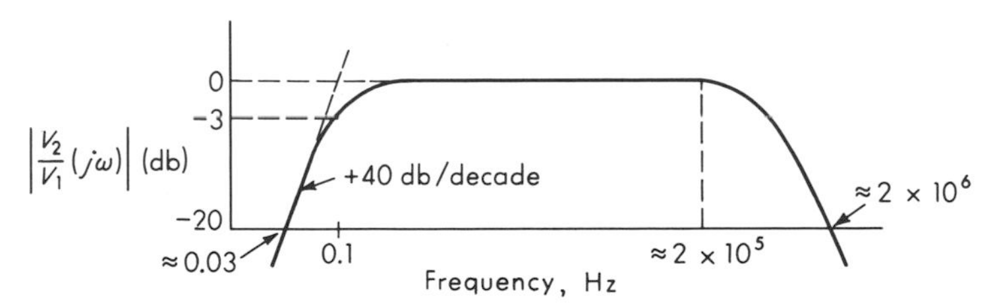

* The operational amplifier used in constructing this realization was a Burr-Brown Model 3003/15.

Circuit 12 Design procedure for the realization of a second-degree bandpass voltage transfer function using an operational amplifier in a multiple-feedback connection.

General circuit schematic

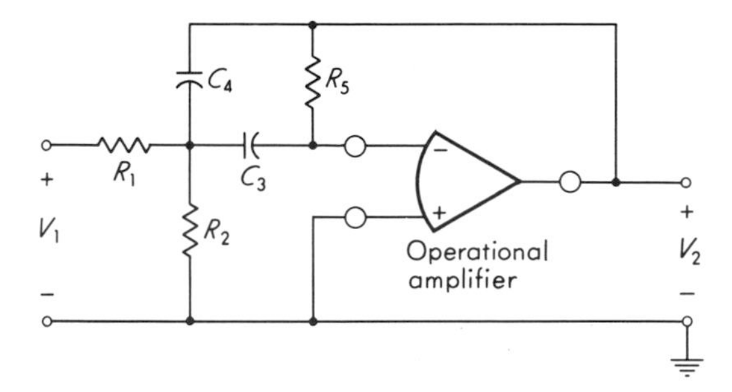

General transfer function The voltage transfer function in terms of the circuit elements and also in terms of the frequency-normalization constant ω_0 and the constant a is

$$\frac{V_2}{V_1} \approx \frac{-p(C_3/R_1)}{p^2C_3C_4 + p(1/R_5)(C_3 + C_4) + (1/R_5)[(1/R_1) + (1/R_2)]} = \frac{-H\omega_0 p}{p^2 + a\omega_0 p + \omega_0^2}$$

General circuit characteristics An idealized Bode plot illustrating the relative gain characteristics of the transfer function and of the (open-loop) operational amplifier is shown below:

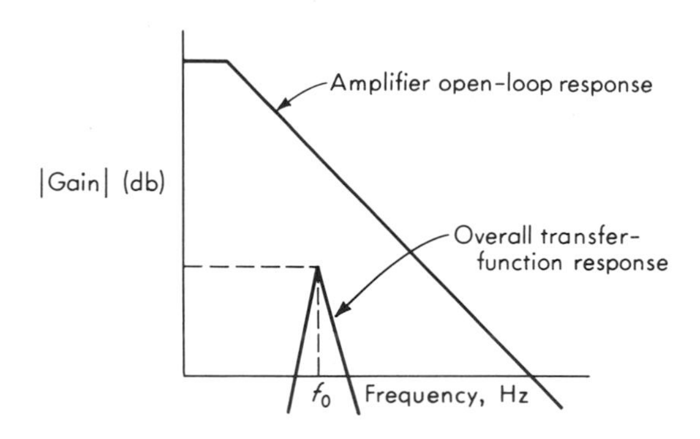

Design procedure Given a, ω_0, H:

1. Choose a convenient value of C_3
2. Define the constant $b = C_3\omega_0$

3. Calculate (ohms and farads)

$$C_4 = C_3 \qquad R_2 = \frac{1}{[(2/a) - H]b}$$

$$R_1 = \frac{1}{Hb} \qquad R_5 = \frac{2}{ab}$$

Example of Circuit 12 The realization of a typical bandpass transfer function with a Q of 10 follows:

Given $f_0 = \frac{\omega_0}{2\pi} = 1.6$ Hz, $a = 0.1$, $H = 1$

$$b = 10^{-4} \qquad C_3 = 10\ \mu\text{F}$$
$$C_4 = 10\ \mu\text{F} \qquad R_2 = 527 \text{ ohms}$$
$$R_1 = 10 \text{ kilohms} \qquad R_5 = 200 \text{ kilohms}$$

Transfer function for example problem

$$\frac{V_2}{V_1} = \frac{-10p}{p^2 + p + 100}$$

*Circuit schematic for example problem**

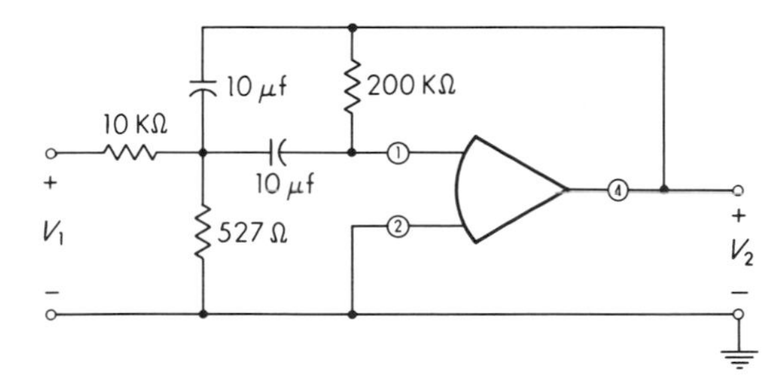

Circuit characteristic for example problem

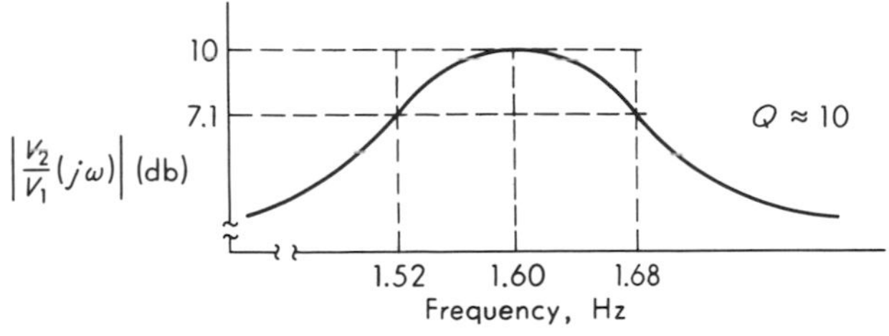

Note: 100 sec. count used to determine frequency

* The operational amplifier used in constructing this realization was a Burr-Brown Model 3003/15.

6.7 *Conclusion*

In this chapter we have considered the use of "infinite-gain" elements as active devices for use in active *RC* realization techniques. This class of active realizations is quite different from the controlled-source, negative-immittance converter, and gyrator classes discussed previously. One of the major differences is that when ideal devices (i.e., devices in which the gain approaches infinity) are considered, the gain constant of the device does not appear in the equations describing the overall network behavior. Thus, the concepts of polynomial decomposition introduced in Chap. 2 are not directly applicable to this class of realizations. It is possible, however, to make sensitivity studies for specific network realizations by taking the limiting case as the gain of the device approaches infinity. Such studies will establish the low sensitivities which are a characteristic of this class of realizations.

In addition to the advantage of low sensitivity of realizations using infinite-gain VCVS active devices (operational amplifiers), such realizations also have several other advantages. One of these is the low output impedance of the active device, which permits the cascading of low-degree functions without the necessity for isolating amplifiers. Another advantage lies in the fact that operational amplifiers are well developed from a technological viewpoint and thus are readily available both in integrated and lumped form over a wide range of prices and specifications.

The fact that the gain constant of the operational amplifier does not occur explicitly in the network function may be a disadvantage in some applications in which it is desired to vary certain properties of the network functions. Another disadvantage is that this class of realizations may require more passive elements to realize a given network function than some of the classes previously discussed.

PROBLEMS

6.1 Verify the y parameters given in (1) for the four-port network with a VCVS connected as shown in Fig. 6.1, for the limiting case of infinite gain.

6.2 Repeat Prob. 6.1 for the network configurations shown in Figs. 6.2, 6.3, and 6.4.

6.3 Find a realization using a single operational amplifier for the multiple-input transfer function that follows:

$$V_0 = \frac{V_1 + pV_2 + p^2V_3}{p^2 + 0.1p + 1}$$

6.4 Find an infinite-gain single-feedback realization for the bandpass transfer function

$$\frac{V_2}{V_1} = \frac{-10p}{p^2 + 0.01p + 1}$$

6.5 The infinite-gain multiple-feedback realization shown in Fig. 6.15 realizes a second-degree bandpass function. Find three other realizations of the general form given in Fig. 6.12 which realize second-degree bandpass functions.

6.6 Find an infinite-gain multiple-feedback realization for the following bandpass transfer function:

$$\frac{V_2}{V_1} = \frac{-Hp}{p^2 + 0.01p + 1}$$

6.7 Apply both of the two general techniques given in Sec. 6.4 to find realizations for the bandpass transfer function given in Prob. 6.4.

6.8 Use the state-variable technique given in Sec. 6.5 to obtain a realization for the following transfer function:

$$\frac{V_2}{V_1} = \frac{p^2 + 1.21}{p^2 + 0.01p + 1}$$

6.9 Analyze the integrator circuit shown in Fig. 6.22 to verify the relation of (28).

6.10 Analyze the general summer circuit shown in Fig. 6.23 to verify the relation of (29).

6.11 Derive the expression for the coefficient b_1 as given in (36).

Chapter 7 Summary and general comments

The goal of this text has been to provide the reader with an introduction to the theory and practice of active *RC* circuits. In the earlier portion of the book, the mathematical theory of sensitivity and polynomial decomposition was developed to provide a common basis for the treatment of all types of active *RC* circuits. Later portions of the book then applied this theory to the details of circuit realization, using several different approaches based on the utilization of different types of active devices. For purposes of comparison, typical realizations of similar network functions were given for each different approach, i.e., for each different active device.

In the mind of the reader who has studied the text material to this point a question now arises, if indeed it has not arisen many pages before. The question is, since there are so many different ways of realizing a given type of network function, e.g., a low-pass, bandpass, or high-pass function, what criteria can be applied to select one form of realization, i.e., one type of active element, over another? This is obviously an exceedingly practical question. The answer to it basically lies in the observation that the specification of only the transfer function does not usually completely express the desired characteristics for the network realization. Other criteria hover outside the sharply defined boundaries of the complex-frequency plane, and these criteria must provide the final factors in choosing between realizations which, in terms of their transfer functions, provide equivalent results.

There are an almost limitless number of such criteria. Perhaps, for example, the circuit is to be fabricated from lumped elements of a type which are relatively expensive. If a large number of circuits are to be built, a minimal element realization may be the most attractive from an economic viewpoint. Perhaps an extremely high-Q realization is desired, in which case sensitivity will certainly become most important, and therefore low-sensitivity approaches are preferable. As another example, if the designer requires that the resulting realization be variable in some special way, e.g., variable bandwidth, some realizations may prove much more applicable in this regard than others. Perhaps the designer has a mother-in-law who owns a gyrator factory, in which case, for peace in the family, only gyrator realizations are acceptable. The list is obviously easily extended.

Many examples may be found in the preceding chapters to verify the suitability of certain realizations over others when specific design criteria are employed. A few of these are given below:

Example 7.1 It is desired to realize a second-degree low-pass network with the criterion that the low-frequency gain may be adjusted without varying the frequency characteristics and that the cutoff frequency may be varied without affecting the gain. The low-pass realization of the controlled-source type, using an operational amplifier with a feedback connection as shown in Fig. 3.23, meets these criteria, although none of the other low-pass realizations meet them. Changes in gain are simply made by varying R_a or R_b. Changes in the cutoff frequency are accomplished by simultaneous equal-percentage variations of G_1 and G_2. These conclusions are easily verified from (52) in Chap. 3.

Example 7.2 It is desired to realize a second-degree bandpass network function in which the Q of the realization is easily adjustable. For such a criteria, the controlled-source realization shown in Fig. 3.13 with the transfer function given in (35) of Chap. 3 or the NIC realization shown in Fig. 4.33 with the transfer function given in (42) of Chap. 4 are both suitable. A secondary criterion, such as the desirability of low output impedance, might be used to differentiate between the two realizations, favoring the controlled-source realization. On the other hand, a secondary criterion based on sensitivity would favor the NIC realization with its optimum insensitivity.

Example 7.3 It is desired to realize a second-degree bandpass network in which the bandwidth is constant, but the center frequency is variable. In addition, varying the center frequency should not change the gain in the passband. For such a criteria, the gyrator realization shown in Fig. 5.22 with the transfer function given in (31) of Chap. 5 is suitable. If the realization for the gyrator shown in Fig. 5.29 is employed, the term G^2 in the denominator of (31) becomes G_1G_2. Similarly, the term G in the numerator of (31) becomes simply G_2. Thus, we see that varying G_1 changes the resonant frequency of the network without affecting either the bandwidth or the gain.

Table 7.1 Summary of the advantages and disadvantages of the various realization techniques

Property	Realization technique (active element)						
	Controlled-source		Negative-immittance converter	Gyrator	Infinite-gain		
	Noninverting	Inverting			Single-feedback	Multiple-feedback	State-variable
Simplicity of realization for active element	+	+	+	−	+	+	+
Small number of active elements required	+	+	+	+	+	+	−
Summing input available	−	−	+	−	+	−	+
Low output impedance	+	+	−	−	+	+	+
Poles always remain in left half-plane	+	−	−	+	+	+	+
Optimum polynomial decomposition possible	−	−	+	+	−	−	−
Low spread of element values	O	+	+	O	O	−	−
High-Q realizations possible	−	+	+	O	+	−	+
High gain available	+	+	+	−	+	−	+
Characteristics easily adjustable	O	+	+	+	−	−	+

In order to provide a summary of some of the significant properties of the various classes of active *RC* realization techniques, Table 7.1 has been prepared. This table lists some of the desirable properties that might be sought in a given network realization. It also gives, by means of the symbols "+," "0," and "−," an indication of what classes of realizations have relatively favorable, average, or relatively unfavorable characteristics with respect to each of the properties. Although there is some subjectiveness in the classification, the table should serve as a useful summary of the properties of the various classes of realizations covered in the preceding chapters. As such, it is the author's hope that it may serve as a chart by means of which the reader may plot his own journeys into the world of active *RC* circuits, a world without inductors.

Appendix A *The properties of driving-point functions*

In this appendix we shall study the properties of driving-point functions which may be produced by various classes of passive and active *RC* networks. The classes of networks will be arranged in the order of increasing generality and usefulness.

A.1 *The properties of passive RC driving-point immittances*

In this section we shall briefly review the basic characteristics of driving-point immittances of passive *RC* networks, i.e., those whose elements are positive-valued resistors and capacitors. The material will be presented in such a manner as to be readily extendible to the active cases which follow.

The nodal equations for a passive *RC* network may be written in matrix form as

$$\mathbf{I} = (\mathbf{G} + p\mathbf{C})\mathbf{V} \tag{1}$$

where $\mathbf{I}$ is a column matrix with elements $I_i(p)$, the excitation currents at the various nodes, and $\mathbf{V}$ is a column matrix with elements $V_i(p)$, the independent nodal voltages. All the above elements are functions of p, the complex-frequency variable. $\mathbf{G}$ and $\mathbf{C}$ are the real symmetric matrices whose elements specify the self- and (with appropriate signs) mutual conductances and capacitances of the network branches. Thus, (1) represents the Laplace transformation of the differential equations describing the network under the condition that the initial conditions are zero. If we multiply both sides of (1) by $\bar{\mathbf{V}}^t$, we obtain

$$\bar{\mathbf{V}}^t\mathbf{I} = \bar{\mathbf{V}}^t\mathbf{G}\mathbf{V} + p\bar{\mathbf{V}}^t\mathbf{C}\mathbf{V} \tag{2}$$

We may now define the quadratic forms*

$$
\begin{aligned}
F_0 &= \bar{\mathbf{V}}^t\mathbf{G}\mathbf{V} \\
H_0 &= \bar{\mathbf{V}}^t\mathbf{C}\mathbf{V}
\end{aligned}
\tag{3}
$$

In terms of these functions, (2) becomes

$$
\bar{\mathbf{V}}^t\mathbf{I} = F_0 + pH_0 \tag{4}
$$

If we restrict our observations of the above equations to the case in which only sinusoidal steady-state conditions are considered, the quadratic form F_0 is proportional to the average power dissipated in the resistive portions of the network. Thus, it can never be negative. It is also, of course, real. From this physical consideration we see that F_0 must be a positive semidefinite quadratic form. Similarly, under these conditions, H_0 is proportional to the average energy stored in the electric field associated with the capacitors of the network. As such it also is a real positive semidefinite quadratic form. These quadratic forms are frequently referred to as energy functions.† Since the properties of the above quadratic forms are determined by the properties of the matrices **G** and **C** and are independent of the form of the variables $V_i(p)$, we see that F_0 and H_0 are positive semidefinite not only for the sinusoidal case, but for all values of excitation. In this more general case, the forms no longer represent power and energy, but their positive semidefiniteness is still assured.

Now consider the case where only I_1 is nonzero. Equation (4) becomes

$$
\bar{V}_1 I_1 = F_0 + pH_0 \tag{5}
$$

If we divide both sides of (5) by $V_1\bar{V}_1$ ($= |V_1|^2$), we obtain

$$
Y(p) = \frac{I_1}{V_1} = \frac{1}{|V_1|^2}(F_0 + pH_0) \tag{6}
$$

This may be considered as a general expression for the driving-point admittance function of a one-port passive RC network. The zeros of such an admittance occur when

$$
F_0 + pH_0 = 0 \tag{7}
$$

This may be written

$$
p = -\frac{F_0}{H_0} \tag{8}
$$

* A treatment of quadratic forms is given in most texts on matrix algebra. For example, see F. Hohn, "Elementary Matrix Algebra," chap. 9, The Macmillan Company, New York, 1960. See also, L. P. Huelsman, "Circuits, Matrices, and Linear Vector Spaces," chap. 5, McGraw-Hill Book Company, New York, 1963.

† A very thorough treatment of energy functions covering the instantaneous case, the sinusoidal case, and the generalized frequency case may be found in E. A. Guillemin, "Introductory Circuit Theory," chap. 10, John Wiley & Sons, Inc., New York, 1953.

Note that (8) cannot be solved for the explicit values of p at which the admittance $Y(p)$ is zero because the functions F_0 and H_0 are functions of the voltages $V_i(p)$ which are themselves functions of p. However, since we know that F_0 and H_0 are real and nonnegative for all values of p, we may conclude that the zeros of a passive RC driving-point admittance occur only on the negative-real axis or at the origin. A development parallel to the above but starting with loop equations may be used to show that the zeros of an RC driving-point impedance occur on the negative-real axis or at infinity.

Thus, we may list a first property of RC driving-point functions:

Property 1 *The poles and zeros of passive RC driving-point immittances are located on the negative-real axis.*

We may develop further properties of the passive RC driving-point admittance $Y(p)$ by defining $p = \sigma + j\omega$ and considering $dY(\sigma)/d\sigma$, that is, the derivative of the function evaluated along the real axis. To do this, let us consider the real and the imaginary parts of $Y(p)$.

We may write

$$Y(p) = G(\sigma,\omega) + jB(\sigma,\omega) \tag{9}$$

For convenience, and without loss of generality, we may take $|V_1|^2$ as unity. Then, from (6) and (9) we see that

$$\begin{aligned} G(\sigma,\omega) &= F_0 + \sigma H_0 \\ B(\sigma,\omega) &= \omega H_0 \end{aligned} \tag{10}$$

Since $Y(p)$ is an analytic function of p, the Cauchy-Riemann conditions may be used to relate the real and the imaginary parts of the function.* One of these conditions is that

$$\frac{\partial G(\sigma,\omega)}{\partial\sigma} = \frac{\partial B(\sigma,\omega)}{\partial\omega} \tag{11}$$

Thus, from (9), (10), and (11) we see that

$$\frac{dY(\sigma)}{d\sigma} = \frac{\partial G(\sigma,\omega)}{\partial\sigma}\bigg|_{\omega=0} = \frac{\partial B(\sigma,\omega)}{\partial\omega}\bigg|_{\omega=0} = \left(H_0 + \omega\frac{\partial H_0}{\partial\omega}\right)\bigg|_{\omega=0} = H_0 \tag{12}$$

It has been shown that H_0 is always real and nonnegative and, except in trivial cases, it will also be nonzero. Thus, we see that the slope of $Y(\sigma)$ is positive.

* These conditions are described in any of the standard mathematical texts covering complex-variable theory. See, for example, I. S. Sokolnikoff and R. M. Redheffer, "Mathematics of Physics and Modern Engineering," chap. 7, p. 543, McGraw-Hill Book Company, New York, 1958.

A similar development may be made for the case of a passive RC driving-point impedance. We find that $dZ(\sigma)/d\sigma$ is always negative. We now have the following property:

Property 2 *For a passive RC driving-point immittance,* $dY(\sigma)/d\sigma \geq 0$, and $dZ(\sigma)/d\sigma \leq 0$.

From considerations of energy, it is easy to see that the value of a passive driving-point immittance evaluated at $p = 0$ or $p = \infty$ must be nonnegative. Therefore, we have the following property:

Property 3 *For a passive RC driving-point immittance,* $Y(0)$, $Y(\infty)$, $Z(0)$, and $Z(\infty)$ *are all real and nonnegative.*

In Figs. A.1 and A.2, typical plots for $Y(\sigma)$ and $Z(\sigma)$ are shown. Consideration of these plots leads to the following properties:

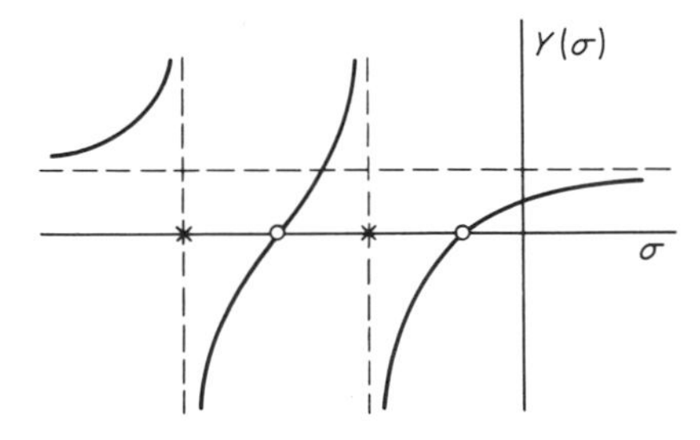

***Figure A.1** A typical plot of* $Y(\sigma)$ *for a passive RC network.*

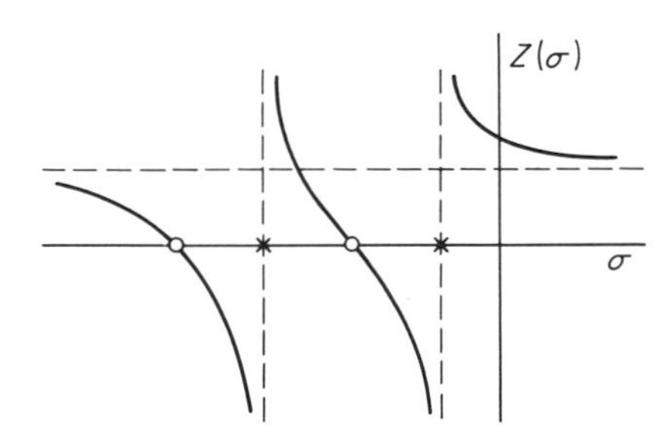

***Figure A.2** A typical plot of* $Z(\sigma)$ *for a passive RC network.*

Property 4 *For a passive RC driving-point immittance, the poles and zeros alternate on the negative-real axis and are simple.*

Property 5 *For a passive RC driving-point immittance* $Y(0) \leq Y(\infty)$, and $Z(0) \geq Z(\infty)$.

Property 6 *The singularity (pole or zero) of a passive RC driving-point admittance closest to the origin is a zero; the singularity closest to infinity is a pole.*

Property 7 *The singularity (pole or zero) of a passive RC driving-point impedance closest to the origin is a pole; the singularity closest to infinity is a zero.*

If a passive RC driving-point admittance function with the properties defined above is expressed in the form of a partial-fraction expansion, we obtain

$$Y(p) = k_a p + k_b + \sum_i \frac{k_i}{p + \sigma_i} \tag{13}$$

Now let us investigate the properties of the various k's in this expression. From (9) and (10) we see that since $Y(\sigma)$ is real, all the k's must be real. Since k_a is the residue for the pole at infinity and since such a pole is the result of a positive-valued capacitor, k_a must be positive. Now let us investigate the behavior of $Y(\sigma)$ in the immediate vicinity of a pole at $-\sigma_i$. In this region,

$$Y(\sigma) \approx \frac{k_i}{\sigma + \sigma_i} \tag{14}$$

If $\sigma > -\sigma_i$, the denominator of the right-hand member of (14) is positive. Therefore, the polarity of $Y(\sigma)$ is the same as the polarity of k_i. From Fig. A.1 we see that in this region, $Y(\sigma) < 0$. Therefore, k_i is negative. Since k_i represents the residues of $Y(p)$ at its negative-real poles, we see that these residues are negative. The remaining constant, k_b, must be positive since $Y(\sigma)$ is positive. It must also be greater than or equal to $\sum_i |k_i/\sigma_i|$.

Similarly, it may be shown that if a passive RC driving-point impedance is expressed in the form of a partial-fraction expansion, we obtain

$$Z(p) - k_\infty + \frac{k_0}{p} + \sum_i \frac{k_i}{p + \sigma_i} \tag{15}$$

All the k's in this expression may be shown to be real and positive. The results of the above paragraphs may be expressed by the following properties:

Property 8 *The residues at the finite negative-real poles of a passive RC driving-point admittance are real and negative. The residue at a pole at infinity is real and positive.*

Property 9 *The residues at the negative-real poles and the pole at the origin of a passive RC driving-point impedance are real and positive.*

Frequently it is convenient to express $Y(p)$ in a different form of partial-fraction expansion than that given in (13). The new form of expansion has the advantage that the terms are separately realizable as RC networks. The form is

$$Y(p) = k_\infty p + k_0 + \sum_i \frac{k_i p}{p + \sigma_i} \tag{16}$$

The k's of such an expansion are all nonnegative. The realization for the various terms is given in Fig. A.3. A parallel connection of the individual

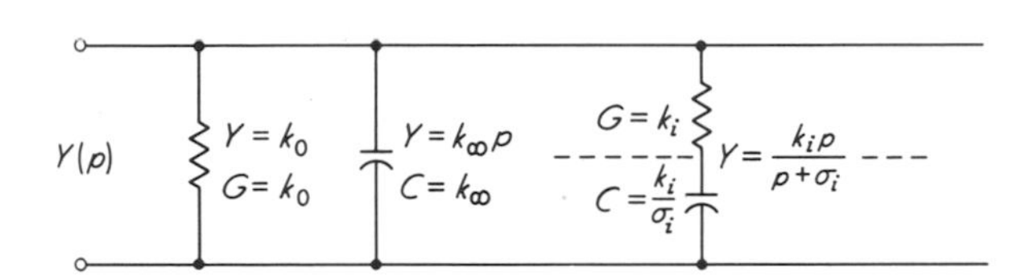

***Figure A.3** A realization of (16) for a passive RC driving-point admittance.*

networks realizes the given admittance. We shall call the partial-fraction expansion of (16) a *realizable* partial-fraction expansion to distinguish between it and the type given in (13). Similarly, a realization of the partial-fraction expansion of an impedance as given in (15) may be made by the separate realization of the terms as shown in Fig. A.4.

***Figure A.4** A realization of (15) for a passive RC driving-point impedance.*

We may summarize the above properties as follows:

Property 10 *A passive RC driving-point admittance may be expressed in the form given in (16) with all the k's nonnegative. A realization may be made in the manner indicated in Fig. A.3.*

Property 11 *A passive RC driving-point impedance may be expressed in the form given in (15) with all k's nonnegative. A realization may be made in the manner indicated in Fig. A.4.*

The realization of Figs. A.3 and A.4 are called *Foster forms*. They are referred to as *canonic* realizations since they have the minimum number of elements possible to realize a given driving-point function.*

A.2 *The properties of $\pm R$, $+C$ driving-point immittances*

In this and the sections that follow, we shall consider how the properties which were derived in the last section for passive *RC* driving-point immittances are altered when various active elements are included. As a first case we shall investigate the effects of including negative-valued resistors with the positive-valued resistors and capacitors discussed to this point. Thus, we shall consider the class of networks which may be symbolized as $\pm R$, $+C$. We may again derive the quadratic forms given in (3). Since negative-valued resistors are being considered, however, F_0 may be negative. Thus, it is no longer a positive semidefinite quadratic form. H_0, of course, is still positive semidefinite. The zeros of the driving-point admittance, as determined by (8), may have both positive- and negative-real values. In a similar fashion it may be shown that the zeros of a driving-point impedance may also have positive- or negative-real values. Since either the zeros of the numerator or the zeros of the denominator of a driving-point function may constitute the natural frequencies of the network,† stability considerations require that at least one of these polynomials have no right-half-plane zeros. This, however, is a limitation of application (and a rather important one) rather than a limitation on the class of networks being considered. Property 1 now becomes

Property 1a *The poles and zeros of $\pm R$, $+C$ driving-point functions are located on the real axis.*

* Another well-known canonic realization is the Cauer form, which is based on continued-fraction expansions for the driving-point admittance and impedance functions. Another canonic form was described in the article by H. B. Lee, A New Canonic Realization Procedure, *IEEE Trans. Circuit Theory*, vol. CT-10, no. 1, pp. 81–85, March, 1963.

† In the case of a driving-point impedance function, the zeros of the numerator are referred to as the *short-circuit natural frequencies*, i.e., those resulting from excitation of the network by a voltage source, whereas the zeros of the denominator are referred to as the *open-circuit natural frequencies*, i.e., those resulting from excitation of the network by a current source.

From (12) we see that the function $dY(\sigma)/d\sigma$ depends only on H_0. Therefore this slope is positive just as it was in the passive RC case. Similarly, we find that $dZ(\sigma)/d\sigma$ is negative, as before. Property 2 is therefore unchanged. The values of the driving-point immittance evaluated at $p = 0$ or $p = \infty$, however, can be negative as well as positive. Thus, property 3 becomes

Property 3a *For a $\pm R$, $+C$ driving-point immittance, $Y(0)$, $Y(\infty)$, $Z(0)$, and $Z(\infty)$ may be positive or negative.*

In Figs. A.5 and A.6, typical plots for $Y(\sigma)$ and $Z(\sigma)$ are shown. From these plots, we see that the poles and zeros alternate, and thus property 4

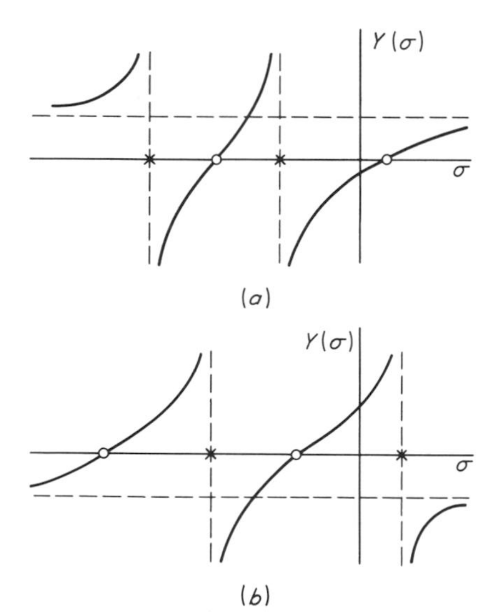

Figure A.5 ***Typical plots of $Y(\sigma)$ for a $\pm R$, $+C$ driving-point admittance.***

is unchanged. The restriction specified by property 5 does not apply to the $\pm R$, $+C$ class of networks. To see this, consider a network consisting of a negative-valued resistor in parallel with a capacitor. If both elements have unity value, the impedance $Z(p) = 1/(p - 1)$. Thus, $Z(0) = -1$, and $Z(\infty) = 0$. We see that $Z(0) < Z(\infty)$, violating property 5. Counterexamples may also be found on an admittance basis.

In considering properties 6 and 7, we first make the surprising observation that it is possible to have a pole of admittance at the origin and, correspondingly, a pole of impedance at infinite frequency. To see this, consider the circuit shown in Fig. A.7. The T configuration of ± 1-ohm

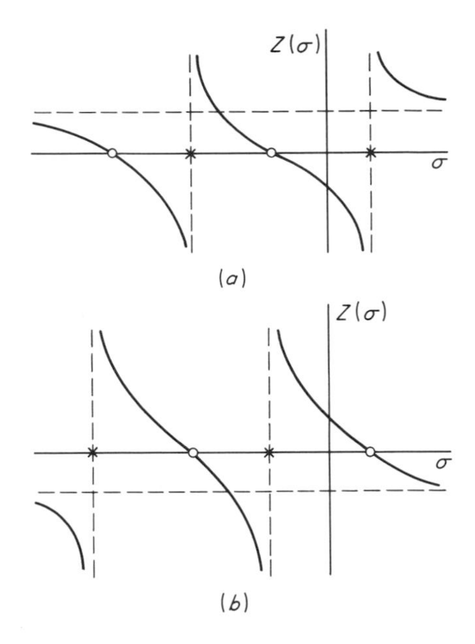

***Figure A.6** Typical plots of* $Z(\sigma)$ *for a* $\pm R$, $+C$ *driving-point impedance.*

resistors acts as a negative-immittance *inverter;* i.e., it inverts an impedance to an admittance and multiplies it by a negative sign. Thus, the input impedance of the circuit has a pole at infinity, and the admittance has a pole at the origin. The residues of such poles are negative. Therefore, for such a circuit, in the limit, $Z(\infty) = -\infty$, and $Y(0) = -\infty$. We may verify the negativeness of the residue at an infinite pole for a driving-point impedance function in another way. For such a function, in the limit as p approaches infinity, $Z(p)$ approaches the value kp, where k is the residue. Thus, $dZ(\sigma)/d\sigma = k$. We have shown, however, that the slope must be negative. Therefore, k is negative. A similar argument verifies the negativeness of the residue of a pole at the origin of a driving-point admittance function. Thus, properties 6 and 7 are changed, and may be stated as follows:

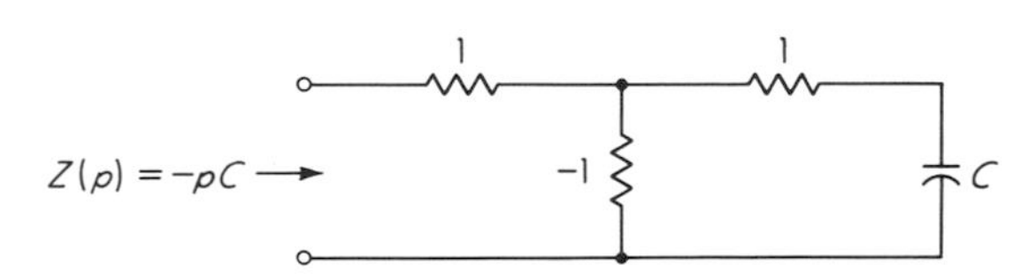

***Figure A.7** A* $\pm R$, $+C$ *network with a driving-point impedance possessing a pole at infinity.*

Property 6a *A ±R, +C driving-point admittance may have a zero or a pole (with a negative residue) at the origin. It may have a pole or a zero at infinity.*

Property 7a *A ±R, +C driving-point impedance may have a pole or a zero at the origin. It may have a pole (with a negative residue) or a zero at infinity.*

A consideration of the partial-fraction expansion for a ±R, +C driving-point admittance in the form of (13) leads to the conclusion that the residues of all the finite poles (including the one at the origin) on the real axis are real and negative. The partial-fraction expansion will be of the form

$$Y(p) = \frac{k_a}{p} + k_b + k_c p + \sum_i \frac{k_i}{p + \sigma_i} \tag{17}$$

where k_a and the k_i are negative, k_b may be positive or negative, and k_c is positive. This expansion is similar to the one given in (13), but the term k_a/p has been added. The partial-fraction expansion for a ±R, +C driving-point impedance function will be of the form

$$Z(p) = k_\infty + k_n p + \frac{k_0}{p} + \sum_i \frac{k_i}{p + \sigma_i} \tag{18}$$

This expression is similar to the one given in (15), but the term $k_n p$ has been added. All the residues will be positive except the residue at the pole at infinity which will be negative. Thus, we may restate properties 8 and 9 for this class of networks as

Property 8a *The residues at the finite real poles of a ±R, +C driving-point admittance are real and negative. The residue at a pole at infinity is real and positive.*

Property 9a *The residues at the finite real poles of a ±R, +C driving-point impedance are real and positive. The residue at a pole at infinity is real and negative.*

The *realizable* partial-fraction expansion for $Y(p)$ is of the form

$$Y(p) = k_\infty p + k_0 + \frac{k_n}{p} + \sum_i \frac{k_i p}{p + \sigma_i} \tag{19}$$

This expansion is similar to the one given in (16), but the term k_n/p has been added. It should be noted that the constants k_i in this expression may be considered as the residues at the real poles of the function $Y(p)/p$. As such, they will have the same signs as the residues of $Y(p)$ for positive values of p, i.e., for poles on the positive-real axis. They will, however, have the opposite signs from the residues of $Y(p)$ for negative values of p, i.e., for poles on the negative-real axis. Since all the residues at the real poles of $Y(p)$ are negative, we conclude that the coefficients k_i in (19) will be negative for right-half-plane poles and positive for left-half-plane poles. The realizations for the separate terms of (19) are easily obtainable from Figs. A.3 and A.7. Thus, property 10, for this class of networks, becomes

Property 10a *A $\pm R$, $+C$ driving-point admittance may be expressed in the form given in (19), where k_∞ is nonnegative, k_0 is positive or negative (or zero), k_n is nonpositive, the k_i associated with negative-real poles are positive, and the k_i associated with positive-real poles are negative. A realization may be made in the manner indicated in Figs. A.3 and A.7.*

The above considerations, which differentiate between the sign of the residues for left-half-plane and right-half-plane poles for driving-point admittances, are not applicable to the driving-point impedance case in which all the k_i terms in (18) are positive. The realizations for the separate terms of (18) are easily obtainable from Figs. A.4 and A.7. Property 11 thus becomes

Property 11a *A $\pm R$, $+C$ driving-point impedance may be expressed in the form given in (18), where k_∞ may be positive or negative (or zero), k_n is nonpositive, k_0 is nonnegative, and the k_i are all positive. A realization may be made in the manner indicated in Figs. A.4 and A.7.*

This concludes our treatment of the driving-point immittances of the $\pm R$, $+C$ class of networks.*

A.3 *The properties of RC-gyrator driving-point immittances*

The next class of networks that we shall consider is the class which includes positive-valued resistors, positive-valued capacitors, and

* A detailed treatment of this case is given by P. Bello, Extension of Brune's Energy Function Approach to the Study of LLF Networks, *IRE Trans. Circuit Theory,* vol. CT-7, no. 3, pp. 270–280, Sept., 1960. The article also covers the properties of various other classes of networks including those realized with various nonreciprocal devices. A development of the properties of this class of networks without using the energy function approach is given by B. K. Kinariwala, Necessary and Sufficient Conditions for the Existence of $\pm R$, $+C$ Networks, *IRE Trans. Circuit Theory,* vol. CT-7, no. 3, pp. 330–335, Sept., 1960.

gyrators. This will be called the *RC-gyrator class* of networks. A detailed study of the properties of the gyrator will be found in Chap. 5. Here it will suffice to describe it as a lossless two-port nonreciprocal device defined by the relations

$$I_1 = GV_2 \qquad I_2 = -GV_1 \tag{20}$$

The constant G is usually referred to as the *gyration conductance.* The nodal equations for the RC-gyrator class of networks may be written in matrix form as

$$\mathbf{I} = (\mathbf{G} + p\mathbf{C} + \mathbf{S})\mathbf{V} \tag{21}$$

where $\mathbf{S}$ is a skew-symmetric matrix which specifies the effects of any gyrators. Following the development of Sec. A.1 we may write

$$\bar{\mathbf{V}}^t\mathbf{I} = \bar{\mathbf{V}}^t\mathbf{G}\mathbf{V} + p\bar{\mathbf{V}}^t\mathbf{C}\mathbf{V} + \bar{\mathbf{V}}^t\mathbf{S}\mathbf{V} \tag{22}$$

The quadratic form $\bar{\mathbf{V}}^t\mathbf{S}\mathbf{V}$ is not an easy form to work with because of the skew-symmetric nature of $\mathbf{S}$. If we multiply the elements of $\mathbf{S}$ by $-j$, however, the resulting matrix is hermitian. Let us now introduce the term F_g, defining it as

$$F_g = \bar{\mathbf{V}}^t(-j)\mathbf{S}\mathbf{V} \tag{23}$$

Then, F_g is a hermitian form. Such a form has the property that F_g will be real for any possible $\mathbf{V}$. We may rewrite (22) in terms of F_g and the quadratic forms F_0 and H_0 defined in (3) as

$$\bar{\mathbf{V}}^t\mathbf{I} = F_0 + pH_0 + jF_g \tag{24}$$

Manipulations similar to those made in (5) and (6) give us a general expression for the driving-point admittance of an RC-gyrator network as

$$Y(p) = \frac{I_1}{V_1} = \frac{1}{|V_1|^2}(F_0 + pH_0 + jF_g) \tag{25}$$

The zeros of such an admittance occur at

$$p = \frac{F_0 + jF_g}{-H_0} \tag{26}$$

Since both F_0 and H_0 are real and nonnegative and since F_g is real, we see that the real part of the zeros of $Y(p)$ must be nonpositive; i.e., the zeros are constrained to the left half-plane and the $j\omega$ axis. A similar development on an impedance basis may be used to show that the poles of $Y(p)$ must be in the left half-plane or on the $j\omega$ axis. Now let us evaluate $Y(p)$ for the case where $p = \sigma$; i.e., for the case in which p is real. It may be shown that $F_g(\sigma) = 0$. Therefore, we see that $Y(p)$, the driving-point admittance of an *RC*-gyrator network, has the property that $Y(\sigma)$ is real. Another property of $Y(p)$ may be found by examining the real part of $Y(j\omega)$. It is given as

$$\text{Re } Y(j\omega) = \frac{1}{|V_1|^2}(F_0) \tag{27}$$

This is clearly positive for all ω. The above properties are sufficient to ensure that $Y(p)$ is a *pr* function.* This of course requires that $Z(p)$ also be a *pr* function. Thus, the properties of driving-point immittances of the *RC*-gyrator class of networks are exactly those of the passive *RLC* class of networks. This conclusion is quite palatable in view of the property (developed in Chap. 5) that a gyrator terminated in a capacitor at one of its ports presents the immittance of an inductor at its other port. Since the properties of *pr* functions are well known, these will not be tabulated separately in this text.

A.4 *The properties of* $\pm R$, $\pm C$ *driving-point immittances*

In the preceding sections we have explored the properties of driving-point immittances that may be realized by the passive network class consisting of $+R$, $+C$ elements and the active class consisting of $\pm R$, $+C$ elements. Now let us consider another active class of networks, the class consisting of positive- and negative-valued resistors and positive- and negative-valued capacitors, i.e., the $\pm R$, $\pm C$ class of networks, and see what properties the driving-point immittances of such networks will have.† This class of networks is sufficient to realize any driving-point immittance which is a rational function of the complex-frequency variable (with real coefficients).‡ To see the sufficiency, consider the following immittance function:

$$F(p) = \frac{a_0 + a_1p + a_2p^2 + \cdots + a_np^n}{b_0 + b_1p + b_2p^2 + \cdots + b_mp^m} \tag{28}$$

* The reader who wishes to review the properties of *pr* functions should consult any of the modern books on network synthesis. The book by D. F. Tuttle, Jr., "Network Synthesis," vol. 1, John Wiley & Sons, Inc., New York, 1958, has an especially complete coverage of this topic.

† Actually, we might also have considered the driving-point immittances realized by the $+R$, $\pm C$ class of networks. Since such a class, however, is rarely encountered in practice and since its properties may be found by a process similar to that used for the $\pm R$, $+C$ class, no treatment will be made of it.

‡ This class of networks cannot be treated directly by the energy-function approach used in the preceding sections. The reasons for this are discussed in Bello, *op. cit.*

The only restriction on the constants a_i and b_i is that they must be real. They may be positive, negative, or zero. Such a function may always be expanded in the form of a continued fraction as follows:

$$F(p) = \sum_i c_i p_i + \cfrac{1}{\sum_j d_j p^j + \cfrac{1}{\sum_k e_k p^k + \cdots}} \tag{29}$$

In the last expression, the constants c_i, d_j, e_k, etc., may be positive, negative, or zero, but they will be real. The exponents i, j, k, etc., will be nonnegative. Thus, the problem of realizing such an immittance function simply becomes that of realizing immittances of the form $c_i p^i$.

That such functions can be realized by the $\pm R$, $\pm C$ class of networks may be seen as follows: Consider the network shown in Fig. A.8. In this

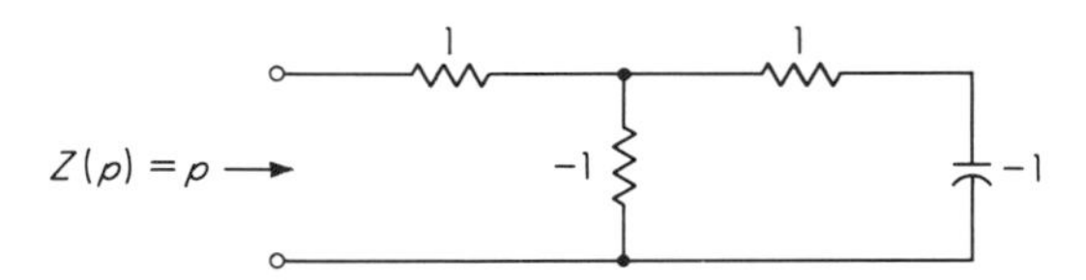

***Figure A.8** The use of $\pm R$, $\pm C$ network elements to realize an inductance.*

figure, the nature of the elements, i.e., whether they are resistive or capacitive, is shown by the use of conventional symbols. The polarity and numerical value of the elements (in ohms and farads) are given by the numbers associated with each element. The driving-point impedance of this network is easily shown to be p, i.e., the same as that of a 1-henry inductor. The network of Fig. A.8 has been redrawn in Fig. A.9. A differ-

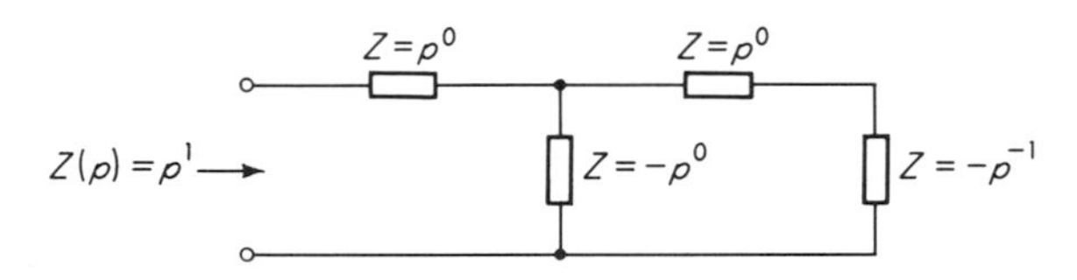

***Figure A.9** The use of $\pm p^0$ and $\pm p^{-1}$ impedance elements to realize the impedance p^1.*

ent convention is used in this figure in that the same symbol is used for all the elements whether they are resistors or capacitors. The nature and the numerical value of the elements are shown by specifying the impedance of each one. From this latter figure it is easy to make the following conclusion: *If we have available elements with impedance* ap^{-1} *and elements with impedance* bp^0, *we can realize impedances* cp^1, *where* a, b, *and* c *are real constants which may be positive or negative.* Now consider the network shown in Fig. A.10. From this figure we see that, in general, if we have

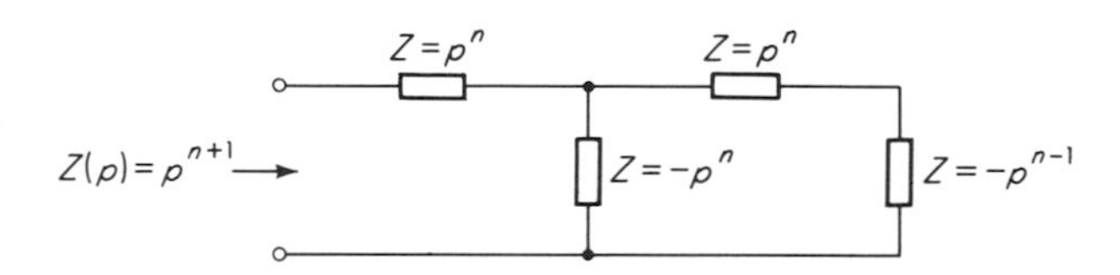

Figure A.10 *The use of* $\pm p^n$ *and* $\pm p^{n-1}$ *impedance elements to realize the impedance* p^{n+1}.

available elements with impedances ap^{n-1} and bp^n, we can realize impedances of cp^{n+1}. Again, the real constants a, b, and c may be positive or negative. Therefore, since we know that we can produce impedances kp, we can produce impedances kp^2, by means of which we can produce impedances kp^3, etc. We conclude that all impedances of the type c_ip^i may be produced by the $\pm R$, $\pm C$ class of networks.

In a dual manner, given admittances ap^{n-1} and bp^n, where a and b may be positive or negative, we can produce admittances cp^{n+1}. A circuit for accomplishing this is shown in Fig. A.11.* Therefore we can always

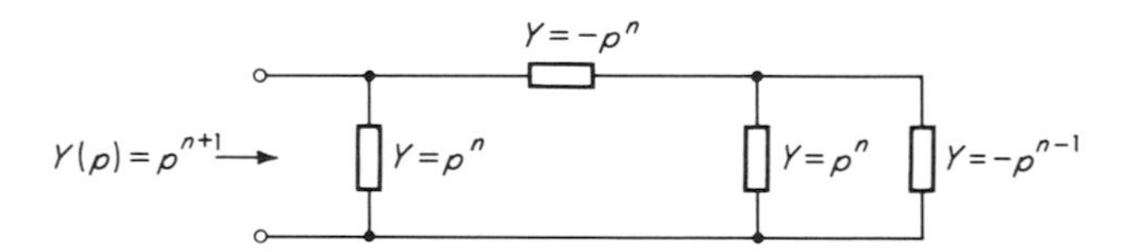

Figure A.11 *The use of* $\pm p^n$ *and* $\pm p^{n-1}$ *admittance elements to realize the admittance* p^{n+1}.

realize both admittances and impedances of the type c_ip^i, and thus, the realization of the general driving-point function of (28) may always be made by using the continued-fraction expansion indicated in (29). Thus, we have established the sufficiency of the $\pm R$, $\pm C$ class of networks for the realization of arbitrary driving-point functions.

* This circuit was presented by H. J. Carlin, in the article entitled, General N-port Synthesis with Negative Resistors, *Proc. IRE*, vol. 48, no. 6, part I, pp. 1174–1175, June, 1960.

It should be pointed out that the development of the preceding paragraphs does not, in general, provide a very practical means of physically realizing a given driving-point function. The primary usage for this discussion has been to show that the $\pm R$, $\pm C$ class of networks is sufficient to realize any driving-point function. It should be quite apparent that

Table A.1 Comparison of the properties of various classes of active and passive RC driving-point immittances

Property		$+R$, $+C$	$\pm R$, $+C$	$\pm R$, $\pm C$
1. ***Location of finite poles and zeros***		Negative-real axis	Real axis	Anywhere
2. ***Sign of derivative along real axis***	$\dfrac{dZ(\sigma)}{d\sigma}$	Nonpositive		No restriction
	$\dfrac{dY(\sigma)}{d\sigma}$	Nonnegative		No restriction
3. $Y(0)$, $Y(\infty)$, $Z(0)$, $Z(\infty)$		Nonnegative	No restriction	
4. ***Properties of poles and zeros***	***Multiplicity***	Simple		Any order
	Alternation required	Yes		No
5. ***Zero- and infinite-frequency behavior***	***Relative values of $Y(0)$ and $Y(\infty)$***	$Y(0) \leq Y(\infty)$	No restriction	
	Relative values of $Z(0)$ and $Z(\infty)$	$Z(0) \geq Z(\infty)$	No restriction	
6. ***Singularities of Y***	***Closest to origin***	Zero	Pole or zero	
	Closest to infinity	Pole	Pole or zero	
7. ***Singularities of Z***	***Closest to origin***	Pole	Pole or zero	
	Closest to infinity	Zero	Pole or zero	
8. ***Residue of Y***	***At finite nonzero pole***	Negative		Positive or negative
	At pole at infinity	Positive		Positive or negative
	At pole at origin	None	Negative	Positive or negative

this class of networks is considerably more general than the $\pm R$, $+C$ class, which only extended our range of natural frequencies by a relatively small amount over the purely passive $+R$, $+C$ case. The extent of the differences between the capabilities of the three classes may be appreciated from a study of Table A.1.

Table A.1 Comparison of the properties of various classes of active and passive RC driving-point immittances (Continued)

Property		$+R$, $+C$	$\pm R$, $+C$	$\pm R$, $\pm C$
9. ***Residue of Z***	***At finite nonzero pole***	Positive		Positive or negative
	At pole at infinity	None	Negative	Positive or negative
	At pole at origin	Positive		Positive or negative
10. $Y = k_\infty p + k_0 + \frac{k_n}{p} + \sum_i \frac{pk_i}{p + \sigma_i}$	k_∞	Positive		Positive or negative
	k_0	Positive	Positive or negative	
	k_n	Zero	Negative	Positive or negative
	k_i	Positive	Positive for LHP poles, negative for RHP poles	Positive or negative
11. $Z = k_\infty + k_n p + \frac{k_0}{p} + \sum_i \frac{k_i}{p + \sigma_i}$	k_∞	Positive	Positive or negative	
	k_n	Zero	Negative	Positive or negative
	k_0	Positive		Positive or negative
	k_i	Positive		Positive or negative

A.5 *Driving-point immittances of other classes of active networks*

The next class of networks that we shall consider is the one which includes positive-valued resistors, positive-valued capacitors, and an active device called a *negative-immittance converter* (NIC). A detailed study of the properties of the NIC is made in Chap. 4. This class of networks will be referred to as the RC-NIC class. Since NICs can be used to produce negative-valued resistors and capacitors from positive-valued ones, we may apply the conclusions reached for the $\pm R$, $\pm C$ class to the RC-NIC class. Thus, we see that the RC-NIC class is sufficient to realize an arbitrary driving-point immittance of the form of (28). Actually, it may be shown that a single NIC and an RC network are sufficient to realize any driving-point function.*

Two other classes of networks may be considered briefly. The first of these is the class which includes positive-valued resistors, positive-valued capacitors, and controlled sources. It is shown in Chap. 4 that a single controlled source may be used to realize an NIC. Therefore, this class of networks will realize the same arbitrary driving-point functions as will the RC-NIC class of networks. The second class of networks is the class which includes positive-valued resistors, positive-valued capacitors, and operational (high-gain) amplifiers. It is also shown in Chap. 4 that a single operational amplifier may be used to realize an NIC. Thus, this class of networks will realize the same types of driving-point functions as will the RC-NIC class of networks.

A.6 *Conclusion*

In this appendix we have discussed the properties of driving-point functions that may be realized by various classes of passive and active RC networks. It was shown that the addition of negative-valued resistors to the class of passive RC networks provides only a small additional amount of freedom in the types of driving-point functions that may be realized. The addition of negative-valued resistors and capacitors, however, makes it possible to realize driving-point functions which are only restricted by the requirement that they be rational functions with real coefficients. The use of a single NIC, a single controlled source, or a single operational amplifier in connection with passive RC networks also permits the realization of arbitrary driving-point functions. In Appendix B, we shall make an investigation of the properties of transfer functions for the same classes of networks that were considered in this appendix.

* A method for such a realization is given by J. M. Sipress, Synthesis of Active RC Networks, *IRE Trans. Circuit Theory*, vol. CT-8, pp. 260–269, Sept., 1961.

Appendix B *The properties of transfer functions*

In this appendix we shall study the properties of transfer functions which may be produced by various classes of passive and active RC networks. The four types of transfer functions which will be considered are impedance transfer functions, admittance transfer functions, open-circuit voltage transfer functions, and short-circuit current transfer functions.* These may all be defined in terms of the z parameters or the y parameters of a two-port network. Therefore, for each class of networks, we shall begin by examining the properties of these parameters.

B.1 *Z and y parameters for passive RC networks*

We may define the properties of a general passive two-port RC network by applying the energy-function approach introduced in Appendix A. If we consider the nodal equations under the conditions that only excitation currents I_1 and I_2 are nonzero, (4) of Appendix A becomes

$$\bar{V}_1 I_1 + \bar{V}_2 I_2 = V_0 + pH_0 \tag{1}$$

If we define $\mathbf{V}$ as the column matrix whose elements are $V_1(p)$ and $V_2(p)$, and $\mathbf{I}$ as the column matrix whose elements are $I_1(p)$ and $I_2(p)$, then (1) may be written as

$$\bar{\mathbf{V}}^t \mathbf{I} = F_0 + pH_0 \tag{2}$$

For such a two-port network, the y parameters are defined by the equation $\mathbf{I} = \mathbf{YV}$, where $\mathbf{Y}$ is the 2×2 matrix whose elements are y_{ij}. Substituting this relation in (2), we obtain

$$\bar{\mathbf{V}}^t \mathbf{YV} = F_0 + pH_0 \tag{3}$$

* The designation of open-circuit or short-circuit applies to the terminating condition imposed on the network port at which the response is measured.

The right-hand member of (3) has been shown to be a positive-real function. Therefore, the quadratic form in the left-hand member will also be a positive-real function and will be referred to as a *positive-real quadratic form*. Since the properties of a quadratic form are determined by the properties of the square matrix of the form, we shall refer to **Y** as a *positive-real matrix*.* A similar development may be made on an impedance basis. Thus, if we specify the z parameters of a passive RC two-port network by the 2×2 matrix **Z** with elements z_{ij}, where $\mathbf{V} = \mathbf{ZI}$, then **Z** is a positive-real matrix. We now have the following property:

Property 1 *The y-parameter matrix and the z-parameter matrix of a passive RC two-port network are positive-real matrices.*

Let us interconnect the two ports of a passive RC network by two ideal transformers with turns ratios n_1 and n_2 as shown in Fig. B.1.

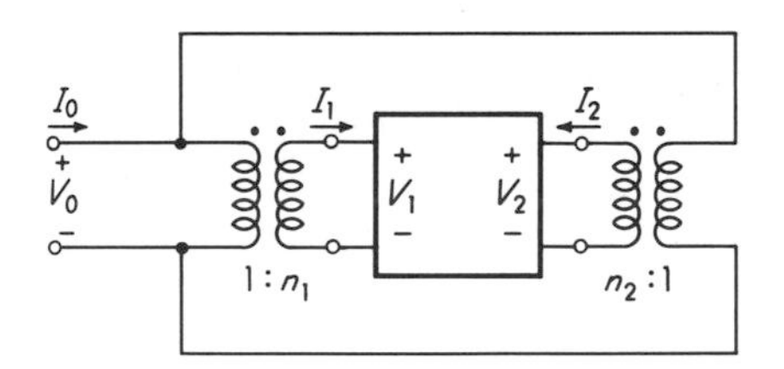

Figure B.1 *A two-port network with ideal transformers interconnecting the two ports.*

For the variables defined in this figure we have the relationships

$$I_0 = n_1 I_1 + n_2 I_2$$
$$V_0 = \frac{V_1}{n_1} = \frac{V_2}{n_2} \tag{4}$$

If we define a column matrix $\mathbf{n}$ with elements n_1 and n_2, the above relations may be written in matrix form as

$$I_0 = \mathbf{n}^t\mathbf{I} \qquad \mathbf{V} = \mathbf{n}V_0 \tag{5}$$

Thus, we may write

$$I_0 = \mathbf{n}^t\mathbf{I} = \mathbf{n}^t\mathbf{Y}\mathbf{V} = \mathbf{n}^t\mathbf{Y}\mathbf{n}V_0 \tag{6}$$

The driving-point admittance Y_{IN} for the network is the ratio I_0/V_0.

* More generally, any symmetric matrix **A**, whose elements are rational functions of the complex-frequency variable p with real coefficients and whose quadratic form $\mathbf{x}^t\mathbf{A}\mathbf{x}$ is a positive-real function for all real finite values of the variables x_i (the elements of the column matrix **x**), will be said to be a positive-real matrix. For a discussion of some of the properties of a positive-real matrix see R. W. Newcomb, "Linear Multiport Synthesis," chap. 5, McGraw-Hill Book Company, New York, 1966, or D. Hazony, "Elements of Network Synthesis," chap. 13, Reinhold Publishing Corporation, New York, 1963.

From (6) we see that

$$Y_{IN} = \mathbf{n}^t\mathbf{Y}\mathbf{n} \tag{7}$$

The right-hand member of (7) is a quadratic form, and, since **Y** is a positive-real matrix, the quadratic form is positive real. Therefore, the driving-point admittance Y_{IN} is also positive real. Since the quadratic form $\mathbf{n}^t\mathbf{Y}\mathbf{n}$ may be considered as a special case of the quadratic form $\bar{\mathbf{V}}^t\mathbf{Y}\mathbf{V}$ of (3), Y_{IN} also has the property that it may be expressed in the form

$$Y_{IN} = F_0 + pH_0 \tag{8}$$

Therefore Y_{IN} is a passive *RC* driving-point admittance, and all the properties of such functions derived in Appendix A apply.*

If we now expand each element y_{ij} of **Y** in the form of a realizable partial-fraction expansion as given in (16) of Appendix A, we obtain

$$y_{ij} = pk_{ij}^{(\infty)} + k_{ij}^{(0)} + \sum_m \frac{p}{p + \sigma_m} k_{ij}^{(m)} \tag{9}$$

Thus, in matrix form we may write

$$\mathbf{Y} = p\mathbf{k}^{(\infty)} + \mathbf{k}^{(0)} + \sum_m \frac{p}{p + \sigma_m} \mathbf{k}^{(m)} \tag{10}$$

where $\mathbf{k}^{(\infty)}$ is the 2×2 matrix with elements $k_{ij}^{(\infty)}$ which specifies the behavior of the y_{ij} in the limit as p approaches infinity, $\mathbf{k}^{(0)}$ is the 2×2 matrix with elements $k_{ij}^{(0)}$ which determines the behavior of the y_{ij} in the limit as p approaches zero, and the $\mathbf{k}^{(m)}$ are 2×2 matrices with elements $k_{ij}^{(m)}$ which determine the behavior of the functions y_{ij}/p in the limit as p approaches the negative-real poles of these functions. If we now express Y_{IN} in the realizable partial-fraction-expansion form given in (16) of Appendix A, then (7) becomes

$$Y_{IN} = k_\infty p + k_0 + \sum_m \frac{k_m p}{p + \sigma_m} = p\mathbf{n}^t\mathbf{k}^{(\infty)}\mathbf{n} + \mathbf{n}^t\mathbf{k}^{(0)}\mathbf{n} + \sum_m \frac{p}{p + \sigma_m} \mathbf{n}^t\mathbf{k}^{(m)}\mathbf{n} \tag{11}$$

If we examine (11) in the limiting cases as p approaches infinity, zero, and the locations of the various negative-real poles, we see that

$$\begin{aligned} k_\infty &= \mathbf{n}^t\mathbf{k}^{(\infty)}\mathbf{n} \\ k_0 &= \mathbf{n}^t\mathbf{k}^{(0)}\mathbf{n} \\ k_m &= \mathbf{n}^t\mathbf{k}^{(m)}\mathbf{n} \end{aligned} \tag{12}$$

* A somewhat more rigorous development may be made by hypothesizing the existence of transformers with complex turns ratios. See P. Bello, Extension of Brune's Energy Function Approach to the Study of LLF Networks, *IRE Trans. Circuit Theory,* vol. CT-7, no. 3, pp. 270–280, Sept., 1960.

Since the various k's in the left-hand members of the above equations will always be nonnegative, the terms on the right must always be nonnegative for all values of n_1 and n_2 (the elements of $\mathbf{n}$). Therefore, the $\mathbf{k}$ matrices in the right-hand members of the above equations must be positive semidefinite. The relations

$$k_{11} \geq 0 \qquad k_{22} \geq 0 \qquad k_{11}k_{22} - k_{12}k_{21} \geq 0 \tag{13}$$

are the conditions that ensure positive semidefiniteness in a 2×2 matrix $\mathbf{k}$. These relations must therefore be true for each of the $\mathbf{k}$ matrices in (10).

The actual residues of the y_{ij} at the negative-real poles are the constants that occur in the summation when the y_{ij} are expressed in the form of the partial-fraction expansion given in (13) in Appendix A. If we expand both sides of (7) in this form and compare corresponding elements, we see that the matrix of residues at each negative-real pole must be negative semidefinite. The relations

$$k_{11} \leq 0 \qquad k_{22} \leq 0 \qquad k_{11}k_{22} - k_{12}k_{21} \geq 0 \tag{14}$$

are the conditions that ensure negative semidefiniteness in a 2×2 matrix $\mathbf{k}$. These conditions must be satisfied by the elements of the residue matrices for each of the negative-real poles of the y_{ij}.

A development similar to the above is easily made for the z parameters. Let $\mathbf{Z}$ be a 2×2 matrix with elements z_{ij} which are the z parameters of a passive RC two-port network. If we expand the z_{ij} in the form of (15) of Appendix A, we obtain

$$z_{ij} = k_{ij}{}^{(\infty)} + \frac{1}{p}\, k_{ij}{}^{(0)} + \sum_m \frac{1}{p + \sigma_m}\, k_{ij}{}^{(m)} \tag{15}$$

Thus, in matrix form we may write

$$\mathbf{Z} = \mathbf{k}^{(\infty)} + \frac{1}{p}\,\mathbf{k}^{(0)} + \sum_m \frac{1}{p + \sigma_m}\,\mathbf{k}^{(m)} \tag{16}$$

where the elements of the matrix $\mathbf{k}^{(0)}$ are the residues of the z_{ij} at the poles at the origin, the elements of the matrices $\mathbf{k}^{(m)}$ are the residues at the negative-real poles, and the elements of the matrix $\mathbf{k}^{(\infty)}$ represent the behavior of the z_{ij} in the limit as p approaches infinity. If we interconnect the two ports of the network as shown in Fig. B.2, the driving-point

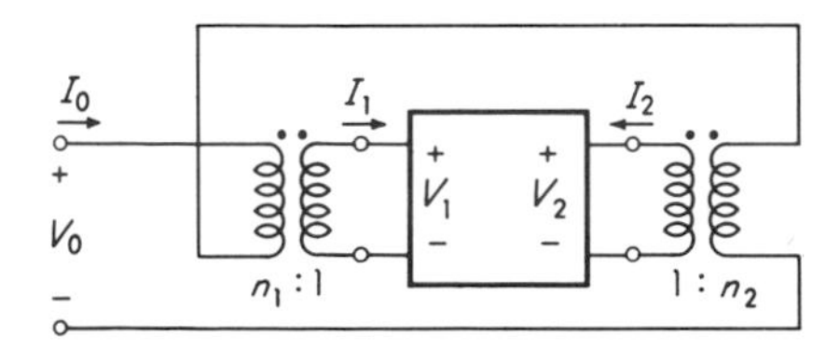

***Figure B.2** A two-port network with ideal transformers interconnecting the two ports.*

impedance Z_{IN} is given by the relation

$$Z_{IN} = \mathbf{n}^t\mathbf{Z}\mathbf{n} \tag{17}$$

where $\mathbf{n}$ is the column matrix whose elements are n_1 and n_2. Considerations similar to those for the y parameters show that all the $\mathbf{k}$ matrices in (16) must be positive semidefinite. We may summarize the discussion in the above paragraphs as follows:

Property 2 *The residue matrix for the y parameters of a passive RC two-port network for a pole at infinity will be positive semidefinite. The residue matrix for a negative-real pole will be negative semidefinite.*

Property 3 *The residue matrix for the z parameters of a passive RC two-port network for a pole at the origin or a negative-real pole will be positive semidefinite.*

Property 4 *If* $\mathbf{Y}$, *the y-parameter matrix of a passive RC two-port network, is expressed in the modified partial-fraction-expansion form given in (10), all the* $\mathbf{k}$ *matrices are positive semidefinite.*

Property 5 *If* $\mathbf{Z}$, *the z-parameter matrix of a passive RC two-port network, is expressed in the partial-fraction-expansion form given in (16), all the* $\mathbf{k}$ *matrices are positive semidefinite.**

This concludes our treatment of the z and y parameters of passive RC networks. In the next section we shall use the properties that have been developed in this section to determine the characteristics of the transfer functions of this class of networks.

B.2 *Transfer functions for passive RC networks*

In this section we shall derive the properties of various classes of transfer functions for the two-port passive RC network. First of all, we shall consider the transfer admittance function $-y_{21}$. In passive RC networks, it is not possible for the transfer admittance $-y_{21}$ to have any poles which are not present in the driving-point admittances y_{11} and y_{22}. Thus, we see that the poles of $-y_{21}$ must be simple and lie on the negative-real axis, excluding the origin but including infinity. The condition of positive semidefiniteness required of the $\mathbf{k}$ matrices in (10) and (16) permits the k_{12} and k_{21} elements of these matrices to be either positive or negative. The nature of the quadratic form and the positive realness of Y_{IN} in (11)

* In the case of the z parameters, the $\mathbf{k}$ matrices of property 5 and the residue matrices of property 3 are identical.

require that k_{12} and k_{21} be real. Reciprocity, of course, requires that $k_{12} = k_{21}$ in each matrix. We conclude that a transfer admittance function $-y_{21}$ may be expanded in the form of (9), where the various k_{21} constants are real but may be positive or negative. Such an expansion may be made from an arbitrary numerator polynomial, i.e., one in which the various coefficients may be positive or negative. Therefore, we conclude that the zeros of $-y_{21}$ may lie anywhere on the complex-frequency plane and be of any order, subject only to the restriction that the degree of the numerator cannot exceed the degree of the denominator by more than 1, since a possible pole of $-y_{21}$ at infinity can only be simple. We may summarize the above conclusions in the following property:

Property 6 *The poles of a passive RC transfer admittance $-y_{21}$ are simple, have real residues, and are restricted to the negative-real axis (excluding the origin) and infinity. The residues at these poles and the limiting behavior at the origin may be positive or negative. The zeros may occur anywhere on the complex-frequency plane.*

The sufficiency of these properties may be demonstrated by a realization in the form of a symmetrical lattice network of the type shown in Fig. B.3.

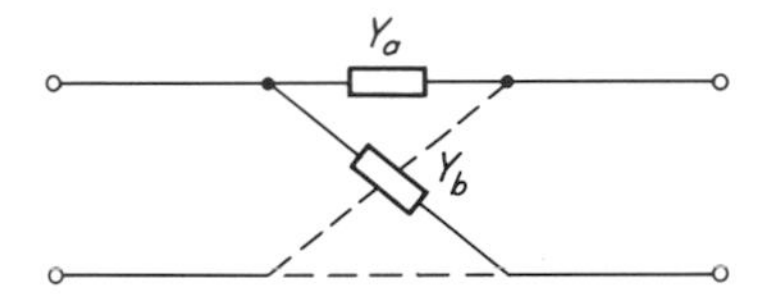

Figure B.3 *A lattice network.*

Dashed lines are used in this figure to simplify the drawing while indicating that an additional Y_a element and an additional Y_b element are present. For this network the transfer admittance is

$$-y_{21} = \tfrac{1}{2}(Y_a - Y_b)$$

Thus, if we make a realizable partial-fraction expansion of $-y_{21}$, we need merely associate the positive terms with Y_a and the negative terms with Y_b, and our realization is complete.

In a similar manner, we may show that a transfer impedance function z_{21} may be expanded in the form shown in (15), in which the various k_{21} terms may be either positive or negative. Since an arbitrary numerator polynomial of degree equal to or less than the degree of the denominator polynomial of z_{21} may be expressed in this form, we conclude that a transfer impedance z_{21} may have zeros anywhere in the complex-frequency plane. We may summarize the characteristics of z_{21} as the following:

Property 7 *The poles of a passive RC transfer impedance z_{21} are simple, have real residues, and are restricted to the negative-real axis, including the origin but excluding infinity. The residues at these poles and the limiting behavior at infinity may be positive or negative. The zeros may occur anywhere on the complex-frequency plane.*

The open-circuit voltage transfer function for a two-port network may be defined in terms of the y parameters as $V_2/V_1 = -y_{21}/y_{22}$. Thus, we may examine the properties of the voltage transfer function in terms of the properties of the y parameters. Let us first consider how a pole of the voltage transfer function might be produced. There are two possibilities: a zero of y_{22} which is not a zero of y_{21} or a pole of y_{21} which is not a pole of y_{22}. The latter case will not occur, however, since the positive semidefinite and negative semidefinite conditions on the residue matrices of the y parameters require that if k_{12} and k_{21} are nonzero, then k_{11} and k_{22} must also be nonzero. Therefore, the poles of the voltage transfer function can only occur at the zeros of y_{22} which are not zeros of y_{21}. Thus, they will be simple and on the negative-real axis. Note that if y_{22} has a zero at the origin, y_{21} must also have a zero there. Otherwise the $\mathbf{k}^{(0)}$ matrix of (10) will not be positive definite. Thus, the voltage transfer function cannot have a pole at the origin. The zeros of the voltage transfer function can come about in two ways: a zero of y_{21} which is not a zero of y_{22} or a pole of y_{22} which is not a pole of y_{21}. Obviously, from the first possibility, we may have zeros anywhere on the complex-frequency plane. Therefore, the residues at the poles of V_2/V_1 may be positive or negative. They will, of course, be real.

Another equivalent definition of the voltage transfer function is $V_2/V_1 = z_{21}/z_{11}$. Note that if z_{11} has a zero at infinity, z_{21} must also have a zero there. Otherwise the $\mathbf{k}^{(\infty)}$ matrix of (16) will not be positive semidefinite. Thus, the voltage transfer function cannot have a pole at infinity. Although poles at the origin and infinity are not permitted, the arbitrariness of the numerator of the voltage transfer function permits the limiting behavior at the origin or infinity to be either positive or negative.

Now let us consider the short-circuit current transfer function for a two-port network. This may be defined in terms of the y and z parameters as $I_2/I_1 = y_{21}/y_{11} = -z_{21}/z_{22}$. The conclusions about the possible locations of the poles and zeros, the residues, and the limiting behavior at the origin and infinity are exactly the same as for the voltage transfer function. We may summarize the above discussion as follows:

Property 8 *The poles of either an open-circuit voltage transfer function or a short-circuit current transfer function for a passive RC network are simple and lie on the negative-real axis, excluding the origin and infinity. They have* *real residues which may be positive or negative. The zeros may lie anywhere on the complex-frequency plane.*

An additional necessary condition for the transfer functions of passive *RC* networks is the Fialkow-Gerst condition.* This condition requires, for a given two-port network of the class we are considering, that if the $-y_{21}$, y_{11}, and y_{22} parameters have the same denominator,† the magnitude of each coefficient of the numerator of $-y_{21}$ must be less than or equal to the corresponding coefficient of the numerator of y_{11} or y_{22}, whichever is lower in value. Thus, if we let

$$
\begin{aligned}
y_{11} &= \frac{a_0 + a_1 p + a_2 p^2 + \cdots}{d_0 + d_1 p + d_2 p^2 + \cdots} \\
y_{22} &= \frac{b_0 + b_1 p + b_2 p^2 + \cdots}{d_0 + d_1 p + d_2 p^2 + \cdots} \\
-y_{21} &= \frac{c_0 + c_1 p + c_2 p^2 + \cdots}{d_0 + d_1 p + d_2 p^2 + \cdots}
\end{aligned}
\tag{18}
$$

then the above condition requires that

$$|c_i| \le a_i \qquad \text{and} \qquad |c_i| \le b_i \tag{19}$$

for all i. The a_i and b_i coefficients, of course, can only be positive. A similar condition applies to the z parameters; that is, the magnitude of each of the numerator coefficients of z_{21} must be less than or equal to the corresponding coefficients of the numerators of z_{11} and z_{22}, assuming that all z_{ij} functions have the same denominator polynomial. Since the voltage and current transfer functions are defined in terms of the y or z parameters, we may relate the Fialkow-Gerst condition to these transfer functions by the following property:

Property 9 *The numerator coefficients of either an open-circuit voltage transfer function or a short-circuit current transfer function for a passive RC network may be positive or negative, but their magnitude must be less than or equal to the magnitude of corresponding denominator coefficients, i.e., coefficients associated with like powers of the complex-frequency variable.*

In this section we have discussed the general properties of the transfer functions of passive *RC* networks. In the next section we shall see that

* A. Fialkow and I. Gerst, The Transfer Function of General Two-pair *RC* Networks, *Quart. Appl. Math.*, vol. 10, pp. 113–127, July, 1952.

† Note that if these parameters do not have the same denominator, this can only be the result of y_{11} or y_{22} (or both) having private poles. It is only necessary to multiply the numerator and denominator of the various y parameters by appropriate factors to make all their denominators be the same in order to apply this condition.

some additional properties may be developed for the case where the network is restricted to a certain configuration.

B.3 *Three-terminal and ladder passive RC networks*

In addition to the restrictions imposed on the transfer function because of the type of network, i.e., the type of elements used in the network, another set of restrictions will be imposed on the transfer functions by reason of the particular type of configuration specified for the network. We shall consider first the restrictions that result from limiting our scope of investigation to those two-port networks which have a common ground terminal. This type of network is usually referred to as a *three-terminal network.** Under this restriction, for a passive RC network, properties 1 through 5 are unchanged. It may be shown, however, that the numerator coefficients of $-y_{21}$ and z_{21} can only be positive. Thus, the zeros of these transfer immittances can only be the zeros of a polynomial all of whose coefficients are positive. The zeros of such a polynomial can be no closer to the positive-real axis than an angle of π/n rad, where n is the degree of the polynomial.† Thus, we see that it is not possible to obtain zeros on the positive-real axis for such transfer immittances. Since the numerator coefficients are all positive, the residue at a pole at infinity must be positive. Similarly, the limiting behavior at the origin must be positive. The residues at the poles on the negative-real axis, however, may be positive or negative. Thus, property 6 becomes

Property 6a *For a passive RC three-terminal network, the poles of the transfer admittance $-y_{21}$ are simple, have real residues, and are restricted to the negative-real axis (excluding the origin) and infinity. The residues at the negative-real poles may be positive or negative. The residue at the infinite pole and the limiting behavior at the origin must be positive. The zeros may occur anywhere on the complex plane except the positive-real axis and a wedge of angle $2\pi/n$ rad surrounding it, where n is the degree of numerator polynomial.*

In a similar manner we may modify properties 7 and 8 as follows:

Property 7a *For a passive RC three-terminal network, the poles of the transfer admittance z_{21} are simple, have real residues, and are restricted to the*

* Such a network is also sometimes referred to as an "unbalanced" network, whereas a network with four terminals, none of which are common, is called a "balanced" network. Thus, a lattice network is a balanced network. If a lattice is converted to a three-terminal network (this is not possible in all cases), we refer to this procedure as "unbalancing the lattice."

† See P. M. Lewis II, The Concept of the One in Voltage Transfer Synthesis, *IRE Trans. Circuit Theory,* vol. CT-2, no. 4, pp. 316–319, Dec., 1955.

negative-real axis (excluding infinity) and the origin. The residues at the negative-real poles may be positive or negative. The residue at a pole at the origin and the limiting behavior at infinity must be positive. The zeros may occur anywhere on the complex-frequency plane except the positive-real axis and a wedge of angle $2\pi/n$ rad surrounding it, where n is the degree of the numerator polynomial.

Property 8a *For a passive RC three-terminal network, the poles of either an open-circuit voltage transfer function or a short-circuit current transfer function are simple and lie on the negative-real axis (excluding the origin and infinity). They have real residues which may be positive or negative. The zeros may lie anywhere on the complex-frequency plane except the positive real-axis and a wedge of angle $2\pi/n$ rad surrounding it, where n is the degree of the numerator polynomial.*

The Fialkow-Gerst condition for the three-terminal case requires the following version of property 9:

Property 9a *For a passive RC three-terminal network, the numerator coefficients of either an open-circuit voltage transfer function or a short-circuit current transfer function are positive and less than or equal to corresponding denominator coefficients, i.e., coefficients associated with like powers of the complex-frequency variable.*

An even more restrictive network configuration is the ladder configuration, i.e., a network of the type shown in Fig. B.4, which is composed of a

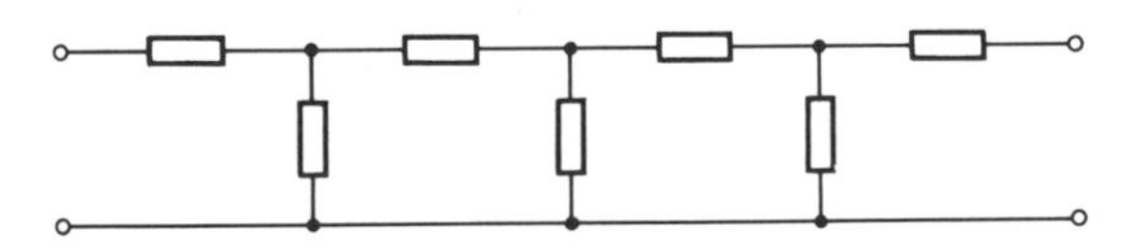

Figure B.4 A ladder network.

cascade connection of two-terminal *RC* elements alternatively connected in series and shunt. The transmission zeros of such a configuration are produced by the poles of series impedances and zeros of shunt impedances.* Thus, we see that for this type of network configuration, the zeros of any transfer function can only lie on the negative-real axis. For net-

* Any shunt or series elements which represent partial pole removals in the realization of a given driving-point function do not produce transmission zeros. See N. Balabanian, "Network Synthesis," pp. 151–153, Prentice-Hall, Inc., Englewood Cliffs, N.J., 1958.

works with this configuration properties 1 through 5 are unchanged. Properties 6 through 8 may be expressed as follows:

Property 6b *For a passive RC ladder network, the poles of the transfer admittance* $-y_{21}$ *are simple, have real residues, and are restricted to the negative-real axis (excluding the origin) and infinity. The residues at the negative-real poles may be positive or negative. The residue at the infinite pole and the limiting behavior at the origin must be positive. The zeros are restricted to the negative-real axis (including the origin and infinity).*

Property 7b *For a passive RC ladder network, the poles of the transfer impedance* z_{21} *are simple, have real residues, and are restricted to the negative-real axis (excluding infinity) and the origin. The residues at the negative-real poles may be positive or negative. The residue at the pole at the origin and the limiting behavior at infinity must be positive. The zeros are restricted to the negative-real axis (including the origin and infinity).*

Property 8b *For a passive RC ladder network, the poles of either an open-circuit voltage transfer function or a short-circuit current transfer function are simple and lie on the negative-real axis (excluding the origin and infinity). They have real residues which may be positive or negative. The zeros are restricted to the negative-real axis (including the origin and infinity).*

Property 9*a* is unchanged for the ladder network.

B.4 *Z and y parameters for* $\pm R$, $+C$ *two-port networks*

The properties of the $+R$, $+C$ class of networks which were developed in the preceding sections will now be extended to the class of networks whose elements are positive- and negative-valued resistors and positive-valued capacitors, i.e., the $\pm R$, $+C$ class of networks. The development will closely follow the steps outlined in the preceding sections, but as a result of the inclusion of the negative-valued resistors, many of the conclusions will be considerably different.

Let us begin by considering the result of applying the energy-function approach to this class of network. If we follow the same steps that led to (3), we see that the quadratic form for the two-port network can be again expressed as

$$\bar{\mathbf{V}}^t\mathbf{Y}\mathbf{V} = F_0 + pH_0 \tag{20}$$

For this class of networks, however, the term F_0 may be negative. Thus, although the right side of the equation will be real, it need not be positive.

Therefore the **Y** matrix is not necessarily positive real. Similarly, the **Z** matrix will not necessarily be positive real. We conclude, therefore, that property 1 does not apply for this class of networks.

In a manner identical with that followed in the last section, we may interconnect the two ports of the $\pm R$, $+C$ network with ideal transformers as shown in Fig. B.1. The driving-point admittance is again given by

$$Y_{IN} = \mathbf{n}^t\mathbf{Y}\mathbf{n} \tag{21}$$

If each element y_{ij} of **Y** is expanded in the form of a realizable partial-fraction expansion as given in (19) of Appendix A, we obtain

$$y_{ij} = pk_{ij}^{(\infty)} + k_{ij}^{(0)} + \frac{1}{p}k_{ij}^{(n)} + \sum_m \frac{p}{p+\sigma_m}k_{ij}^{(m)} \tag{22}$$

Thus, in matrix form we may write

$$\mathbf{Y} = p\mathbf{k}^{(\infty)} + \mathbf{k}^{(0)} + \frac{1}{p}\mathbf{k}^{(n)} + \sum_m \frac{p}{p+\sigma_m}\mathbf{k}^{(m)} \tag{23}$$

If Y_{IN} is now also expressed in the realizable partial-fraction-expansion form given in (19) of Appendix A, then (21) above becomes

$$\begin{aligned} Y_{IN} &= k_\infty p + k_0 + \frac{k_n}{p} + \sum_m \frac{p}{p+\sigma_m}k_m \\ &= p\mathbf{n}^t\mathbf{k}^{(\infty)}\mathbf{n} + \mathbf{n}^t\mathbf{k}^{(0)}\mathbf{n} + \frac{1}{p}\mathbf{n}^t\mathbf{k}^{(n)}\mathbf{n} + \sum_m \frac{p}{p+\sigma_m}\mathbf{n}^t\mathbf{k}^{(m)}\mathbf{n} \end{aligned} \tag{24}$$

From the behavior of (24) as p approaches the various critical frequencies, we see that

$$\begin{aligned} k_\infty &= \mathbf{n}^t\mathbf{k}^{(\infty)}\mathbf{n} \\ k_0 &= \mathbf{n}^t\mathbf{k}^{(0)}\mathbf{n} \\ k_n &= \mathbf{n}^t\mathbf{k}^{(n)}\mathbf{n} \\ k_m &= \mathbf{n}^t\mathbf{k}^{(m)}\mathbf{n} \end{aligned} \tag{25}$$

It was shown in Sec. A.2 that k_∞ must be nonnegative. Therefore we see that the matrix $\mathbf{k}^{(\infty)}$ must be positive semidefinite. Since k_0 may be either positive or negative, the matrix $\mathbf{k}^{(0)}$ is indefinite, i.e., unrestricted as to the polarity of its quadratic form. Similarly, since k_n is always nonpositive, the matrix $\mathbf{k}^{(n)}$ must be negative semidefinite. Finally, since the residues k_m are positive for left-half-plane poles and negative for right-half-plane poles, we see that the matrices $\mathbf{k}^{(m)}$ must be positive semidefinite for left-half-plane poles and negative semidefinite for right-half-plane poles.

If rather than using the realizable partial-fraction expansion for the y

parameters, we use the partial-fraction expansion of the general form given in (17) of Appendix A, we see that the y-parameter matrix may be expanded in the form

$$\mathbf{Y} = \frac{1}{p}\mathbf{k}^{(a)} + \mathbf{k}^{(b)} + p\mathbf{k}^{(c)} + \sum_i \frac{1}{p + \sigma_i}\mathbf{k}^{(i)} \tag{26}$$

It is easily shown that $\mathbf{k}^{(a)}$ must be positive semidefinite, $\mathbf{k}^{(b)}$ is indefinite, and $\mathbf{k}^{(c)}$ and the $\mathbf{k}^{(i)}$ are negative semidefinite.

A development similar to the above may be used to determine the properties of the $\mathbf{Z}$ matrix for the two-port $\pm R$, $+C$ class of networks. If we expand the z_{ij}, the elements of the $\mathbf{Z}$ matrix, in the form given by (18) of Appendix A, we obtain

$$z_{ij} = k_{ij}{}^{(\infty)} + pk_{ij}{}^{(n)} + \frac{1}{p}k_{ij}{}^{(0)} + \sum_m \frac{1}{p + \sigma_m}k_{ij}{}^{(m)} \tag{27}$$

Thus, in matrix form we may write

$$\mathbf{Z} = \mathbf{k}^{(\infty)} + p\mathbf{k}^{(n)} + \frac{1}{p}\mathbf{k}^{(0)} + \sum_m \frac{1}{p + \sigma_m}\mathbf{k}^{(m)} \tag{28}$$

Considerations similar to those given for the y parameters lead us to the conclusion that the $\mathbf{k}^{(0)}$ and $\mathbf{k}^{(m)}$ matrices of (28) are positive semidefinite, the $\mathbf{k}^{(n)}$ matrix is negative semidefinite, and the $\mathbf{k}^{(\infty)}$ matrix is indefinite. We may summarize the characteristics of the z and y parameters for the $\pm R$, $+C$ class of networks by the following properties:

Property 2c *The residue matrix for the y parameters of a $\pm R$, $+C$ two-port network for a pole at infinity will be positive semidefinite. The residue matrix for a real pole or for a pole at the origin will be negative semidefinite.*

Property 3c *The residue matrix for the z parameters of a $\pm R$, $+C$ two-port network for a pole at the origin, or for a real pole, will be positive semidefinite. The residue matrix for a pole at infinity will be negative semidefinite.*

Property 4c *If the y parameter matrix for a $\pm R$, $+C$ two-port network is expanded in the form given in (23), the matrix $\mathbf{k}^{(\infty)}$ is positive semidefinite, the matrix $\mathbf{k}^{(n)}$ is negative semidefinite, and the matrix $\mathbf{k}^{(0)}$ is indefinite. The matrices $\mathbf{k}^{(m)}$ will be positive semidefinite for poles on the negative-real axis and negative semidefinite for poles on the positive-real axis.*

Property 5c *If $\mathbf{Z}$, the z-parameter matrix for a $\pm R$, $+C$ two-port network, is expanded in the form given in (28), the matrices $\mathbf{k}^{(0)}$ and $\mathbf{k}^{(m)}$ are positive semidefinite, the matrix $\mathbf{k}^{(n)}$ is negative semidefinite, and the matrix $\mathbf{k}^{(\infty)}$ is indefinite.*

B.5 Transfer functions for $\pm R$, $+C$ networks

In this section we shall derive some of the properties of the various types of transfer functions for $\pm R$, $+C$ two-port networks. First of all, let us consider the transfer admittance function $-y_{21}$. The poles of such a function must also be present in the driving-point admittances y_{11} and y_{22}. Thus, they must be simple and are restricted to the real axis, including the origin and infinity. Since the k_{12} and k_{21} terms in the various $\mathbf{k}$ matrices in (23) are real and equal, they may be either positive or negative without violating the positive or negative semidefinite conditions on the matrices developed in the preceding section. Thus, $-y_{21}$ may be expanded in the form given in (22), where the various k_{21} constants are real but may be positive or negative. From this we conclude that the numerator polynomial of $-y_{21}$ is unrestricted except by the requirement that its degree cannot exceed the degree of the denominator polynomial by more than 1. Thus property 6 becomes

Property 6c *The poles of a $\pm R$, $+C$ transfer admittance function $-y_{21}$ are simple, have real residues, and are restricted to the real axis including the origin and infinity. The residues at these poles and the limiting behavior at the origin or at infinity may be positive or negative. The zeros may occur anywhere on the complex-frequency plane.*

As in the passive RC case, a symmetrical lattice may be used to demonstrate the sufficiency of this property. Similarly, a transfer impedance function z_{21} may be expressed in the form given in (27), where the various k_{21} terms may be either positive or negative but are real. Since a pole at infinity is permitted in this class of network, the numerator polynomial is unrestricted except by the requirement that its degree cannot exceed the degree of the denominator polynomial by more than 1. Thus, property 7 becomes

Property 7c *The poles of a $\pm R$, $+C$ transfer impedance z_{21} are simple, have real residues, and are restricted to the real axis, including the origin and infinity. The residues at these poles and the limiting behavior at the origin and at infinity may be positive or negative. The zeros may occur anywhere on the complex plane.*

The properties of the open-circuit voltage transfer function V_2/V_1 may be derived in the same manner as was done for the passive RC case. They are identical with two exceptions. First, the $\mathbf{k}^{(0)}$ matrix of (23) is no longer required to be positive semidefinite. Therefore, it is possible for y_{22} to have a zero at the origin without requiring y_{21} to have a zero there. Since $V_2/V_1 = -y_{21}/y_{22}$, we conclude that it is possible for the voltage transfer function to have a pole at the origin. Since $y_{21}^{(0)}$ may be positive or negative, the residue at such a pole may be positive or negative. An example of such a network with a positive residue is shown in Fig. B.5. Similarly,

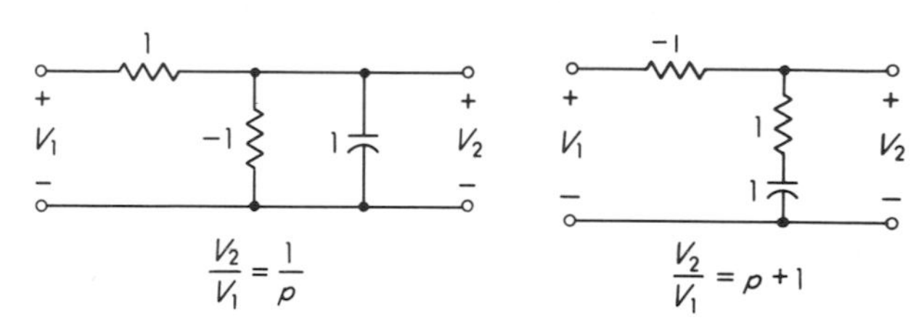

Figure B.5 *A voltage transfer function with a pole at the origin.*

Figure B.6 *A voltage transfer function with a pole at infinity.*

the $\mathbf{k}^{(\infty)}$ matrix of (28) is permitted to be indefinite. Thus, z_{11} may have a zero at infinity without the necessity of z_{21} having a zero there. Since $V_2/V_1 = z_{21}/z_{11}$, we see that it is possible for the voltage transfer function to have a pole at infinity. Again the residue may be positive or negative. An example of a network with a positive residue is shown in Fig. B.6. Similar arguments lead to the conclusion that the short-circuit current transfer function I_2/I_1 may have poles at the origin and infinity, a condition that was not possible in the passive *RC* case. Property 8 now becomes

Property 8c *The poles of either an open-circuit voltage transfer function or a short-circuit current transfer function for a* $\pm R$, $+C$ *two-port network are simple and lie on the real axis including the origin and infinity. They have real residues which may be positive or negative. The zeros may lie anywhere on the complex-frequency plane.*

The final property that was developed for the passive *RC* case, i.e., property 9, the Fialkow-Gerst condition, does not apply to the $\pm R$, $+C$ class of networks.

B.6 *Three-terminal and ladder* $\pm R$, $+C$ *networks*

In this section we shall consider the restrictions imposed on the transfer functions of $\pm R$, $+C$ networks because of the configuration of the network. As was done for the passive *RC* case, we shall consider the two most common cases, the three-terminal network and the ladder network. First let us consider the three-terminal network. The poles are restricted in the same way as the more general $\pm R$, $+C$ network; i.e., they must be simple and are restricted to the real axis, including the origin and infinity. The residues at the finite poles are real, but they may be positive or negative. A pole at infinity, however, will have its residue determined by the capacitive elements of the circuit. Thus, it must have a positive residue. Similarly, a pole at the origin must have its behavior determined by network elements of the type shown in Fig. A.7; thus, its residue must be negative. If there is no pole at the origin, the behavior of the function may be positive or negative since it will be determined by the resistive elements of the network.

Now let us consider the possible locations of zeros. It was shown that a passive *RC* three-terminal network could have transmission zeros anywhere except on the positive-real axis. In $\pm R$, $+C$ class of networks, however, if we parallel each capacitor of value C_i by a resistor of value $G_i = -aC_i$ mhos, we, in effect, change the complex-frequency variable from p to $p - a$, thus achieving a linear translation of all poles and zeros a units to the right on the complex-frequency plane. Clearly we can now obtain zeros anywhere on the complex-frequency plane by this technique. Thus, the location of the zeros of the three-terminal $\pm R$, $+C$ class of networks is unrestricted. For this class of networks property 6 becomes

Property 6d *For a three-terminal $\pm R$, $+C$ network, the poles of the transfer admittance $-y_{21}$ are simple, have real residues, and are restricted to the real axis, including the origin and infinity. The residues at the finite poles may be positive or negative, the residue at the pole at infinity must be positive, and the residue at the pole at origin must be negative. The limiting behavior at the origin (if no pole is present) may be positive or negative. The zeros may occur anywhere on the complex-frequency plane.*

In a similar manner we may modify properties 7 and 8 as follows:

Property 7d *For a three-terminal $\pm R$, $+C$ network, the poles of the transfer impedance z_{21} are simple, have real residues, and are restricted to the real axis, including the origin and infinity. The residues at the finite poles may be positive or negative, the residue at the pole at infinity must be negative, and the residues at the pole at the origin must be positive. The limiting behavior at infinity (if no pole is present) may be positive or negative. The zeros may occur anywhere on the complex-frequency plane.*

Property 8d *For a three-terminal $\pm R$, $+C$ network, the poles of either an open-circuit voltage transfer function or a short-circuit current transfer function are simple and lie on the real axis, including the origin and infinity. They have real residues which may be positive or negative. The zeros may lie anywhere on the complex-frequency plane.*

The most restricted configuration of $\pm R$, $+C$ networks is the ladder network. Since the transmission zeros are the result of poles of series impedances and zeros of shunt impedances, properties 6 through 8 must be modified as follows:

Property 6e *For a $\pm R$, $+C$ ladder network, the poles of the transfer admittance $-y_{21}$ are simple, have real residues, and are restricted to the real axis, including the origin and infinity. The residues at the real poles may be positive or negative, the residue at the pole at infinity must be positive, and the residue at the pole at the origin must be negative. The limiting behavior at the origin may be positive or negative. The zeros are restricted to the real axis, including the origin and infinity.*

Property 7e *For a $\pm R$, $+C$ ladder network, the poles of the transfer impedance z_{21} are simple, have real residues, and are restricted to the real axis, including the origin and infinity. The residues at the finite poles may be positive or negative. The residue at the pole at infinity must be negative, and the residue at the pole at the origin must be positive. The limiting behavior at infinity (if no pole is present) may be positive or negative. The zeros are restricted to the real axis, including the origin and infinity.*

Property 8e *For a $\pm R$, $+C$ ladder network, the poles of either an open-circuit voltage transfer function or a short-circuit current transfer function are simple and lie on the real axis, including the origin and infinity. They have real residues which may be positive or negative. The zeros are restricted to the real axis, including the origin and infinity.*

Property 9 does not apply to this class of networks.

In the preceding sections of this chapter we have developed the properties of two-port networks and transfer functions for the passive *RC* class of networks and also for the $\pm R$, $+C$ class. For each of these classes, properties have been specified for the general four-terminal network configuration, for the three-terminal network configuration, and for the ladder network. Table B.1 lists the various properties for all of the above six cases and provides a ready comparison between the different cases.

B.7 *The properties of RC-gyrator two-port networks*

In this section we shall derive some of the properties of the *RC*-gyrator class of two-port networks. If such a network has its two ports interconnected by transformers in the same manner as was done in Sec. B.1 and as shown in Fig. B.1, we obtain a normalized driving-point admittance

Table B.1 Comparison of properties of various types of RC two-port networks

Property		$+R$, $+C$			$\pm R$, $+C$		
		General network	***Three-terminal network***	***Ladder network***	***General network***	***Three-terminal network***	***Ladder network***
1. ***Z** and **Y** matrices are positive-real*		Yes			Not necessarily		
2. *Residue matrices for y parameters*	*Finite nonzero poles*	Negative semidefinite					
	Pole at infinity	Positive semidefinite					
	Pole at origin	None			Negative semidefinite		
3. *Residue matrices for z parameters*	*Finite nonzero poles*	Positive semidefinite					
	Pole at infinity	None			Negative semidefinite		
	Pole at origin	Positive semidefinite					
4. $\mathbf{Y} = p\mathbf{k}^{(\infty)} + \mathbf{k}^{(0)} + \sum_m \frac{p}{p+\sigma_m}\mathbf{k}^{(m)} + \frac{1}{p}\mathbf{k}^{(n)}$	$\mathbf{k}^{(\infty)}$ *matrix*	Positive semidefinite					
	$\mathbf{k}^{(0)}$ *matrix*	Positive semidefinite			Indefinite		
	$\mathbf{k}^{(m)}$ *matrices*	Positive semidefinite			Positive semidefinite for LHP poles Negative semidefinite for RHP poles		
	$\mathbf{k}^{(n)}$ *matrix*	Null			Negative semidefinite		
5. $\mathbf{Z} = \mathbf{k}^{(\infty)} + \frac{1}{p}\mathbf{k}^{(0)} + \sum_m \frac{1}{p+\sigma_m}\mathbf{k}^{(m)} + p\mathbf{k}^{(n)}$	$\mathbf{k}^{(\infty)}$ *matrix*	Positive semidefinite			Indefinite		
	$\mathbf{k}^{(0)}$ *matrix*	Positive semidefinite					
	$\mathbf{k}^{(m)}$ *matrices*	Positive semidefinite					
	$\mathbf{k}^{(n)}$ *matrix*	Null			Negative semidefinite		

<table>
<tr><td rowspan="8">6. Transfer admittance $-y_{21}$</td><td>Pole locations</td><td colspan="3">Negative-real axis, including infinity, excluding origin</td><td colspan="3">Real axis, including infinity and origin</td></tr>
<tr><td>Multiplicity of poles</td><td colspan="6">Simple</td></tr>
<tr><td>Finite pole residues</td><td colspan="6">Positive or negative</td></tr>
<tr><td>Infinite pole residue</td><td>Positive or negative</td><td colspan="2">Positive</td><td>Positive or negative</td><td colspan="2">Positive</td></tr>
<tr><td>Origin pole residue</td><td colspan="3">None</td><td>Positive or negative</td><td colspan="2">Negative</td></tr>
<tr><td>Behavior at origin (if no pole there)</td><td>Positive or negative</td><td colspan="2">Positive</td><td colspan="3">Positive or negative</td></tr>
<tr><td>Maximum degree of numerator</td><td colspan="6">Degree of denominator plus 1</td></tr>
<tr><td>Zero locations</td><td>Anywhere</td><td>Not on positive real axis</td><td>Negative-real axis, origin and infinity</td><td colspan="2">Anywhere</td><td>Real axis, origin and infinity</td></tr>
<tr><td rowspan="6">7. Transfer impedance z_{21}</td><td>Pole locations</td><td colspan="3">Negative-real axis, excluding infinity, including origin</td><td colspan="3">Real axis, including infinity and origin</td></tr>
<tr><td>Multiplicity of poles</td><td colspan="6">Simple</td></tr>
<tr><td>Finite pole residues</td><td colspan="6">Positive or negative</td></tr>
<tr><td>Infinite pole residue</td><td colspan="3">None</td><td>Positive or negative</td><td colspan="2">Negative</td></tr>
<tr><td>Origin pole residue</td><td>Positive or negative</td><td colspan="2">Positive</td><td>Positive or negative</td><td colspan="2">Positive</td></tr>
<tr><td>Behavior at infinity (if no pole there)</td><td>Positive or negative</td><td colspan="2">Positive</td><td colspan="3">Positive or negative</td></tr>
</table>

Table B.1 Comparison of properties of various types of RC two-port networks (Continued)

Property		$+R$, $+C$			$\pm R$, $+C$		
		General network	*Three-terminal network*	*Ladder network*	*General network*	*Three-terminal network*	*Ladder network*
7. *Transfer impedance z_{21}*	***Maximum degree of numerator***	Degree of denominator			Degree of denominator plus 1		
	Zero locations	Anywhere	Not on positive-real axis	Negative-real axis, origin, and infinity	Anywhere		Real axis, origin and infinity
8. *Transfer ratios V_2/V_1 and I_2/I_1*	***Pole locations***	Negative-real axis, excluding origin and infinity			Real axis, including origin and infinity		
	Multiplicity of poles	Simple					
	Pole residues	Positive or negative					
	Behavior at origin and infinity (if no pole)	Positive or negative	Positive		Positive or negative		
	Maximum degree of numerator	Degree of denominator			Degree of denominator plus 1		
	Location of zeros	Anywhere	Not on positive-real axis	Negative-real axis, origin, and infinity	Anywhere		Real axis, origin, and infinity
9. *Fialkow condition on V_2/V_1 and I_2/I_1*	***Sign of numerator coefficients***	Positive or negative	Positive		Positive or negative		
	Magnitude of numerator coefficients	Less than or equal to magnitude of denominator coefficients			Does not apply		

which must have the form given in (25) in Appendix A, namely

$$Y_{IN} = F_0 + pH_0 + jF_g = \mathbf{n}^t\mathbf{Yn} \tag{29}$$

It was pointed out in Sec. A.3 that the function Y_{IN} must be positive real; i.e., it must have the following properties:

1. It is real for real values of p.
2. Its poles are restricted to the left half-plane and the $j\omega$ axis.
3. Its real part is nonnegative on the $j\omega$ axis.
4. Its $j\omega$-axis poles must be simple with real positive residues.

These conditions infer related conditions on the y-parameter matrix as follows:

1. Since Y_{IN} is real for real values of p, the matrix $\mathbf{Y}$, evaluated under the conditions $p = \sigma$, must have the property that $\mathbf{n}^t\mathbf{Yn}$ is real. This requires the matrix $\mathbf{Y}(\sigma)$ to be hermitian, a condition which is satisfied for the usual case where the y_{ij} are rational functions with real coefficients.
2. Since the poles of Y_{IN} will be the poles of the elements of the matrix $\mathbf{Y}$, these elements can only have poles in the left half-plane and on the $j\omega$ axis.
3. If we evaluate the $\mathbf{Y}$ matrix for $p = j\omega$, we may decompose it into a hermitian part $\mathbf{Y}^{(H)}$ and a skew-hermitian part $\mathbf{Y}^{(SH)}$. Thus, we have

$$\mathbf{n}^tY(j\omega)\mathbf{n} = \mathbf{n}^t\mathbf{Y}^{(H)}\mathbf{n} + \mathbf{n}^t\mathbf{Y}^{(SH)}\mathbf{n} \tag{30}$$

It is easily shown that the skew-hermitian form $\mathbf{n}^t\mathbf{Y}^{(SH)}\mathbf{n}$ is purely imaginary. As such it does not contribute to determining the real part of Y_{IN}. Thus, for the real part of Y_{IN} to be nonnegative, we see that the real part of the hermitian part of $\mathbf{Y}(j\omega)$ must be positive semidefinite.

4. For the $j\omega$-axis poles of Y_{IN} to be simple requires that the $j\omega$ axis poles of the elements of the matrix $\mathbf{Y}$ be simple. Since the residues in such poles of Y_{IN} are required to be real and positive, the residue matrix of $\mathbf{Y}$ for such a pole must be hermitian and positive semidefinite.

The conditions on the z-parameter matrix may be derived in the same manner. It is easily shown that they are identical with the properties for the y-parameter matrix.

The properties on the y- and z-parameter matrix of the RC-gyrator class of active RC networks are basically those of the parameter matrices of the passive RLC class of networks. There is, however, an important exception. This is the result of the gyrator being a nonreciprocal device. As an example of this, assume the elements of $\mathbf{Y}$ have only negative-real poles, and let the $\mathbf{Y}$ matrix be expressed in the realizable partial-fraction-expansion form given in (10). If the network is to have nonreciprocal properties, we may indicate this by writing each of the $\mathbf{k}$ matrices in (10) as the sum of a symmetric and a skew-symmetric matrix; i.e., we may let $\mathbf{k}^{(\infty)} = \mathbf{k}_s^{(\infty)} + \mathbf{k}_{ss}^{(\infty)}$, where $\mathbf{k}_s^{(\infty)}$ is the symmetric part of $\mathbf{k}^{(\infty)}$ and $\mathbf{k}_{ss}^{(\infty)}$ is the skew-symmetric part. Thus, (10) may be written in the form

$$\mathbf{Y} = p(\mathbf{k}_s^{(\infty)} + \mathbf{k}_{ss}^{(\infty)}) + \mathbf{k}_s^{(0)} + \mathbf{k}_{ss}^{(0)} + \sum_m \frac{p}{p + \sigma_m} (\mathbf{k}_s^{(m)} + \mathbf{k}_{ss}^{(m)}) \quad (31)$$

Some of the skew-symmetric matrices in (31) may be realized by appropriate combinations of gyrators and RC elements. For example, the $\mathbf{k}_{ss}^{(0)}$ matrix simply represents a conventional gyrator of appropriate gyration conductance connected between port 1 and port 2. Similarly, terms of the type

$$\frac{p}{p + \sigma_m} \mathbf{k}_{ss}^{(m)} \quad (32)$$

may be realized by the network configuration shown in Fig. B.7, where

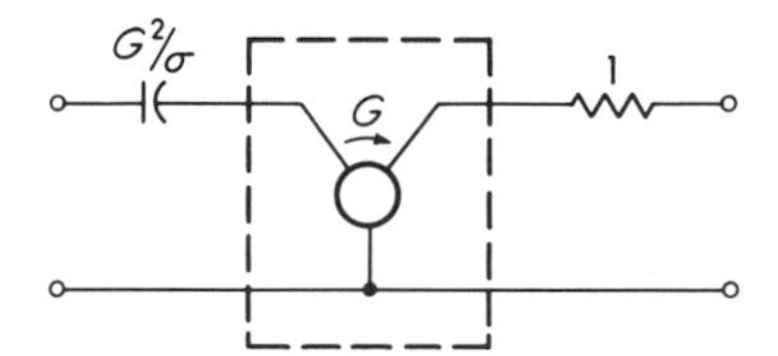

***Figure B.7** A nonreciprocal network with complex transfer admittances.*

the symbol shown within the dashed lines is the conventional schematic representation for a two-port device with the properties defined by (20) of Appendix A, i.e., a gyrator. For this figure the transfer admittances are

$$y_{12} = -y_{21} = \frac{G}{p + \sigma} \quad (33)$$

Thus, this circuit may be thought of as realizing a gyrator with a complex gyration admittance equal to the right-hand member of (33).* The matrix $p\mathbf{k}_{ss}^{(\infty)}$ may be thought of as representing a gyrator with a gyration admittance of the form kp. Such a device is sometimes referred to as a capacitive gyrator. This device is not realizable by this class of networks. It can be shown that such an element is capable of producing non-*pr* driving-point functions.†

* This circuit also has nonzero driving-point admittances y_{11} and y_{22}. Therefore, its elements must be considered as also contributing to the symmetric portion of the residue matrices. See L. P. Huelsman, "Circuits, Matrices, and Linear Vector Spaces," App. B, McGraw-Hill Book Company, New York, 1963.

† Bello, *op. cit.*

B.8 *Transfer functions for other classes of active RC networks*

In this section we shall consider the characteristics of other classes of active *RC* two-port networks. The first of these is the $\pm R$, $\pm C$ class of networks. Such networks are completely general both with respect to the location and the degree of the poles and to the location and degree of the zeros. The generality applies to all three network-configuration classes that have been discussed, namely, the general network, the three-terminal network, and the ladder network. Actually, a simple "pi" network suffices to realize an arbitrary set of y parameters, subject only to the restriction that the y_{12} and y_{21} parameters are equal, i.e., that the network is reciprocal. We assume, of course, that the y_{ij} are rational functions, i.e., ratios of polynomials with real coefficients. To see this, consider the "pi" network shown in Fig. B.8. This may also be considered as a simple ladder network.

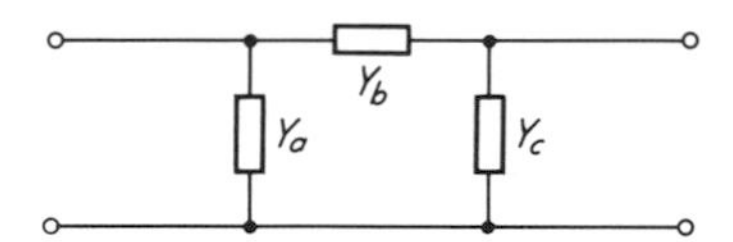

***Figure B.8** A "pi" network of admittances.*

The three admittances Y_a, Y_b, and Y_c may be expressed in terms of the y parameters of the network as

$$\begin{aligned} Y_a &= y_{11} + y_{12} \\ Y_b &= -y_{12} \\ Y_c &= y_{22} + y_{12} \end{aligned} \tag{34}$$

Therefore, since the y_{ij} are rational functions, the admittances Y_a, Y_b, and Y_c will also be rational functions. As such they are realizable as $\pm R$, $\pm C$ driving-point immittances by the methods given in Sec. A.4. Thus, we see that a ladder-network realization can always be achieved for a reciprocal set of y parameters by the $\pm R$, $\pm C$ class of networks. It should be readily apparent that, since the y parameters are unrestricted, the z parameters, the open-circuit voltage transfer function, and the short-circuit current transfer functions are similarly unrestricted; i.e., this class of networks can be used to realize a reciprocal network with completely general characteristics.

As an example, consider the network parameters

$$\begin{aligned} y_{11} &= 0 \\ y_{12} &= y_{21} = \frac{-0.2p}{p^2 + 0.2p + 1} \\ y_{22} &= 1 \end{aligned}$$

It is easily seen that

$$Y_a = \frac{-0.2p}{p^2 + 0.2p + 1}$$
$$Y_b = \frac{0.2p}{p^2 + 0.2p + 1} \tag{35}$$
$$Y_c = \frac{p^2 + 1}{p^2 + 0.2p + 1}$$

The realizations for these admittances are easily made in the manner described in Sec. A.4. The complete network is shown in Fig. B.9. Note

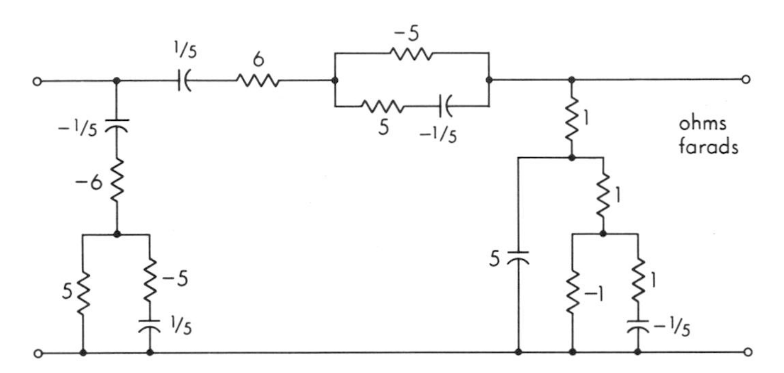

Figure B.9 A realization of the y parameters of (35).

that this network, when operated under the usual short-circuit conditions, has the rather unique properties of infinite input impedance, a bandpass transfer admittance, constant output impedance independent of frequency; yet it is still a reciprocal network! An inspection of the schematic for this network brings out the impracticability of using $\pm R$, $\pm C$ networks for actually synthesizing networks. Despite their theoretical universality, practically they are almost useless because of the large number of difficult-to-realize negative-valued elements. We shall see that some of the other classes of active *RC* networks have more practicality.

The next class of active *RC* circuits to consider is the *RC*-NIC class, i.e., the one which includes positive-valued resistors and capacitors and NICs (negative-immittance converters). A detailed discussion of the NIC may be found in Chap. 4. Here, however, for completeness, we point out that since NICs can be used to realize negative-valued resistors and capacitors, this class of networks is at least as general as the $\pm R$, $\pm C$ class discussed above. Actually, it is considerably more general since the NIC is a nonreciprocal device. Therefore with it as an active element, we can realize networks in which y_{12} is not equal to y_{21}.

Two other classes of networks may be considered briefly. The first is the class that includes positive-valued resistors and capacitors and controlled sources. It has been shown that the controlled source can be used to realize an NIC. Therefore this class of networks is at least as general a class as the *RC*-NIC class. Further discussion of this class of networks is given in Chap. 3. The second class is the class of networks including positive-valued resistors and capacitors and operational (high-gain) amplifiers. Again, as has been pointed out, this class is at least as general a class as the *RC*-NIC class. Further discussion of this class of networks is given in Chap. 6.

B.9 *Z and y parameters for n-port networks*

Although the primary concern of this book is with the development of the properties of active *RC* networks as applied to the transfer function case, it is desirable, for completeness, to include some of the basic concepts concerning the properties of n-port networks. The reader who is interested in the more applied aspects of active *RC* networks may easily skip this section without loss of continuity.

The discussion and development in Sec. B.1 which led to a determination of the properties of the two-port passive *RC* network are easily extended to the n-port case. All that is required is to permit each of the column matrices $\mathbf{V}$ and $\mathbf{I}$ used in (2) to have n elements $V_i(p)$ and $I_i(p)$, respectively. Thus the $\mathbf{Y}$ matrix becomes an $n \times n$ matrix rather than a 2×2 matrix. The positive-real property based on the energy functions F_0 and H_0, however, remains the same. Thus we conclude that the $\mathbf{Y}$ matrix and similarly the $\mathbf{Z}$ matrix are positive real. Thus, property 1 of Sec. B.1 applies if "two-port" is changed to "n-port."

An interconnection of transformer networks for the n-port case similar to that used for the two-port case is shown in Fig. B.10. The input admit-

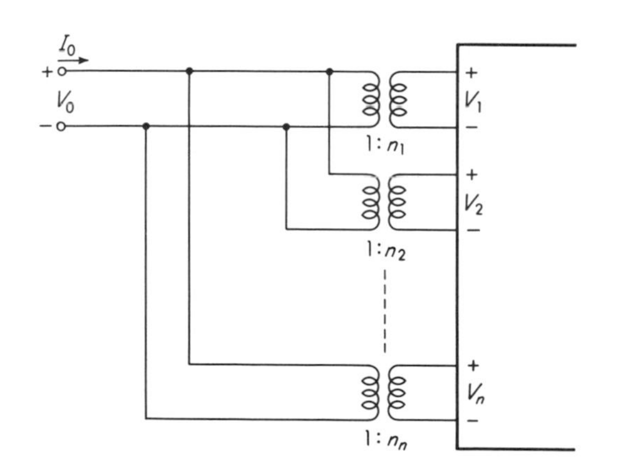

Figure B.10 *An n-port network with ideal transformers interconnecting the n ports.*

tance Y_{IN} is specified by the same quadratic form given in (7), where in the n-port case $\mathbf{n}$ is a column matrix with n elements n_i giving the turns ratios of the transformers shown in Fig. B.10. The elements y_{ij} of the $n \times n$ matrix $\mathbf{Y}$ may be expanded in the identical form given in (9), and the same conclusions that were made about the positive or negative semidefiniteness of the residue matrices are true. As a matter of fact, the entire development of Sec. B.1 applies to the n-port case, the only exception being that the conditions for positive and negative semidefiniteness given in (13) and (14) must be replaced with the more complex relations for the $n \times n$ matrix case.* Thus, we see that properties 2 through 5 apply to the n-port case by merely changing "two-port" to "n-port."

In a similar fashion, the conclusions reached in Sec. B.4 regarding the properties of the two-port z- and y-parameter matrices for $\pm R$, $+C$ networks may be shown to apply equally well to the $\mathbf{Z}$ and $\mathbf{Y}$ matrices for the n-port case. The conclusions reached regarding the two-port parameters of the RC-gyrator class of networks in Sec. B.7 are also directly applicable to the n-port case, as are the conclusions of Sec. B.8 for $\pm R$, $\pm C$ networks.

B.10 *Conclusion*

In this appendix we have analyzed the properties of various classes of active and passive RC networks with a view to determining the properties of transfer functions for the various classes of networks. As in the case for the driving-point functions, it was shown that the addition of negative-valued resistors to the passive RC class of networks provided only a small gain with respect to the types of transfer functions that could be realized. In contrast with this, however, the addition of controlled sources (or NICs or operational amplifiers) provided complete generality with respect to transfer function realization. The $\pm R$, $\pm C$ class was also shown to be completely general.

* Such relations may be found in any of the standard texts on matrix algebra. See also L. Weinberg, "Network Analysis and Synthesis," chap. 6, McGraw-Hill Book Company, New York, 1962.

Appendix C *Optimum decomposition of a polynomial*

In Sec. 2.6 of Chap. 2, a method is given for decomposing a polynomial containing only complex conjugate zeros into the difference of two polynomials, with each of the latter containing only negative-real zeros. The decomposition may be written in the form

$$P(p) = \prod_{i=1}^{n/2} (p - p_i)(p - \bar{p}_i) = a_0 A(p) - k b_0 B(p) \tag{1}$$

where

$$\begin{aligned} A(p) &= \prod_{i=1}^{n} (p + a_i) \\ B(p) &= \prod_{i=1}^{n} (p + b_i) \end{aligned} \tag{2}$$

and k has a nominal value of unity. If the decomposition satisfies the criteria that

1. The zero determined by $-b_n$ is at infinity
2. The zero determined by $-b_1$ is at the origin
3. All the other zeros of $A(p)$ and $B(p)$ occur in pairs and have an alternation satisfying the relation

$$-b_n < -a_n = -a_{n-1} < -b_{n-1} = -b_{n-2} < \cdots < a_2 = a_1 < b_1$$

then it is said to be optimum in the sense that the magnitude of the sensitivity which is defined by the relation

$$|S_k{}^{p_i}| = \left| \frac{dp_i}{dk/k} \right| \tag{3}$$

is minimized at all the zeros p_i of $P(p)$. In this appendix, a proof of the optimality of this decomposition is given.*

From the derivation given in Sec. 2.2 of Chap. 2, the sensitivity defined in (3) may be shown to be

$$|S_k{}^{p_i}| = \left| \frac{a_0 A(p_i)}{dP(p_i)/dp} \right| \tag{4}$$

Thus, the sensitivity will be minimized if $|a_0 A(p_i)|$ is minimized. Now let us assume that the zero of $B(p)$ located at $-b_n$ is not at infinity. We may form the new decomposition

$$P(p) = a_0' A'(p) - k b_0' B'(p) \tag{5}$$

where

$$\begin{aligned} a_0' A'(p) &= a_0 A(p) - d_0 D(p) \\ b_0' B'(p) &= b_0 B(p) - d_0 D(p) \end{aligned} \tag{6}$$

The polynomial $D(p)$ is assumed to contain only negative-real zeros. Thus, it may be written in the form

$$D(p) = \prod_{i=1}^{n} (p + d_i) \tag{7}$$

where

$$-d_n < -d_{n-1} < \cdots < -d_1 \tag{8}$$

In addition, let it be required that a zero of $D(p)$ be located between each pair of the zeros of $A(p)$ and $B(p)$ such that

$$\theta_d = \frac{\theta_i + \theta_{i+1}}{2} \tag{9}$$

where the quantities θ_k are angles defined as shown in Fig. C.1. Also, let

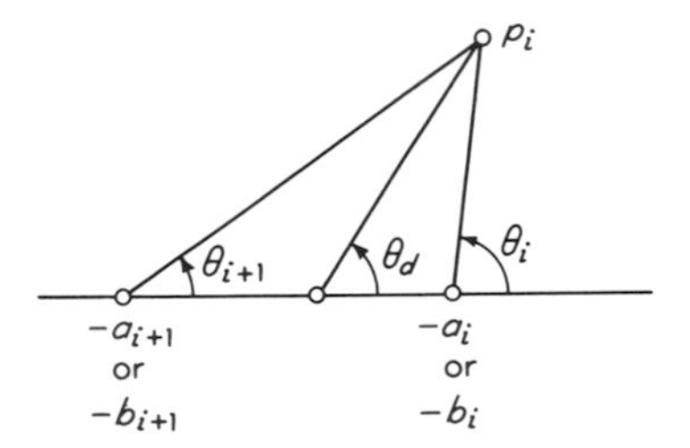

Figure C.1 Definition of the angles in (9).

the zero of $D(p)$ at $-d_1$ coincide with the zero of $B(p)$ at $-b_1$. It may be

* The proof is due to D. A. Calahan, Notes on the Horowitz Optimization Procedure, *IRE Trans. Circuit Theory*, vol. CT-7, no. 3, pp. 352–354, Sept., 1960.

shown that if

$$|\arg A(p_i) - \arg D(p_i)| < \frac{\pi}{2} \tag{10}$$

then a positive constant d_0 exists such that

$$|a_0'A'(p_i)| = |a_0A(p_i) - d_0D(p_i)| < |a_0A(p_i)| \tag{11}$$

Thus, in such a case, the decomposition of (5) will have a lower sensitivity than the decomposition given in (1). We now proceed to show that (10) may be satisfied.

If we define the various angles shown in Fig. C.2, we see that

$$\arg D(p_i) = \sum_{i=2}^{n} \theta_{d_i} + \theta_{b_1} \tag{12}$$

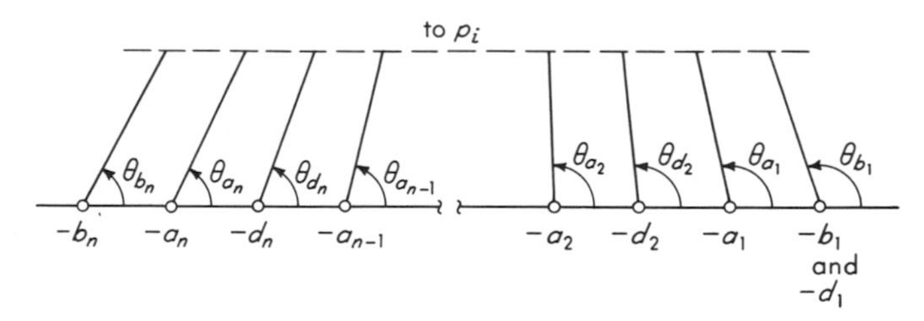

Figure C.2** **Definition of the angles in (12).

Also, from the figure and using (9), we see that

$$\begin{aligned} \arg A(p_i) &= 2\sum_i \theta_{d_i} \qquad i = 2, 4, 6, \ldots, n \\ \arg B(p_i) &= 2\sum_i \theta_{d_i} + \theta_{b_1} + \theta_{b_n} \qquad i = 3, 5, \ldots, n-1 \end{aligned} \tag{13}$$

Therefore, we may write

$$\arg D(p_i) = \tfrac{1}{2}[\arg A(p_i) + \arg B(p_i) + \theta_{b_1} + \theta_{b_n}] \tag{14}$$

From a consideration of (1) we see that

$$\arg A(p_i) = \arg B(p_i) \tag{15}$$

Substituting (15) in (14) and rearranging, we obtain

$$|\arg A(p_i) - \arg D(p_i)| = |\tfrac{1}{2}(\theta_{b_1} - \theta_{b_n})| < \frac{\pi}{2} \tag{16}$$

Thus, we conclude that if $-b_n$ is not at infinity, a d_0 may be chosen such that the sensitivity of the decomposition given in (5) is less than the sensitivity of the decomposition given in (1). In addition, the zero at $-b_n$ of the polynomial $B'(p)$ will be closer to infinity than the corresponding zero of the polynomial $B(p)$.

A similar argument may be made for the case where the zero of $B(p)$ at $-b_1$ is not at the origin. For this case, the zero of $D(p)$ at $-b_1$ is deleted. This reduces the order of $D(p)$. Summing the arguments from the various polynomials, we see that

$$|\arg A(p_i) - \arg D(p_i)| = |\tfrac{1}{2}\theta_{b_1}| < \frac{\pi}{2} \tag{17}$$

Therefore, a positive d_0 exists such that a new decomposition with reduced sensitivity may be found. In this case the zero of $B(p)$ at $-b_1$ is closer to the origin than the corresponding zero of $B(p)$.

Finally, by a similar argument, we may show that if the zeros of $B(p)$ at $-b_n$ and $-b_1$ are located at infinity and the origin, respectively, but the zeros of any of the pairs of zeros of $A(p)$ or $B(p)$ are not coincident, a new decomposition may be formed with a lower sensitivity. For such a case, if we let $-d_m$ be the zero of $D(p)$ located between a pair of noncoincident zeros of $A(p)$ or $B(p)$, then if that zero is eliminated from $D(p)$, we see that

$$|\arg A(p_i) - \arg D(p_i)| = |\tfrac{1}{2}\theta_{b_1} - \theta_{d_m}| < \frac{\pi}{2} \tag{18}$$

and a d_0 must exist such that a new decomposition of the form given in (5) may be found with a reduced sensitivity. In the new decomposition, the zeros of the pair of zeros of $A'(p)$ or $B'(p)$ will be closer together than they were in $A(p)$ or $B(p)$.

By continued application of the above steps we arrive at an optimum decomposition satisfying the criteria given at the beginning of this appendix. A similar argument may be applied to prove the optimality of the sum decomposition described in Sec. 2.7 of this text.*

* D. A. Calahan, Sensitivity Minimization in Active *RC* Synthesis, *IRE Trans. Circuit Theory*, vol. CT-9, no. 1, pp. 38–42, March, 1962.

Appendix D *Bibliography*

In this appendix, a bibliography of material pertinent to the subject matter of this text is presented. The material is divided into five classifications, namely general material on active *RC* circuits (including realizations using controlled sources), sensitivity and polynomial decomposition, negative-immittance converters and related synthesis techniques, gyrators, and operational amplifier realization techniques. Although there are over 200 entries in this bibliography, no claim can be made that the listing is an all-inclusive one. Rather, it is hoped that it will present a collection of significant references that will serve as a starting point for the serious researcher in this field, who will go on to make his own literature discoveries.

The reader should also be aware of two books which contain material pertinent to the topics covered in this text. They are K. L. Su, "Active Network Synthesis," McGraw-Hill Book Company, New York, 1965, and P. M. Chirlian, "Integrated and Active Network Analysis and Synthesis," Prentice-Hall, Inc., Englewood Cliffs, N.J., 1967.

D.1 *General active RC circuits and controlled-source realizations*

Armstrong, D. B., and F. M. Reza: Synthesis of Transfer Functions by Active *RC* Networks with Feedback Loops, *IRE Trans. Circuit Theory,* vol. CT-1, no. 2, pp. 8–17, June, 1954.

Balabanian, N., and B. Patel: Active Realization of Complex Zeros, *IEEE Trans. Circuit Theory,* vol. CT-10, no. 2, pp. 299–300, June, 1963.

Bennett, W. R.: Synthesis of Active Networks, *Proc. Symp. Modern Networks Synthesis, Polytechnic Inst. Brooklyn,* vol. 5, pp. 45–61, 1956.

Blecher, F. H.: Application of Synthesis Techniques to Electronic Circuit Design, *IRE Trans. Circuit Theory,* vol. CT-7, special supplement, pp. 79–91, Aug., 1960.

Bobrow, L. S., and S. L. Hakimi: A Note on Active RC Realization of Voltage Transfer Functions, *IEEE Trans. Circuit Theory,* vol. CT-11, no. 4, pp. 493–494, Dec., 1964.

Bongiorno, J. J.: Synthesis of Active RC Single-tuned Bandpass Filters, *IRE Nat. Conv. Record,* part 2, pp. 30–41, 1958.

DeClaris, N.: Driving Point Impedance Functions of Active Networks, *IRE Nat. Conv. Record,* part 2, pp. 26–37, 1956.

———: Synthesis of Active Networks Driving-point Functions, *IRE Nat. Conv. Record,* part 2, pp. 23–39, 1959.

Ford, R. L., and F. E. J. Girling: Active Filters and Oscillators Using Simulated Inductance, *Electron. Letters,* vol. 2, no. 2, p. 52, Feb., 1966.

Foss, R. C., and B. J. Green: Qfactor, Qstability, and Gain in Active Filters, *Electron. Letters,* vol. 2, no. 3, pp. 99–100, March, 1966.

Fritzinger, G.: Frequency Discrimination by Inverse Feedback, *Proc. IRE,* vol. 26, no. 2, p. 207, Feb., 1938.

Gorski-Popiel, J.: RC Active Networks, *Electron. Letters,* vol. 1, no. 10, pp. 288–289, Dec., 1965.

Gorski-Popiel, J., and A. J. Drew: RC Active Ladder Networks, *Proc. IEE,* vol. 112, pp. 2213–2219, Dec., 1965.

Haines, G. W.: An Integrated Stabilized Gain Block, *IEEE Int. Conv. Record,* part 7, pp. 296–307, 1966.

Hakim, S. S.: RC Active Filters Using Amplifiers as Active Elements, *Proc. IEE,* vol. 112, no. 5, pp. 901–912, May, 1965.

———: Synthesis of RC Active Filters with Prescribed Pole Sensitivity, *Proc. IEE,* vol. 112, no. 12, pp. 2235–2242, Dec., 1965.

Holt, A. G. J., and R. Linggard: Active Chebyshev Filters, *Electron. Letters,* vol. 1, no. 5, pp. 130–131, July, 1965.

———: RC Active Synthesis Procedure for Polynomial Filters, *Proc. IEE,* vol. 113, no. 5, pp. 777–782, May, 1966.

Horowitz, Isaac M.: Active Network Synthesis, *IRE Nat. Conv. Record,* part 2, pp. 38–45, 1956.

———: Exact Design of Transistor RC Band-pass Filters with Prescribed Active Parameter Insensitivity, *IRE Trans. Circuit Theory,* vol. CT-7, no. 3, pp. 313–320, Sept., 1960.

———: Optimum Design of Single-stage Gyrator-RC Filters with Prescribed Sensitivity, *IRE Trans. Circuit Theory,* vol. CT-8, no. 2, pp. 88–94, June, 1961.

———: Active RC Synthesis, *IEEE Trans. Circuit Theory,* vol. CT-13, no. 1, pp. 101–102, March, 1966.

Huelsman, L. P.: Stability Criteria for Active RC Synthesis Techniques, *Proc. Nat. Electron. Conf.,* vol. 20, pp. 731–736, 1964.

Jones, H. E., and B. A. Shenoi: Worst Case Gain Sensitivity with Zero Phase Sensitivity in Active RC Network Synthesis, *Proc. Fourth Ann. Allerton Conf. Circuit and System Theory,* pp. 259–268, 1966.

Kawakami, M.: Some Fundamental Considerations on Active Four-terminal Linear Networks, *IRE Trans. Circuit Theory,* vol. CT-5, no. 2, pp. 115–121, June, 1958.

Kerwin, W. J.: An Active RC Elliptic Function Filter, *IEEE Region Six Conf. Record,* vol. 2, pp. 647–654, 1966.

———: RC Active Networks, *Proc. Inst. Modern Solid State Circuit Design, Univ. of Santa Clara,* pp. 77–91, 1966.

Kerwin, W. J., and L. P. Huelsman: Design of High Performance Active RC Band-pass Filters, *IEEE Int. Conv. Record,* vol. 14, part 10, pp. 74–80, March, 1966.

Kinariwala, B. K.: Synthesis of Driving-point Impedances Using Active RC Filters, *IRE WESCON Conv. Record,* part 2, pp. 53–64, 1959.

———: Necessary and Sufficient Conditions for the Existence of ±R, C Networks, *IRE Trans. Circuit Theory,* vol. CT-7, no. 3, pp. 330–335, Sept., 1960.

Kuh, E. S.: Transfer Function Synthesis of Active RC Networks, *IRE Trans. Circuit Theory,* vol. CT-7, special supplement, pp. 3–7, Aug., 1960.
Kuo, F. F.: Transfer Function Synthesis with Active Elements, *Proc. Nat. Electron. Conf.,* vol. 13, pp. 1049–1056, 1957.
Linvill, J. G.: The Synthesis of Active Filters, *Proc. Symp. Modern Network Synthesis, Polytechnic Inst. of Brooklyn,* vol. 5, 1955.
———: Synthesis Techniques and Active Networks, *IRE Nat. Conv. Record,* part 2, pp. 90–94, 1957.
McVey, P. J.: Sensitivity in Some Simple RC Active Networks, *Proc. IEE,* vol. 112, no. 7, pp. 1263–1269, July, 1965.
Mitra, S. K.: Notes on Sandberg's Method of Active RC One-port Synthesis, *IRE Trans. Circuit Theory,* vol. CT-9, no. 4, pp. 422–423, Dec., 1962.
———: A Unique Synthesis Method of Transformerless Active RC Networks, *J. Franklin Inst.,* vol. 274, no. 2, pp. 115–129, Aug., 1962.
———: A New Approach to Active RC Network Synthesis, *J. Franklin Inst.,* vol. 274, no. 3, pp. 185–197, Sept., 1962.
Myers, B. R.: Transistor-RC Network Synthesis, *IRE WESCON Conv. Record,* part 2, pp. 65–74, 1959.
Newell, W. E.: Selectivity and Sensitivity in Functional Blocks, *Proc. IRE,* vol. 50, no. 12, p. 2517, Dec., 1962.
———: Tuned Integrated Circuits—A State-of-the-art Survey, *Proc. IEEE,* vol. 52, no. 12, pp. 1603–1608, Dec., 1964.
Orchard, H. J.: Inductorless Filters, *Electron. Letters,* vol. 2, no. 6, pp. 224–225, June, 1966.
Paul, R. J. A.: Active Network Synthesis Using One-port RC Networks, *Proc. IEE,* vol. 113, no. 1, pp. 83–86, Jan., 1966.
Sallen, R. P., and E. L. Key: A Practical Method of Designing RC Active Filters, *IRE Trans. Circuit Theory,* vol. CT-2, no. 1, pp. 74–85, March, 1955.
Sandberg, I. W.: Synthesis of n-port Active RC Networks, *Bell System Tech. J.,* vol. 40, no. 1, pp. 329–347, Jan., 1961.

D.2 *Sensitivity and polynomial decomposition*

Biswas, R. N., and E. S. Kuh: Multiparameter Sensitivity Analysis for Linear Systems, *Proc. Third Ann. Allerton Conf. Circuit and System Theory,* pp. 384–393, 1965.
Blecher, F. H.: Application of Synthesis Techniques to Electronic Circuit Design, *IRE Trans. Circuit Theory,* vol. CT-7, special supplement, pp. 79–91, Aug., 1960.
Bongiorno, J. J.: Synthesis of Active RC Single-tuned Bandpass Filters, *IRE Nat. Conv. Record,* part 2, pp. 30–41, 1958.
Branner, G. R.: On Methods of Polynomial Decomposition in Active Network Synthesis, *IEEE Trans. Circuit Theory,* vol. CT-10, no. 4, pp. 525–526, Dec., 1963.
———: On Active Networks Using Current Inversion-type Negative-impedance Converters, *IEEE Trans. Circuit Theory,* vol. CT-10, no. 2, p. 290, June, 1963.
Calahan, D. A.: Notes on the Horowitz Optimization Procedure, *IRE Trans. Circuit Theory,* vol. CT-7, no. 3, pp. 352–354, Sept., 1960.
———: Restrictions on the Natural Frequencies of an RC-RL Network, *J. Franklin Inst.,* vol. 272, no. 2, pp. 112–133, Aug., 1961.
———: Sensitivity Minimization in Active RC Synthesis, *IRE Trans. Circuit Theory,* vol. CT-9, no. 1, pp. 38–42, March, 1962.

———: A Numerical Algorithm for the Minimization of Sensitivity, *Proc. Third Ann. Allerton Conf. Circuit and System Theory,* pp. 394–406, 1965.

Cartianu, G., and D. Poenaru: Variation of Transfer Functions with the Modification of Pole Location, *IRE Trans. Circuit Theory,* vol. CT-9, no. 1, pp. 98–99, March, 1962.

Cruz, J. B., and W. R. Perkins: The Role of Sensitivity in the Design of Multivariable Linear Systems, *Proc. Nat. Electron. Conf.,* vol. 20, pp. 742–745, 1964.

———: A New Approach to the Sensitivity Problem in Multivariable Feedback System Design, *IEEE Trans. Auto. Control,* vol. AC-9, no. 3, pp. 216–223, July, 1964.

Dorato, P.: On Sensitivity in Optimal Control Systems, *IEEE Trans. Auto. Control,* vol. AC-8, no. 3, pp. 256–257, July, 1963.

Fu, K. S.: Sensitivity of a Linear System with Variations of One or Several Parameters, *IRE Trans. Circuit Theory,* vol. CT-7, no. 3, pp. 348–349, Sept., 1960.

Geller, S. B.: Synthesis of an Immittance Function with Two Negative Impedance Converters, *IRE Trans. Circuit Theory,* vol. CT-9, no. 3, p. 291, Sept., 1962.

Goldstein, A. J., and F. F. Kuo: Multiparameter Sensitivity, *IRE Trans. Circuit Theory,* vol. CT-8, no. 2, pp. 177–178, June, 1961.

Gorski-Popiel, J.: Classical Sensitivity—A Collection of Formulas, *IEEE Trans. Circuit Theory,* vol. CT-10, no. 2, pp. 300–302, June, 1963.

———: Horowitz Minimum-sensitivity Decomposition, *Electron. Letters,* vol. 2, no. 9, pp. 334–335, Sept., 1966.

Hakim, S. S.: RC Active Filters Using Amplifiers as Active Elements, *Proc. IEE,* vol. 112, no. 5, pp. 901–912, May, 1965.

———: Synthesis of RC Active Filters with Prescribed Pole Sensitivity, *Proc. IEE,* vol. 112, no. 12, pp. 2235–2242, Dec., 1965.

Hakimi, S. L., and J. B. Cruz: Measures of Sensitivity for Linear Systems with Large Multiple Parameter Variations, *IRE WESCON Conv. Record,* part 2, pp. 109–115, 1960.

Herbst, N. M.: Optimization of Pole Sensitivity in RC Networks, *Cornell Univ. Res. Rept.* EE 569, 1963.

Holmes, W. H., S. Gruetzmann, and W. E. Heinlein: High-quality Active-RC Filters Using Gyrators, *Digest 1967 Int. Solid State Circuits Conf.,* pp. 122–123, Feb., 1967.

Horowitz, I. M.: Optimization of Negative-impedance Conversion Methods of Active RC Synthesis, *IRE Trans. Circuit Theory,* vol. CT-6, no. 3, pp. 296–303, Sept., 1959.

———: Exact Design of Transistor RC Band-pass Filters with Prescribed Active Parameter Insensitivity, *IRE Trans. Circuit Theory,* vol. CT-7, no. 3, pp. 313–320, Sept., 1960.

———: Optimum Design of Single-stage Gyrator-RC Filters with Prescribed Sensitivity, *IRE Trans. Circuit Theory,* vol. CT-8, no. 2, pp. 88–94, June, 1961.

Huang, R. Y.: The Sensitivity of the Poles of Linear, Closed-loop Systems, *Trans. AIEE Applications and Industry,* no. 38, pp. 182–187, Sept., 1958.

Huelsman, L. P.: Active RC Synthesis with Prescribed Sensitivities, *Proc. Nat. Electron. Conf.,* vol. 16, pp. 412–426, 1960.

———: Use of Two Negative-impedance Converters to Synthesize RC Transfer Functions, *IRE Trans. Circuit Theory,* vol. CT-9, no. 3, p. 357, Sept., 1961.

———: Matrix Analysis of Network Sensitivities, *Proc. Nat. Electron. Conf.,* vol. 19, pp. 1–5, 1963.

Jones, H. E., and B. A. Shenoi: Worst Case Gain Sensitivity with Zero Phase Sensitivity in Active RC Network Synthesis, *Proc. Fourth Ann. Allerton Conf. Circuit and System Theory,* pp. 259–268, 1966.

Kuh, E. S.: Some Results in Linear Multiple Loop Feedback Systems, *Proc. First Ann. Allerton Conf. Circuit and System Theory,* pp. 471–487, 1963.

Kuo, F. F.: Transfer Function Synthesis with Active Elements, *Proc. Nat. Electron. Conf.,* vol. 13, pp. 1049–1056, 1957.

———: Pole-Zero Sensitivity in Network Functions, *IRE Trans. Circuit Theory,* vol. CT-5, no. 4, pp. 372–373, Dec., 1958.

———: Sensitivity of Transmission Zeros in RC Network Synthesis, *IRE Nat. Conv. Record,* part 2, pp. 18–22, 1959.

———: A Sensitivity Theorem, *IRE Trans. Circuit Theory,* vol. CT-6, no. 1, p. 131, March, 1959.

Lee, S. C.: Sensitivity Minimization in Active RC Integrated Circuit Design, *Proc. Fourth Ann. Allerton Conf. Circuit and System Theory,* pp. 269–281, 1966.

———: On Multiparameter Sensitivity, *Proc. Third Ann. Allerton Conf. Circuit and System Theory,* pp. 407–420, 1965.

Linvill, J. G.: The Synthesis of Active Filters, *Proc. Symp. Modern Network Synthesis, Polytechnic Inst. of Brooklyn,* vol. 5, 1955.

———: RC Active Filters, *Proc. IRE,* vol. 42, no. 3, pp. 555–564, March, 1954.

Martinelli, G.: On the Matrix Analysis of Network Sensitivity, *Proc. IEEE,* vol. 54, no. 1, pp. 72–73, Jan., 1963.

McVey, P. J.: Sensitivity in Some Simple RC Active Networks, *Proc. IEE,* vol. 112, no. 7, pp. 1263–1269, July, 1965.

Mikulski, J. J.: "The Correlation between Classical and Pole-Zero Sensitivity," Ph.D. thesis, University of Illinois, Department of Electrical Engineering, 1959.

Mitra, S. K., and J. Delansky: A Polynomial Decomposition Approach to the Synthesis of Driving-point Functions, *Proc. Seventh Midwest Symp. Circuit Theory,* May, 1964.

Newell, W. E.: Pole-Zero Sensitivity Relationships, *Proc. IRE,* vol. 49, no. 12, p. 1959, Dec., 1961.

———: Selectivity and Sensitivity in Functional Blocks, *Proc. IRE,* vol. 50, no. 12, p. 2517, Dec., 1962.

Papoulis, A.: Displacement of the Zeros of the Impedance Z(p) due to Incremental Variations in the Network Elements, *Proc. IRE,* vol. 43, no. 1, pp. 79–82, Jan., 1955.

———: Sensitivity Analysis with Random Increments, *Proc. Third Ann. Allerton Conf. Circuit and System Theory,* pp. 202–211, 1965.

Rohrer, R. A.: Minimum Sensitivity RC-NIC Driving Point Synthesis, *IEEE Trans. Circuit Theory,* vol. CT-10, no. 3, pp. 442–443, Sept., 1963.

Saito, M.: Sensitivity in Active RC Networks, *Electron. Commun. Japan,* vol. 47, pp. 54–62, Feb., 1964.

Schoeffler, J. D.: The Synthesis of Minimum Sensitivity Networks, *IEEE Trans. Circuit Theory,* vol. CT-11, no. 2, pp. 271–276, June, 1964.

Storey, D. J.: Effect of Small Variations of Impedance on the Pole and Zero Locations for a Passive Linear Network, *Proc. IEE,* vol. 110, no. 12, p. 2181, Dec., 1963.

Thomas, R. E.: Polynomial Decomposition in Active Network Synthesis, *IRE Trans. Circuit Theory,* vol. CT-9, no. 3, pp. 270–274, Sept., 1961.

Tomovic, R.: "Sensitivity Analysis of Dynamic Systems," McGraw-Hill Book Company, New York, 1963.

Truxal, J. G., and I. M. Horowitz: Sensitivity Considerations in Active Network Synthesis, *Proc. 2nd Midwest Symp. Circuit Theory,* pp. 6-1 to 6-11, 1956.

Woodard, J., and R. W. Newcomb: Sensitivity Improvement of Inductorless Filters, *Electron. Letters,* vol. 2, no. 9, pp. 349–350, Sept., 1966.

D.3 *Negative-immittance converters and related synthesis procedures*

Antoniou, A.: New Active RC Synthesis Procedure Using Negative-impedance Converters, *Electron. Letters,* vol. 1, no. 7, pp. 203–204, Sept., 1965.

———: Negative-impedance Converters Using Operational Amplifiers, *Electron. Letters,* vol. 1, no. 4, pp. 88–89, June, 1965.

Barranger, J.: Voltage Transfer Function Matrix Realization Using Current Negative Immittance Converters, *IEEE Trans. Circuit Theory,* vol. CT-13, no. 1, pp. 97–98, March, 1966.

Blecher, F. H.: Application of Synthesis Techniques to Electronic Circuit Design, *IRE Trans. Circuit Theory,* vol. CT-7, special supplement, pp. 79–91, Aug., 1960.

Branner, G. R.: On Active Networks Using Current Inversion-type Negative-impedance Converters, *IEEE Trans. Circuit Theory,* vol. CT-10, no. 2, p. 290, June, 1963.

Brownlie, J. D.: On the Stability Properties of a Negative Impedance Converter, *IEEE Trans. Circuit Theory,* vol. CT-13, no. 1, pp. 98–99, March, 1966.

Calahan, D. A.: Sensitivity Minimization in Active RC Synthesis, *IRE Trans. Circuit Theory,* vol. CT-9, no. 1, pp. 38–42, March, 1962.

Carlin, H. J.: Singular Network Elements, *IEEE Trans. Circuit Theory,* vol. CT-11, no. 1, pp. 67–72, March, 1964.

Chien, R. T.: On the Synthesis of Active Networks with One Negative Impedance Converter, *Proc. Nat. Electron. Conf.,* vol. 16, pp. 405–411, 1960.

Cruz, J. B.: A Synthesis Procedure based on Linvill's RC Active Structure, *IRE Trans. Circuit Theory,* vol. CT-6, no. 1, pp. 133–134, March, 1959.

Drew, A. J., and J. Gorski-Popiel: Directly Coupled Negative Impedance Converter, *Proc. IEE,* vol. 111, no. 7, pp. 1282–1283, July, 1964.

Franklin, D. P.: Direct-coupled Negative-impedance Convertor, *Electron. Letters,* vol. 1, no. 1, p. 1, March, 1965.

Gammie, J., and J. L. Merrill, Jr.: Stability of Negative Impedance Elements in Short Transmission Lines, *Bell System Tech. J.,* vol. 34, pp. 333–360, March, 1955.

Geller, S. B.: Synthesis of an Immittance Function with Two Negative Impedance Converters, *IRE Trans. Circuit Theory,* vol. CT-9, no. 3, p. 291, Sept., 1962.

Gorski-Popiel, J.: RC Active Networks, *Electron. Letters,* vol. 1, no. 10, pp. 288–289, Dec., 1965.

Hakim, S. S.: Some New Negative-impedance Convertors, *Electron. Letters,* vol. 1, no. 1, pp. 9–10, March, 1965.

Hoskins, R. F.: Stability of Negative-impedance Convertors, *Electron. Letters,* vol. 2, no. 9, p. 341, Sept., 1966.

Hudson, F. J.: Synthesis of Transfer Admittance Functions Using Active Components, *IBM J. Res. Develop.,* vol. 7, no. 1, pp. 40–43, Jan., 1963.

Huelsman, L. P.: Use of Two Negative-impedance Converters to Synthesize RC Transfer Functions, *IRE Trans. Circuit Theory,* vol. CT-9, no. 3, p. 357, Sept., 1961.

———: A Fundamental Classification of Negative-immittance Converters, *1965 IEEE Int. Conv. Record,* part 7, pp. 113–118, March, 1965.

———: The Compensation of Negative-immittance Converters, *Proc. IEEE,* vol. 54, no. 7, pp. 1015–1016, July, 1966.

Ingemarsson, I.: A Class of Transistorized Two-Ports, *Proc. IEEE,* vol. 53, no. 8, pp. 1152–1153, Aug., 1965.

Kallmann, H. E.: A Simple AC-DC Negative Impedance Convertor, *Proc. IEEE,* vol. 52, pp. 199–200, Feb., 1964.

Keen, A. W.: Derivation of Some Basic Negative-immittance-Convertor Circuits, *Electron. Letters,* vol. 2, no. 3, pp. 113–114, March, 1966.

Kinariwala, B. K.: Synthesis of Active RC Networks, *Bell System Tech. J.,* vol. 38, pp. 1269–1316, Sept., 1959.

Larky, A. I.: Negative-impedance Converters, *IRE Trans. Circuit Theory,* vol. CT-4, no. 3, pp. 124–131, Sept., 1957.

Linvill, J. G.: Transistor Negative-impedance Converters, *Proc. IRE*, vol. 41, pp. 725–729, June, 1953.

———: The Synthesis of Active Filters, *Proc. Symp. Modern Network Synthesis, Polytechnic Inst. of Brooklyn*, vol. 5, 1955.

———: RC Active Filters, *Proc. IRE*, vol. 42, no. 3, pp. 555–564, March, 1954.

———: Synthesis Techniques and Active Networks, *IRE Nat. Conv. Record*, part 2, pp. 90–94, 1957.

———: A New RC Filter Employing Active Elements, *Proc. Nat. Electron. Conf.*, vol. 9, pp. 342–352, 1953.

Lundry, W. R.: Negative Impedance Circuits—Some Basic Relations and Limitations, *IRE Trans. Circuit Theory*, vol. CT-4, no. 3, pp. 132–139, Sept., 1957.

Merrill, J. L.: Theory of the Negative Impedance Converter, *Bell System Tech. J.*, vol. 30, pp. 88–109, Jan., 1951.

Mitra, S. K., and N. M. Herbst: Synthesis of Active RC One-Ports Using Generalized Impedance Converters, *IEEE Trans. Circuit Theory*, vol. CT-10, no. 4, p. 532, Dec., 1963.

Morse, A. S.: The Use of Operational Amplifiers in Active Network Theory, *Proc. Nat. Electron. Conf.*, vol. 20, pp. 748–752, 1964.

Myers, B. R.: Transistor-RC Network Synthesis, *IRE WESCON Conv. Record*, part 2, pp. 65–74, 1959.

———: New Subclass of Negative-impedance Convertors with Improved Gain-product Sensitivities, *Electron. Letters*, vol. 1, no. 3, pp. 68–70, May, 1965.

Rohrer, R. A.: Minimum Sensitivity RC-NIC Driving Point Synthesis, *IEEE Trans. Circuit Theory*, vol. CT-10, no. 3, pp. 442–443, Sept., 1963.

Sandberg, I. W.: Synthesis of Driving-point Impedances with Active RC Networks, *Bell System Tech. J.*, vol. 39, pp. 947–962, July, 1960.

Sipress, J. M.: Synthesis of Active RC Networks, *IRE Trans. Circuit Theory*, vol. CT-8, no. 3, pp. 260–269, Sept., 1961.

Yanagisawa, T.: RC Active Networks Using Current Inversion Type Negative Impedance Converters, *IRE Trans. Circuit Theory*, vol. CT-4, no. 3, pp. 140–144, Sept., 1957.

D.4 *Gyrators**

Anderson, B. D., W. New, and R. Newcomb: Proposed Adjustable Tuned Circuits for Microelectronic Structures, *Proc. IEEE*, vol. 54, no. 3, p. 411, March, 1966.

Anderson, B. D., and R. W. Newcomb: A Capacitor-Transformer Gyrator Realization, *Proc. IEEE*, vol. 53, no. 10, p. 1640, Oct., 1965.

Anderson, B. D., D. A. Spaulding, and R. W. Newcomb: Useful Time-variable Circuit-element Equivalences, *Electron. Letters*, vol. 1, no. 3, pp. 56–57, May, 1965.

Bello, P.: Extension of Brune's Energy Function Approach to the Study of LLF Networks, *IRE Trans. Circuit Theory*, vol. CT-7, no. 3, pp. 270–280, Sept., 1960.

Blecher, F. H.: Application of Synthesis Techniques to Electronic Circuit Design, *IRE Trans. Circuit Theory*, vol. CT-7, special supplement, pp. 79–91, Aug., 1960.

---

* An additional bibliography is given by M. P. Beddoes and K. R. Morin, Bibliography on Inductance Simulation Using Gyrator Methods, *IEEE Trans. Circuit Theory*, vol. CT-14, no. 1, pp. 107–111, March, 1967.

Bogert, B. P.: Some Gyrator and Impedance Inverter Circuits, *Proc. IRE*, vol. 43, no. 7, pp. 793–796, July, 1955.

Calahan, D. A.: Sensitivity Minimization in Active RC Synthesis, *IRE Trans. Circuit Theory*, vol. CT-9, no. 1, pp. 38–42, March, 1962.

Carlin, H. J.: Singular Network Elements, *IEEE Trans. Circuit Theory*, vol. CT-11, no. 1, pp. 67–72, March, 1964.

Deboo, G. J.: Application of a Gyrator-type Circuit to Realize Ungrounded Inductors, *IEEE Trans. Circuit Theory*, vol. CT-14, no. 1, pp. 101–102, March, 1967.

Ghausi, M. S., and F. D. McCarthy: A Realization of Transistor Gyrators, *Semiconductor Products Solid State Tech.*, pp. 13–17, Oct., 1964.

———: A Realization of Transistor Gyrators, *Proc. Nat. Electron. Conf.*, vol. 19, pp. 396–406, 1963.

Grutzman, S.: Hall Effect Gyrators, Isolators, and Circulators with High Efficiency, *Proc. IEEE*, vol. 51, no. 11, pp. 1584–1588, Nov., 1963.

Harrison, T. J.: A Gyrator Realization, *IEEE Trans. Circuit Theory*, vol. CT-10, no. 2, p. 303, June, 1963.

Holmes, W. H.: A New Method of Gyrator-RC Filter Synthesis, *Proc. IEEE*, vol. 54, p. 1459, 1966.

Holmes, W. H., S. Gruetzmann, and W. E. Heinlein: High-performance Direct-coupled Gyrators, *Electron. Letters*, vol. 1, no. 2, pp. 45–46, Feb., 1967.

———: Direct-coupled Gyrators with Floating Ports, *Electron. Letters*, vol. 3, no. 2, pp. 46–47, Feb., 1967.

Holt, A. G. J., and J. Taylor: Method of Replacing Ungrounded Inductors by Grounded Gyrators, *Electron. Letters*, vol. 1, no. 4, p. 105, June, 1965.

Horowitz, I. M.: Optimum Design of Single-stage Gyrator-RC Filters with Prescribed Sensitivity, *IRE Trans. Circuit Theory*, vol. CT-8, no. 2, pp. 88–94, June, 1961.

Huelsman, L. P.: A Brune Realization Using Gyrator-Capacitor Sections, *IEEE Trans. Circuit Theory*, vol. CT-12, no. 3, pp. 439–440, Sept., 1965.

Ingemarsson, I.: A Class of Transistorized Two-Ports, *Proc. IEEE*, vol. 53, no. 8, pp. 1152–1153, Aug., 1965.

Karni, S.: A Note on n-Port Networks Terminated with n Gyrators, *IEEE Trans. Circuit Theory*, vol. CT-10, pp. 526–527, Dec., 1963.

Morse, A. S.: The Use of Operational Amplifiers in Active Network Theory, *Proc. Nat. Electron. Conf.*, vol. 20, pp. 748–752, 1964.

Morse, A. S., and L. P. Huelsman: A Gyrator Realization Using Operational Amplifiers, *IEEE Trans. Circuit Theory*, vol. CT-11, no. 2, p. 277, June, 1964.

Murdoch, J. B.: RC-Gyrator Cascade Synthesis, *IEEE Trans. Circuit Theory*, vol. CT-11, no. 2, pp. 268–271, June, 1964.

Murdoch, J. B., and D. Hazony: Cascade Driving-point-impedance Synthesis by Removal of Sections Containing Arbitrary Constants, *IRE Trans. Circuit Theory*, vol. CT-9, no. 1, pp. 56–61, March, 1962.

Myers, B. R.: Transistor-RC Network Synthesis, *IRE WESCON Conv. Record*, part 2, pp. 65–74, 1959.

New, W., and R. Newcomb: An Integratable Time-variable Gyrator, *Proc. IEEE*, vol. 53, no. 12, pp. 2161–2162, Dec., 1965.

Orchard, H. J.: Inductorless Filters, *Electron. Letters*, vol. 2, no. 6, pp. 224–225, June, 1966.

Prescott, A. J.: Loss-compensated Active Gyrator Using Differential-input Operational Amplifiers, *Electron. Letters*, vol. 2, no. 7, pp. 283–284, July, 1966.

Rao, T. N., and R. W. Newcomb: Direct-coupled Gyrator Suitable for Integrated Circuits and Time Variation, *Electron. Letters*, vol. 2, no. 7, pp. 250–251, July, 1966.

Riordan, R. H. S.: Simulated Inductors Using Differential Amplifiers, *Electron. Letters,* vol. 3, no. 2, pp. 50–51, Feb., 1967.

Sharpe, G. E.: The Pentode Gyrator, *IRE Trans. Circuit Theory,* vol. CT-4, no. 4, pp. 322–323, Dec., 1957.

Sheahan, D. F.: Gyrator-flotation Circuit, *Electron. Letters,* vol. 3, no. 1, pp. 39–40, Jan., 1967.

Sheahan, D. F., and H. J. Orchard: High Quality Transistorized Gyrator, *Electron. Letters,* vol. 2, no. 7, p. 274, July, 1966.

———: Integratable Gyrator Using M.O.S. and Bipolar Transistors, *Electron. Letters,* vol. 2, no. 10, pp. 390–391, Oct., 1966.

———: Bandpass-filter Realization Using Gyrators, *Electron. Letters,* vol. 3, no. 1, pp. 40–42, Jan., 1967.

Shekel, J.: The Gyrator as a Three Terminal Element, *Proc. IRE,* vol. 41, pp. 1014–1016, Aug., 1953.

———: Reciprocity Relations in Active 3-Terminal Elements, *IRE Trans. Circuit Theory,* vol. CT-1, no. 2, pp. 17–20, June, 1954.

Shenoi, B. A.: A 3-Transistor Gyrator Circuit with Variable Gyration Resistance, *Proc. 2nd Ann. Allerton Conf. Circuit and System Theory,* pp. 782–801, 1964.

———: Practical Realization of a Gyrator Circuit and RC-gyrator Filters, *IEEE Trans. Circuit Theory,* vol. CT-12, no. 3, pp. 374–380, Sept., 1965.

Su, K. L.: A Transistor-circuit Realization of the Inductor, *Proc. IEEE,* vol. 54, no. 12, pp. 2025–2027, Dec., 1966.

Tellegen, B. D. H.: The Gyrator, a New Electric Network Element, *Philips Res. Rept.,* vol. 3, pp. 81–101, April, 1948.

———: The Synthesis of Passive Resistanceless Four-Poles That May Violate the Reciprocity Relation, *Philips Res. Rept.,* vol. 3, pp. 321–327, Oct., 1948.

———: The Synthesis of Passive Two-Poles by Means of Networks Containing Gyrators, *Philips Res. Rept.,* vol. 4, pp. 31–37, 1949.

———: The Gyrator, an Electric Network Element, *Phillips Tech. Rev.,* vol. 18, no. 4/5, pp. 120–124, 1956/57.

Vallese, L. M.: Understanding the Gyrator, *Proc. IRE,* vol. 53, p. 483, 1955.

Yanagisawa, T., and Y. Kawashima: Active Gyrator, *Electron. Letters,* vol. 3, no. 3, pp. 105–107, March, 1967.

D.5 *Operational amplifier realization techniques*

Aggarwal, G. K.: On nth Order Simulation by One Operational Amplifier, *Proc. IEEE,* vol. 52, no. 8, p. 969, Aug., 1964.

———: On Using One Operational Amplifier for nth Order Simulation, *Intern. J. Control,* vol. 1, 1st series, no. 6, pp. 557–564, June, 1965.

Balabanian, N., and C. I. Cinkilie: Expansion of an Active Synthesis Technique, *IEEE Trans. Circuit Theory,* vol. CT-10, no. 2, pp. 290–298, June, 1963.

Bradley, F. R., and R. McCoy: Driftless D-C Amplifiers, *Electronics,* vol. 25, no. 4, pp. 144–148, April, 1952.

Brennan, R., and A. Bridgman: Simulation of Transfer Functions Using Only One Operational Amplifier, *IRE WESCON Conv. Record,* vol. 1, pp. 273–277, 1957.

Brugler, J. S.: "RC Synthesis with Differential Input Operational Amplifiers," in Papers on Integrated Circuit Synthesis (compiled by R. Newcomb and T. Rao), *Stanford Electron. Labs. Rept. No.* 6560-4, June, 1966.

Butler, E.: The Operational Amplifier as a Network Element, *Tech. Rept. No.* 86, *Res. Rept.* EERL 40, Cornell University, June, 1965.

Dietzold, R. L.: Frequency Discriminative Electric Transducer, U.S. Patent No. 2,549,065, April 17, 1951.

Ford, R. L., and F. E. J. Girling: Active Filters and Oscillators Using Simulated Inductance, *Electron. Letters,* vol. 2, no. 2, p. 52, Feb., 1966.

Foss, R. C., and B. J. Green: Qfactor, Qstability, and Gain in Active Filters, *Electron. Letters,* vol. 2, no. 3, pp. 99–100, March, 1966.

Foster, E. J.: Active Low-pass Filter Design, *IEEE Trans. Audio,* vol. AU-13, no. 5, pp. 104–111, Sept./Oct., 1965.

Hakim, S. S.: RC-active Circuit Synthesis Using an Operational Amplifier, *Intern. J. Control,* vol. 1, 1st series, no. 5, pp. 433–446, May, 1965.

Holt, A. G. J., and J. I. Sewell: Table for the Voltage Transfer Functions of Single-amplifier Double-Ladder Feedback Systems, *Electron. Letters,* vol. 1, no. 3, pp. 70–71, May, 1965.

———: Active RC Filters Employing a Single Operational Amplifier to Obtain Biquadratic Response, *Proc. IEE,* vol. 112, no. 12, pp. 2227–2234, Dec., 1965.

Karplus, W. J.: Synthesis of Non-pr Driving Point Impedance Functions Using Analog Computer Units, *IRE Trans. Circuit Theory,* vol. CT-4, no. 3, pp. 170–172, Sept., 1957.

Lovering, W. F.: Analog Computer Simulation of Transfer Functions, *Proc. IEEE,* vol. 53, no. 3, pp. 306–307, March, 1965.

Matthews, M. V., and W. W. Seifert: Transfer-Function Synthesis with Computer Amplifiers and Passive Networks, *Proc. Western Joint Computer Conf.,* pp. 7–12, March, 1955.

McVey, P. J.: Synthesis of Transfer Functions by RC Networks with Two or Three Computing Amplifiers, *Intern. J. Control,* vol. 2, 1st series, no. 2, pp. 125–134, Aug., 1965.

Morse, A. S.: The Use of Operational Amplifiers in Active Network Theory, *Proc. Nat. Electron. Conf.,* vol. 20, pp. 748–752, 1964.

Nathan, A.: Matrix Analysis of Networks Having Infinite-Gain Operational Amplifiers, *Proc. IRE,* vol. 49, no. 10, pp. 1577–1578, Oct., 1961.

Pande, H. C., and R. S. Shukla: Synthesis of Transfer Functions Using an Operational Amplifier, *Proc. IEE,* vol. 112, no. 12, pp. 2208–2212, Dec., 1965.

Paul, R. J. A.: Simulation of Rational Transfer Functions with Adjustable Coefficients, *Proc. IEE,* vol. 110, no. 4, pp. 671–679, April, 1963.

Ponsonby, J. E. B.: Active All-pass Filter Using a Differential Operational Amplifier, *Electronic Letters,* vol. 2, no. 4, pp. 124–125, April, 1966.

Sheingold, D. H.: Constant Current Source for Analog Computer Use, *IEEE Trans. Electron. Computers,* vol. EC-12, no. 3, p. 324, June, 1963.

Sinha, V. P.: Topological Formulas for Passive Transformerless 3-Terminal Networks Constrained by One Operational Amplifier, *IEEE Trans. Circuit Theory,* vol. CT-10, no. 1, pp. 125–126, March, 1963.

Taylor, P. L.: Flexible Design Method for Active *RC* Two-Ports, *Proc. IEE,* vol. 110, no. 9, pp. 1607–1616, Sept., 1963.

Wadhwa, L. K.: Simulation of Third-order Systems with One Operational Amplifier, *Proc. IRE,* vol. 50, no. 2, pp. 201–202, Feb., 1962.

———: Simulation of Third-order Systems with Simple-Lead Using One Operational Amplifier, *Proc. IRE,* vol. 50, no. 4, part I, p. 465, April, 1962.

———: Simulation of Third-order Systems with Double-Lead Using One Operational Amplifier, *Proc. IRE,* vol. 50, no. 6, pp. 1538–1539, June, 1962.

Index

Index